FRACTURE PREVENTION
IN ENERGY AND TRANSPORT SYSTEMS

VOLUME I

The Proceedings of a Conference organized by the International Congress on Fracture/Fracture Group of the Americas and the Metallurgy and Materials Engineering Program of the Co-ordination of Post-Graduate Programs in Engineering (COPPE) at the Federal University of Rio de Janeiro, Brazil, where the Conference was held,
November 28 – December 1, 1983.

EDITORS:
Iain Le May
Sergio Neves Monteiro

EMAS
ENGINEERING MATERIALS
ADVISORY SERVICES LTD.,
339, Halesowen Road, Cradley Heath,
Warley, West Midlands, B64 6PH, U.K.

ISBN 0 947817 02 6 (Set)
ISBN 0 947817 03 4 (Vol. I) ISBN 0 947817 04 2 (Vol. II)

RELATED EMAS PUBLICATIONS –

THE MEASUREMENT OF CRACK LENGTH AND SHAPE DURING FRACTURE AND FATIGUE – Editor: C. J. Beevers – ISBN 0 9506820 0 4 (1980)

FATIGUE THRESHOLDS – Proceedings of an International Conference held in Stockholm, June 1–3, 1981 – Editors: J. Backlund, A. F. Blom and C. J. Beevers – ISBN 0 9506820 1 2 (1982, in two volumes).

FRACTURE AND THE ROLE OF MICROSTRUCTURE – Proceedings of the 4th European Conference on Fracture and Fatigue, Leoben, Austria, September 22–24, 1982 – Editors: K. L. Maurer and F. E. Matzer – ISBN 0 9506820 5 5 (1982, in two volumes).

ADVANCES IN CRACK LENGTH MEASUREMENT – Editor: C. J. Beevers – ISBN 0 9506820 4 7 (1982)

FATIGUE 84 – Proceedings of the 2nd International Conference on Fatigue and Fatigue Thresholds held in Birmingham, U.K., September 3–7, 1984 – Editor: C. J. Beevers – ISBN 0 9506820 8 X (1984, in three volumes).

FORTHCOMING PUBLICATIONS –

A COMPENDIUM OF FATIGUE THRESHOLDS AND CRACK GROWTH RATES – D. Taylor.

THE APPLICATION OF 3-DIMENSIONAL FINITE ELEMENT METHODS TO FRACTURE MECHANICS AND FATIGUE LIFE PREDICTION – A. K. Pickard.

PRINTED BY THE CHAMELEON PRESS LTD.
LONDON, UNITED KINGDOM

PREFACE

The International Conference on Fracture Prevention in Energy and Transport Systems was conceived in April, 1981 at the 5th International Conference on Fracture, ICF 5, held in Cannes, France. At that time a Brazilian Delegation was proposed and later accepted by the Council of the International Congress on Fracture. It was then suggested by fellow delegates that Brazil host an interim conference as a landmark for the initiation of activities on fracture science and technology jointly with other countries. Professor Fernando Bastian and myself, both from the Federal University of Rio de Janeiro, endorsed the suggestion and obtained formal approval from Dr. Roy Nichols, then President of ICF, Professor David Taplin, future President of ICF, Professor George Sih, Chairman of the Fracture Group of the Americas (FGA), and Professor Takeo Yokobori, Founder President of ICF. Thanks to fruitful discussions with experienced colleagues, Professors Pratt, Pelloux, Knott, Averbach and Miller, to mention only a few, the structure of the Fracture Prevention Conference was decided upon. The idea of the main theme came from Professor Iain Le May who, as an authority in technological aspects related to the use of materials in the areas of energy and transportation, was able to identify a point of common interest to industrialized and developing countries such as Brazil. It was then realized that many aspects concerning energy and transportation might be treated together, not only because of technological reasons related to fuel and electricity but also due to the interconnection between these on a global scale. Fracture Prevention was then the aim of the Conference and it was hoped that solutions to these problems would be raised and discussed.

On the Brazilian side, the list of those who contributed in many important aspects would go much beyond the available space. The following general acknowledgements encompass the names of those who have made possible this Conference.

- Colleagues of the Program of Metallurgy and Materials Engineering
- The Directors of COPPE
- Authorities of the Federal University of Rio de Janeiro
- The Brazilian agencies for higher level education, research and development: FINEP, CNPq and CAPES
- The Brazilian Association for Metals
- The Brazilian Association for Non-Destructive Testing
- The Electrical Engineering Research Center, CEPEL

Finally, on behalf of the Organizing Committee, I would like to express my deep appreciation to those who accepted our invitation, attended and collaborated with the Conference.

Sergio Neves Monteiro
Program of Metallurgy and Materials Engineering, COPPE/UFRJ
Caixa Postal, 68505
21,944 – Rio de Janeiro – RJ
Brazil

SPONSORS

Conselho Nacional de Desenvolvimento Científico e Tecnológico - CNPq
(National Research and Development Council)

Financiadora de Estudos e Projetos - FINEP
(Studies and Projects Financing Agency)

Coordenação de Aperfeiçoamento de Pessoal de Nível Superior - CAPES/MEC
(Coordination for Training of High Level Personnel)

Fundação Universitária José Bonifácio - FUJB
(Jose Bonifacio University Foundation)

The British Council

Associação Brasileira de Ensaios Não-Destrutivos - ABENDE
(Brazilian Association for Non-Destructive Testing)

Associação Brasileira de Metais - ABM
(Brazilian Association for Metals)

Centro de Pesquisas de Energia Elétrica - CEPEL
(Electrical Energy Research Center)

International Technology Institute

The Fulbright Commission

FOREWORD

During recent years the whole area encompassing fracture mechanics and the study of the processes and mechanisms of fracture has expanded enormously. One particular sign of maturity has been the greatly increased interest in fracture prevention procedures, rather than only the analysis of fractures that have taken place. It was with this development in mind that the program for the International Conference on Fracture Prevention in Energy and Transport Systems was arranged.

The papers chosen for the program, from the very many submitted, covered a wide range of topics within the overall theme. It is particularly fortunate that keynote papers were able to be commissioned from authorities in the various areas of interest. These are included in these Proceedings, together with the contributed papers.

I particularly wish to thank members of the Scientific Committee and the Local Editorial Committee for their work in reviewing all the conference papers; also the authors for preparing such interesting contributions to this important area. It is hoped that the Proceedings resulting from all these efforts will provide a valuable and continuing source of reference to researchers and designers in industry and university alike, in a critical area for future engineering developments.

Iain Le May
Department of Mechanical Engineering
University of Saskatchewan
Saskatoon, Canada
S7N OWO

INTERNATIONAL CONFERENCE ON FRACTURE PREVENTION IN ENERGY AND TRANSPORT SYSTEMS

CONTENTS

Volume I

PLENARY LECTURE AND KEYNOTE PAPERS

OFFSHORE OIL EXPLORATION AND PRODUCTION

NUCLEAR REACTORS

PIPELINES

Volume II

RAILWAYS

PETROCHEMICAL

NONCONVENTIONAL FUEL

FUNDAMENTALS OF FRACTURE

AERONAUTICS AND AEROSPACE

RECOMMENDED SYMBOLS

a	Crack-Length - One-Half the Total Length of an Internal Crack or Depth of a Surface Crack
Δa	Crack Growth Increment
a.c.	Alternating Current
B	Test Piece Thickness
C	Compliance
$C_1 - C_5$ & D	Constants
da/dN	Rate of Fatigue Crack Propagation
$\Delta\frac{da}{dN}$	Additional Growth Rate due to Environment
$\left[\frac{da}{dN}\right]_{CTB}$	Growth Rate Retarded by Crack Tip Blunting
$\left[\frac{da}{dN}\right]_{LHE}$	Growth Rate Enhanced by Localised Hydrogen Embrittlement
$\left[\frac{da}{dN}\right]_{TCF}$	Overall Growth Rate for 'True Corrosion Fatigue'
$\left[\frac{da}{dN}\right]_{SCF}$	Stress Corrosion Fatigue Crack Growth Rate
$\left[\frac{da}{dt}\right]_{P}$	Stress Corrosion Plateau Growth Rate Per Second
da/dt	Crack Extension Rate
d.c.	Direct Current
δ	Value of Crack Opening Displacement (see British Standard BS5762)
δ_c	Critical Crack Opening Displacement, being One of the Following: (1) Crack Opening Displacement at Fracture (2) Crack Opening Displacement at First Instability or Discontinuity (3) Crack Opening Displacement at which an Amount of Crack Growth Commences
δ_m	Crack Opening Displacement at First Attainment of Maximum Force
D_H	Diffusion Coefficient for Hydrogen in Iron

E	Young's Modulus of Elasticity
exp	Exponential Base of Natural Logarithms
ε	Creep Strain
$\dot{\varepsilon}_S$	Secondary Creep Rate
ε_T	Transient Creep Strain
F	Cyclic Frequency
G	Strain Energy Release Rate
$G_I G_{II} G_{III}$	Crack Extension Forces for Various Modes of Crack Opening
I	Current
i_a	Anodic Current Density
K	Stress Intensity Factor - a Measure of the Stress-Field Intensity Near the Tip of a Perfect Crack in a Linear-Elastic Solid
K_c	Fracture Toughness - The Largest Value of the Stress-Intensity Factor that exists Prior to the Onset of Rapid Fracture
K_{cl}	K in Fatigue Cycle Below which Crack is Closed
K_I	Opening Mode Stress Intensity Factor
K_{IC}	Plane-Strain Fracture Toughness as Defined by ASTM Standard Designation E 399-74 or British Standard BS 5447
K_{Ii}	Elastic Stress-Intensity Factor at the Start of a Sustained-Load Flaw-Growth Test
K_{ISCC}	Plane-Strain K_I Threshold Above which Sustained Load Flaw-Growth Occurs
K_{IH_2S}	Value of K_{ISCC} in Dry H_2S Gas
K_Q	Provisional Fracture Toughness Value Corresponding to a 5% Deviation of the Load/Displacement Relationship from Linearity
K_{max}	Maximum Stress-Intensity Factor
K_{min}	Minimum Stress-Intensity Factor
ΔK	Stress Intensity Range

ΔK_{th}	Threshold Stress Intensity Factor Below which Fatigue Crack Growth will not occur
ΔK_i^o	ΔK_i to just cause Fatigue Initiation
ΔK_n	Next Value of ΔK
ΔK_{th}^o	Value of ΔK_{th} at $R = O$
ΔK_o	Constant Value of ΔK_{th}
$d\Delta K$	Notional Extra Stress Intensity due to Environment
k_T, k_N	Stress Concentration Factor, Neuber Correction Factor
ln	Natural Logarithm
log	Common Logarithm
m	Power Exponent in Paris-Erdogen Expression $\frac{da}{dN} = A \Delta K^m$
N	Cycles
N_i	Cycles to Initiate
N_F	Cycles to Failure
ΔN	Cycles Increment
n	Strain Hardening Exponent
ΔP	Load Range
ν	Poisson's Ratio
Q	Flaw Shape Parameter
σ	Stress
$\Delta\sigma$	Stress Range
σ_{max}	Maximum Stress
σ_{ps}	Proof Stress
σ_{min}	Minimum Stress
σ_u	Ultimate Tensile Strength
σ_y	Yield Stress under Uniaxial Tension
$\Delta\sigma_{net}$	Stress Range on Net Section

R	Minimum Load/Maximum Load
R_{cl}	R below which Crack Closure Occurs
r_p	Plastic Zone Size
ρ	Crack Tip Radius
ρ_o	Notional Minimum Value of ρ
T	Temperature
t	Time
t_h	Hold Time in Load Cycle
t_r	Rise Time in Load Cycle
t_r^o, t_r^{max}	Values of t_r at Minimum and Maximum Environmental Enhancement
V	Potential Difference
V_o	Reference Potential Difference
$V(a)$	Potential Difference at Crack Length, a
W	Test Piece Width
ϕ	Electric Potential
x, y	Cartesian Co-ordinates
Y	Compliance Function
Ω	Ohms

RECOMMENDED ABBREVIATIONS

BFS	Back Face Strain
BRF	Blunting Retardation Factor
CCP	Centre Cracked Plate
COD	Crack Opening Displacement
CT	Compact Tension
CTB	Crack Tip Blunting
DCPD	Direct Current Potential Drop
EEF	Environmental Enhancement Factor
LHE	Localised Hydrogen Embrittlement

PD	Potential Drop
SENB	Single Edge Notched Bend
SENT	Single Edge Notched Tension
SCC	Stress Corrosion Cracking
SCF	Stress Corrosion Fatigue
TCF	True Corrosion Fatigue
T-Type WOL	T-Type Wedge Open Loading
UTS	Ultimate Tensile Strength

PLENARY LECTURE AND KEYNOTE PAPERS

THE FITNESS-FOR-PURPOSE CONCEPT

A.A. Wells*

Fitness for purpose is deemed to be that which is consciously chosen to be the right level of material and fabrication quality for each application, having regard to the risks and consequences of failure; it may be contrasted with the best quality that can be achieved within a given set of circumstances, which may be inadequate for some exacting requirements, and needlessly uneconomic for others which are less demanding. The need for such an approach has already been seen with the development and application of fracture mechanics, but the paper draws attention to a wider scope which also embraces the evolution of the design process, risk analysis and reliability engineering, non-destructive examination, codes and standards, and quality assurance.

INTRODUCTION

The history of technology is dominated by evidence of cyclic growth, mainly created by perpetual imbalance between the commercial and economic forces of demand and supply. Nowhere are these cycles more readily seen than in the occurrence of structural casualties and in the public attitudes adopted towards them. It so happens that the topic of this Conference, Fracture prevention in energy and transport systems, despite its timeless relevance, can be illustrated through two such cyclic events in the industrial development of Britain during the early nineteenth century. Firstly, the provision of steam power for factories led to the incidence of a serious epidemic of boiler explosions, which was followed by stricter legislation. The Manchester Steam Users Association was formed at about this time, together with the Engineering Insurers, now known in Britain as the Associated Offices, which continue regularly to investigate, catalogue and publicise the circumstances of casualties in engineering plant, with the object of diminishing their occurrence. The formation of Lloyd's Register in the shipping field is equally well-known. Secondly, the development of railways led to a very large incidence of accidents due to derailments. The Transactions of the Institution of Mechanical Engineers for 1850 (Parsons (1)) reveal that a significant proportion of these were due to deterioration and breakage of wrought iron railway axles, almost invariably at the sharp corners machined at the inner edges of the wheel seats. We should now categorise these as initiated by fatigue cracking, leading to brittle fracture. In those times of infancy of the science of metallography the fractures were recognised as crystalline, but there was furious debate as to the reasons why the metal would crystallise in service, since the inherent crystal structures of metals remained largely unrecognised. John Ramsbottom, a well-remembered plain-speaking Yorkshire railway engineer, held that whenever fractures of machinery always occurred at the same place it was

* The Welding Institute, Cambridge, England

more important to reconsider the design than to argue about the metal, and his precept still has value in the limited consideration of fatigue failures.

The structural casualties which occurred during the Second World War and during the subsequent period of reconstruction are even more worthy of study, with the added advantages of better documentation and easier retrieval of information. Many such structures employed welding for the first time at this juncture and a popular prejudice developed against this means of fabrication. A scholarly study of the history of casualties by Professor Shank of MIT (2) did much to correct the impression, and remains as one of the best available publications in this area. It also serves to emphasize one of the serious limitations which persist in the study of casualties, which is that the requirements of law almost world-wide preclude the wider discussion of these events by those whose duty it is to study and pronounce upon them. The reason for the limitation is well-understood and accepted since the function of the law is to distribute fairly the financial responsibility for losses, but when the process is protracted there is delay in dissemination of the lessons which have been learned, and the influence of prejudice is prolonged.

Notwithstanding the difficulties in making known the lessons from casualties the ultimate aim must be to create a system which anticipates risks of incurring structural damage and provides means for fracture prevention. One such well-respected approach is concerned with the development and application of workmanship standards. An inherent difficulty is one of definition and translation to other communities and cultures, other countries and other languages. Workmanship standards may be regarded as a prerequisite but are insufficient of themselves, and the subject will be alluded to again.

At the time of his Presidency of the Institute of Welding (1960-61), Edgar Fuchs had been responsible for the specification and use of heavy welded plant in the chemical industry, characteristically operated at high and low temperatures, high pressures, and in conjunction with hostile environments. It had been his earlier experience that the consequences of failures in such plant were so costly as to justify the search for perfection in fabrication. Yet, in his Presidential Address (3), he introduced the term and concept of fitness for purpose, and linked it with what was known of the significance of weld defects. His first example related to the development of porosity in MIG welded aluminium alloys which was then prevalent, and which called for much excavation and repair of welded seams. It had been concluded that this aspect of the search for perfection was totally misdirected, since no destructive test of those welded joints exhibiting moderate porosity could demonstrate a diminution of strength or ductility, whatever the loading condition. Indeed, the repairs were sometimes retrogressive, because they introduced new defects (lack of fusion, etc.) which did have a weakening effect.

As a result of sustained thinking on this topic he concluded that the most suitable quality of welding, even for onerous working conditions, was that which would emerge from all the evidence of mechanical, metallurgical and non-destructive testing (NDT) with the aim to establish the significance of defects. There is a profound difference between such a concept, and its precedent which aimed for the best quality that could be achieved with the available knowledge and means, regardless of application.

The very idea that all constructions contain defects has for long been repugnant to some, in recognising too readily that an ideal of perfection cannot be attained. The attitude is maintained in spite of recognition that acceptance of the alternative fitness-for-purpose concept entails an added responsibility, which is to assess the significance of defects, and to base inspections accordingly. Much has taken place since 1960 in the total development of welding technology to convert the fitness-for-purpose concept into a workable reality, but the old indiscriminate judgements do persist. It was the aim of an International Conference held in 1981 (4) to illustrate the background, the concept itself, and the important concomitants in terms of balance between economy and safety, so that the advantages of the approach might be more fully realised and confusions eliminated. Cost escalations on projects both large and small have increasingly occurred in recent times. Some are related to management problems, and others to inflation over long periods of construction for large plants; it could be said in a few cases that an inadequate balance has been maintained between economy and safety. Lavish expenditure in the pursuit of quality may not always secure more than a diminishing return in terms of safety. The key to this dilemma now rests particularly with public perception: if the public is to be educated with respect to what can reasonably be expected in terms of safety from industrial projects and constructions, it is first necessary for the professional ethic to be clearly described, together with the working procedures which stem from it.

In the contemporary scene the criteria for fitness for purpose are expressed more as a set of principles than as a proliferation of ever more rigid specifications. It follows that the attempt is to define more closely some of those considerations which would formerly have been described as 'good workmanship' and 'sound engineering judgement'.

This is no more than a striving to do better and with more conscious articulation that which was done intuitively in the past. Thus, it was never customary to apply the same criteria to the selection of timber for a public utility pole in a country lane as to that for a sailing ship mast. The contrast was even wider between freestone for a rubble fill and squared blocks for ashlar masonry. The steel industry in a more modern context exhibits perhaps the most extensive hierarchy, with the highly refined and closely specified massive products for such as turbo-alternator rotors and nuclear high-pressure vessels at the apex, and the more loosely specified products known affectionately in the trade as 'clog iron' at the base for undemanding requirements. The monetary values of these products on a tonnage basis will vary by factors of more than 10. No well-qualified [illegible] ignorant of these distinctions: at one extreme he will risk failures and at the other he will unnecessarily waste the money of clients.

EVOLUTION OF THE DESIGN PROCESS IN STEEL STRUCTURES

Large engineering works in the 19th century and earlier were customarily conceived, planned, and executed by talented engineers as individuals, with few assistants and training on the job for those in a master and pupil relationship. Straightforward calculations were performed and confirmed by many tests on models. More complex calculations were pioneered by the French, arising from the flowering of academic engineering science at the time of the Napoleonic Wars. The uses of elastic structural analysis and stress analysis were firmly entrenched everywhere at the commencement of this century. Knowledge of the mechanical behaviour of metals had become firmly established at this time, but the base of experience tended to be broader in this field with independent contributions from the USA, Japan and elsewhere, as well as from Europe and Scandinavia. The complementary art of conceptual design of engineering works and structures can be separately distinguished and has more substance than is confined to structural analysis and strength of materials. It is closely allied to the practical limitations of construction, and to the organisation of large projects which developed extensively in the 19th century with the building of canals and railways, and has continued at an increasing pace ever since, notably through influences initiated in the USA. Nevertheless, it is with detail design, analysis and mechanical properties that we are concerned here.

These activities have been transformed in scope and importance during the past fifty years. In the first place, the capabilities of structural and stress analyses have increased by orders of magnitude through the application of numerical methods handled by digital computers. Experimental model tests have not disappeared, but have been progressively replaced by mathematical modelling. In the second place, mechanical testing has been modified by the orderly development of fracture mechanics methods, but an even more significant revolution has occurred with regard to the improvement of mechanical properties both in scale and consistency, through the development of metallurgical science. Two discrete sets of tools have been provided by and for metallurgists to make this possible. On the one hand wet chemical and similarly tedious methods of analysis have been supplemented by precise and automatic spectrographic methods, and a variety of other complements which provide not only instant readout but also data on molecular form as well as proportional atomic constituents. On the other hand the development of the whole family of electron microscopes has greatly increased the revelation of fracture surfaces, metallic microstructures and other polycrystalline forms, so that the effects of impurities and contaminants as well as microalloy constituents have come into much sharper focus than hitherto. A similarly vigorous revolution, whose effects, both real and potential, are not yet so clearly evident, is now taking place in the methods of nondestructive examination. X-ray methods, long thought to be incapable of illuminating cracks, are increasing their ability to do so, and ultrasonic methods of great sensitivity are beginning to conform to the need for automatic recording. All these new methods for the analysis of metals and minerals have benefited metal processing, but nowhere has the effect been more profound than with regard to metal joining, welding and fabrication.

This burgeoning of new tools and methods is only now being assimilated. A major effect has been to create a challenge to such intangible concepts as 'the responsible engineer'. The new methods of analysis, although they vastly supplement insight and capacity to control on a material basis, also require the services of an army of experts, and call for collective responsibility in implementation of a construction. Since no expert can readily be challenged in his own field, it might be expected that a side effect would be to retard the rate of construction and increase its costs, in exchange for an unquantified increase in safety and quality of the end product.

Assimilation into industry of the 'new metallurgy' has, in fact, been accompanied by several counterpart developments which help to optimise the advantages. These include risk analysis, fracture mechanics, nondestructive examination, computer-aided design, and quality assurance (QA). They are constituents which make up a total package of fitness-for-purpose design.

RISK ANALYSIS AND RELIABILITY ENGINEERING

These are two aspects of quantification which address the same problem from different ends, and which had their origins in Scandinavia and the USA, respectively. Long before it became customary to grace such studies with specific names, the engineering insurers and classification societies world-wide compiled statistics on the incidence and manners of failure of engineering strutures. Excellent work was published and updated from time to time. Specific families of structures were isolated and firm data now exist for aircraft, for fractures of ship hulls and oil storage tanks, and for pressure vessels. The populations of structures in service and therefore at risk over periods of, say, twenty years are sufficiently large that the observed failure rates are as regular as mortality rates, and small changes of rate can be perceived. These changes are mainly downwards, in spite of considerable improvements of service performance over corresponding periods. It is abundantly clear that public tolerance has much to do with the setting of acceptable casualty rates, and that these latter diminish as the number of human beings exposed in a potential casualty becomes larger. A comparison of the data from the several classes above leads to the elementary supposition that an acceptable probability of structural failure is that for which the associated human casualty rates approximately match the risks of death and injury from natural causes. However, the public perception of risk is strongly biased (5) to accept the familiar (motor bicycles and common diseases) and reject the unknown but dreaded risks (nuclear incidents, crashes of large aircraft), irrespective of the actuarial data.

It follows that experimental observation of structural casualty rates should have been supplemented in due course by attempts to calculate them in advance, as for instance in the case of nuclear pressure vessels. Risk analysis has developed from this, and it attempts to compute the overall risk of failure from constituent parts, using statistical and probabilistic methods. The methods first developed in Denmark have taken account of pressure vessel loading, notch toughness and its scatter, characteristic populations of cracklike defects, and efficacy of NDT methods in finding these defects. The value of these methods is best seen when sensitivity analyses are superimposed upon them, since these show where efforts to improve can best be applied. It is of interest to the metallurgist that one of the most required developments is shown in this way to be the improvement of the consistency of notch toughness properties.

The parallel approach known as reliability engineering is believed to have been developed in connection with electronic components for use in aerospace equipments. Standard failure rates have been compiled for such as resistors, capacitors, and transistors, and these can be synthesised to predict failure rates for circuits, both singly and in array. More recent applications have been made to measurement and control units used in the gas and petroleum industries.

It is the experience of this author that the benefits of making use of risk analyses by calculation are obtained at no great cost other than that of the determination of standard deviations on measured mechanical (and other) properties (which require permutation in any case for purposes of quality control). The benefits include the assignment of meaning to occasional low results, and identification of areas where improvement leads to no more than diminishing returns. Risk analysis falls within the province of the engineering designer, and can assert a strong influence on the rational determination of fitness for purpose.

FRACTURE MECHANICS

The main circumstances of the development of fracture mechanics, especially linear elastic fracture mechanics (LEFM), are by now very well-known. The objectives were recently summarised by the author (6) in the following terms:

"The aim of using the fracture mechanics approach to fracture control in engineering structures is to determine the loading (applied, thermal, residual stress, etc.) at which a pre-existing crack of given size will extend in the most vulnerable mode (brittle, ductile tearing, fatigue, stress corrosion, high temperature, creep). The means involves:

1. the determination of loading conditions for crack extension in a sharply notched specimen by using the appropriate material and environmental conditions (temperature, loading rate, gaseous and electrochemical surface condition, pressure)

2. the provision of a stress analysis embracing the sharp notch in both distribution and scale, and the effects of shape and loading conditions."

It may be added in amplification of these stated principles that the first objective is to measure the fracture toughness of the material under precisely standardised conditions, and the second objective is to estimate the driving force at the postulated crack, wherever it may be found in the structure and whatever might be the most onerous conditions. The fracture toughness will exceed the estimated values of driving force under safe working conditions, subject to margins which relate to previous experiences.

Thus, fracture mechanics was specifically developed to help the engineer to determine the significance of defects in terms of susceptibility to fracture, and to reinforce judgements on the necessity to repair defects once they had been detected. Its relevance to fitness for purpose is self-evident.

The concept of defect tolerance has been well established by observation over the past two decades of the behaviour in service of welded structures containing cracks (7, 8). Several practical methods which have been devised to assess levels of tolerance to crack-like defects were described at a recent International Conference (4).

Although fracture mechanics has become widely known, the usefulness of the approach is confined at present to the control of notch ductility or fatigue crack growth rates in a relatively narrow range of structures of high expected performance, usually associated either with high-strength materials or heavy sections. The main reason for this is related to the employment wherever possible of materials, typically ferritic steels, at temperatures and strain rates so that they are above a transition temperature, and therefore exhibit a high margin of tolerance with regard to fracture risk.

The accurate measurement of fracture toughness by fracture mechanics methods is more difficult in the circumstances of superior toughness, and the tests are relatively costly to perform. Such measurements are beyond the range of LEFM and require the use of the crack opening displacement or J-integral criteria. Furthermore, the measurement specimens require in many cases to be of full-section thickness to make valid measurements. It is also necessary in most of such cases to make use of the full resistance curve, taking slow crack growth into account to the point of instability, to mobilise the very high values of fracture toughness which characterise modern steels of very high qualities.

The favourable economics of such approaches are well-established for high-performance structures, and there are no valid alternative procedures for them. Conversely, these procedures are inappropriate for most constructions of a largely repetitive character, for which there are serviceable, empirical alternatives in control through Charpy V notch impact testing, together with correlations with performance of similar constructions in past service. This dichotomy can be regarded as temporary since valid and characteristic fracture toughness values will become available as standard data in the course of time, although this state of affairs does not yet obtain. Despite many careful attempts up to this time it has proved to be relatively unsatisfactory to rely upon empirical correlations between the results of valid fracture toughness tests and those of Charpy V notch impact tests.

NONDESTRUCTIVE EXAMINATION

Structural defects must first be detected and sized by NDT before their significance can be assessed. The methods that are characteristically employed, e.g. X and radiography, magnetic and penetrant testing, and ultrasonics, have all now been in regular service for more than thirty years, but it would be inappropriate to assume that any one of them has yet reached full development, or will lapse into disuse. The importance of magnetic and penetrant testing for surface defects has been emphasized in the light of much careful fatigue testing of fillet welds, which has demonstrated the vulnerability of the latter in circumstances of repeated loading. This arises from the coincidence of superimposed geometric and metallurgical discontinuities at their edges, or toes, to the extent that incipient or very shallow cracks are often present from the time of manufacture. These cracks are readily detected by one or the other of these methods of NDT, and their effects can also be ameliorated by various surface dressing techniques. Such treatments have proved to be of use in the construction of welded steel ocean platforms, particularly those destined for the North Sea where wave loading fatigue effects are present, and in which fillet welded joints are commonplace at the nodes of tubular constructions.

Recording techniques associated with radiography have been improved to such an extent in the recent past that it is no longer held to be conventional wisdom that cracks cannot be detected by this method. The long-recognised advantage of radiography has been the acquisition of permanent visual records, which are suited to the proof of contractual obligation. Ultrasonic observations were earlier regarded as complementary in this regard, in that the method making use of reflections can exhibit considerable sensitivity, but is sometimes lacking in certainty of detection. The method is also penalised by scatter and absorption when associated with coarse microstructures, such as sometimes arise with austenitic materials. There are also difficulties in distinguishing legitimate signals from background noise levels. In spite of these limitations ultrasonics has become the principal tool for sizing defects. Considerable progress has also recently been made in overcoming a similar problem with the transmission of television images through space, through the conversion of data to digital form, coupled with signal processing by numerical methods. Recent attempts to apply similar techniques to ultrasonic imaging have been encouraging (9), and should further assist in defect sizing as an adjunct to the application of fracture mechanics.

Ultrasonic imaging offers a powerful technique for the acquisition of permanent data, even in its present state of development, and has led to the concept of 'fingerprinting' important structures fabricated by welding at the time of commissioning, and at infrequent intervals during service, so that the degree of quiescence or alternative growth of incipient defects can be observed. This technique develops in importance where there are repeated loads which can cause fatigue but where a long service life is also envisaged. Fingerprinting was devised for the special case of nuclear reactor pressure vessels, but is becoming justified for wider application.

QUALITY ASSURANCE

Of all the modern aids to fitness-for-purpose design and construction the simplest and possibly the most useful has been the development of QA concepts and methods. Quality assurance is the commonsense system which joins them all together, and is still best described as the provision of a standard of good housekeeping.* The need for QA arises firstly with the growth in complexity of modern construction and production sequences, coupled with the requirement on behalf of a purchaser for independent verification that all the specified sequences have taken place correctly and in the right order.

Quality assurance methods have their roots in the design process, at which stage the needs and objectives are defined. The interpretation at present embraces the proper selection of methods for structural analysis and design, authentication of design data, and independent checking of calculations, including those making use of computers.

Nowhere is the need for good QA methods more acute than in the deployment of correctly chosen materials, which should also receive the correct treatments during manufacture. The system is therefore applied with uniform attention, firstly in design, then from the stores where the materials and components are first accumulated and disbursed, through the production operation to final inspection of the finished product. It embraces evidence of calibration of the production equipment and the instrumentation used for quality control. It also embraces a sufficient documentation of the work as it passes through the production stages.

Quality assurance procedures supplement the necessary activities of inspectors such as those employed by insurance bodies and classification societies. They are based upon the creation at each plant of a quality assurance manual, prepared by the staff of the plant to satisfy the needs of inspection.

The Quality Assurance Manual aims to describe in detail the design and manufacturing capability of a plant in terms of its skills, resources, and ability to control them, and therefore commences with staff and organisational pattern, including the skills and qualifications of many individuals. It goes on to describe in detail the resources and facilities, both general and specialised, from buildings to individual plant items. It takes account of training facilities and those for acquisition of expertise from outside sources. Considerable attention is given to facilities for measurement, including those associated with machine tools and manufacturing equipment, and those in supporting laboratories. This includes the arrangement for calibration, both within the plant and outside, to which references are made on a routine basis or otherwise. Design/production organisation and documentation methods are set down. Inspection facilities, the methods that are used, their characteristic performances and the associated documentation systems are obvious candidates for detailed attention. The Manual is examined by a responsible outside body both at the outset, and at intervals thereafter; it is also updated when significant changes occur. Omissions and modifications are required to be dealt with, and the outside body conducts and maintains an audit to ensure that the Manual corresponds with actuality.

The QA Manual becomes the basis upon which customers assess the capability and suitability of a potential contracting firm, and Government departments and multinational companies were the first to demand and encourage the use of this approach and to conduct their own audits. The necessity for multiple audits has been diminished in one field in Britain by the founding of the Pressure Vessel Quality Assurance Board (PVQAB), and its affiliation with the Institution of Mechanical Engineers. It is not therefore a Government body,

---

* A term which nevertheless, like good workmanship, is undefinable and cannot be translated to other languages.

but is fully recognised by the Health and Safety Executive. The duties of the compact staff, answerable to the Board, centre upon the appointment of auditors to act at companies seeking and extending recognition, and to ensure that the auditors operate impartially and are themselves suitably qualified. The auditors are drawn from the skilled and experienced staffs of engineering insurers and classification bodies. The advantage of the system to the participating manufacturing companies, including those concerned as subcontractors, is that the need for multiple audits is diminished. Its success will otherwise depend upon the capability to satisfy customers for equipment whose standards have already been created by previous experience. The PVQAB should provide for users of British Standards the facility which has hitherto been provided by the American Society of Mechanical Engineers for users of the corresponding US Standards, a service which has proved to be of such value that it has penetrated many countries of the world, and is well-known for its pragmatism.

It should be emphasized that these systems take care of the need for organisation of quality assurance and provide for its audit; they do not diminish the need on behalf of the customer to make use of independent inspection, which may be provided as before by the insurers and classification societies, nor do they replace internal inspection during the progress of work. The systems do provide unambiguous evidence of what is expected in manufacture, and how it is to be attained.

CODES AND STANDARDS

Nothing that has been described diminishes the need for effective national codes and standards for structural design, materials, fabrication processes, and testing methods, and they are important components in the fitness-for-purpose listing. However, they are always likely to follow rather than to lead in times of change, because of the need to embrace existing good practices to verify fully that which is codified before it can be endorsed. This process has been shortened to some extent in Britain by the issue of Draft for Development Standards and Published Documents, which contain relevant information but warn that it should be used with circumspection, rather than become mandatory as part of the contractual process. Use of these types of document has been made in facture mechanics to deal with test methods, and with topics such as the definition of acceptable defect sizes for welded structures. This approach confers the benefit of unification at the stage of data collection, so that the time to completion of a full standard can be truncated.

DISCUSSION AND CONCLUSIONS

Fitness for purpose is the shorthand name for a concept which has emerged almost spontaneously in more than one country, and one which has not yet been fully defined and applied. The need for it has arisen, if a personal opinion may be stated, in response to the proliferation in recent years of powerful new methods of quality assessment which have been created through the efforts of physical and management scientists and engineers, motivated by the need to provide a more certain prediction of performance than hitherto in large pioneering projects. Aerospace has been an obvious example but there are others too, particularly in the power generation and energy-related fields. The need to achieve good standards of safety and reliability for the protection of the public has become so demanding that no cost will be spared to provide it in those areas where it is most needed.

The correct balance between quality and required performance is thereby measured, defined, and achieved as necessary. This then presents a dilemma, in terms of a conflict of moral and economic choices which can no longer be borne entirely by individuals. When the best approach is recognised who will say that such standards should be relaxed for far less demanding constructions, yet which country can afford to do otherwise, in terms of securing its own economic survival? What is needed is a framework, or basis, upon which such choices are made that can be debated, developed, and eventually accepted widely. It will ultimately have to be international in scope since there is nowadays such interdependence between nations.

An example of this trend has been identified above in the application of fracture mechanics, but the thrust of the attempt to create a perspective has been to demonstrate that there have been many other parallel developments which relate to fitness for purpose. It may be concluded that the topic should be recognised as a whole, with the aim to provide that which is consciously chosen to be the right quality of material and fabrication for every application. There is abundant hope that the tenets of belief relating to fitness for purpose could be accommodated within the framework of QA programmes, since it is the latter which embrace the whole activity of pursuit of quality, and which have the organic characteristic to provide for their own development and updating.

REFERENCES

1. Parsons,R.H.,1947,"History of the Institution of Mechanical Engineers", I.Mech.E.,London,England.

2. Shank,M.E.,1953,WRC Bulletin 17,4.

3. Fuchs,E.,1961,British Welding J.8(1),4.

4. 1981,Welding Institute/AWS/WRC Conference Proceedings "Fitness for Purpose Validation of Welded Constructions",London,England. Publ. by The Welding Institute 1982.

5. Warner,F., and Slater,D.H.,1981,Proc.Roy.Soc.of London A376,1.

6. Ford,H.,et al,1981,Phil.Trans.Roy.Soc.of London A299,19.

7. Wells,A.A.,1979,"Structural Integrity: Evolution of a Technology",ASME Conference Proceedings "Structural Integrity Technology".

8. Burdekin,F.M.,1963,British Welding J.10(4),183.

9. Hanstead,P.D.,1981,Proc.Roy.Soc.of London A374,491.

FRACTURE PREVENTION IN PIPELINES

I. Le May[1], J.T. Justice[2], and R.M. Jamieson[3]

The paper reviews the development of pipeline steels in the context both of fracture problems which have occurred in the past and of future requirements for fracture resistant systems. Methods of assessing toughness and of ensuring that high toughness steels are produced are discussed, and developments in NDE techniques and testing procedures to ensure pipeline integrity are examined.

INTRODUCTION

Failures in oil and gas pipelines can arise from a number of causes. The principal ways in which fracture initiation can take place are through mechanical damage, corrosion, stress corrosion cracking (SCC), and hydrogen induced cracking. Fatigue is also a source of fracture at longitudinal welds in oil pipelines, but is not found to be a problem in gas pipelines.

Fracture initiation may lead to leakage only, the crack arresting after very limited growth, or else a running failure may develop, this being particularly serious in the case of gas pipelines which operate at substantial pressure. Running failures may be either brittle or ductile in nature, depending on the toughness of the pipeline steel.

Figure 1 shows an example of a running brittle failure, this having taken place in Northern Ontario, Canada, in 1979, in a 760 mm diameter natural gas pipeline. The fracture initiated at a region which had been dented and gouged during construction and which is shown in Figure 2. The fracture ran for some 650 m, terminating in one direction at a section of heavier wall pipe at a valve, and at the other end where it ran into a section of tougher pipe.

Figure 3 shows a pipeline which failed by SCC after some 20 years of operation. In this case there had been interaction between the cathodic protection and the soil surrounding the pipe, leading to localized SCC at an imperfectly applied area of the asphalt coating. Figure 4 illustrates the

[1] Department of Mechanical Engineering, University of Saskatchewan, Saskatoon, Sask. Canada S7N 0W0
[2] Manager, Quality Control, TransCanada PipeLines, Toronto, Ont. Canada.
[3] Assistant Manager, Pipeline Monitoring, TransCanada PipeLines, Toronto, Ont. Canada.

localized attack in the steel underlying the coating.

Hydrogen induced cracking can occur preferentially in sour gas pipelines and in oil pipelines carrying higher sulfur crude. It initiates in regions containing non-metallic inclusions, and two cracking modes may be identified; (1) straight cracking parallel to the rolling plane, and (2) stepwise cracking, which is particularly detrimental when the cracks propagate through the thickness as shown schematically in Figure 5. The first evidence of this problem in pipelines occurred when crude oil leaked from an underwater pipeline in the Persian Gulf in 1974, as reported by Abe et al (1): subsequent analysis showed the failure to have originated from stepwise cracking at inclusions, caused by hydrogen gas accumulating there under pressure.

Delayed hydrogen cracking is also a major cause of leaking girth welds in pipelines and is associated with the use of cellulosic electrodes (Justice (2)). Shielded metal arc electrodes with a cellulosic coating were, until recently, the standard consumable used in the field welding of pipelines, because of their ability to deposit a root bead rapidly. Hydrogen assisted cracking at the root bead can be initiated if: (1) there is a susceptible microstructure in the heat affected zone (HAZ) because of too rapid cooling; (2) the residual stresses caused by contraction, the stress concentration at discontinuities, and the lifting stresses associated with construction are together significant; and (3) hydrogen from the shielding gas from the cellulosic electrode coating reaches the susceptible microstructure.

In order to minimize the risk of fractures in pipelines it is necessary to utilize material which is inherently tough and which has good weldability. It is also important to ensure that there is protection against corrosion and SCC during service. However, it is of interest to note that the American Gas Association, in a 1980 report entitled "An Analysis of Reportable Incidents for Natural Gas Transmission and Gathering Lines, 1970 through 1978", concluded that the major cause of service incidents was outside force. This covers the cases where mechanical equipment contacted the line or when earth movements or thermal strains caused excessive loading.

The present paper attempts to review factors leading to the minimizing of the risk of pipeline failure, covering materials aspects, fabrication procedures, inspection during construction, and periodic pipeline monitoring in service.

DEVELOPMENTS IN PIPELINE STEELS

In the past, high carbon contents of the order of 0.25% were used in order to produce adequate tensile properties. In order to improve low temperature toughness and provide good weldability, the carbon content has been reduced steadily, so that today's pipelines suitable for Frontier use in regions such as the Arctic contain less than 0.1%C. The development of pearlite-reduced steels is discussed elsewhere (3), and it may be noted here that by utilizing controlled rolling and austenite grain-refining additions, high strength, tough steels with a polygonal ferrite structure and only a small amount of pearlite were developed for line pipe use.

Subsequently, acicular ferrite steels of improved toughness were developed with carbon contents of the order of 0.06% or less, utilizing controlled rolling and additions of small quantities of niobium to maintain a fine austenite grain size, and with 1.5 to 2.0% Mn and up to 0.5% Mo to provide the desired $\gamma \rightarrow \alpha$ transformation characteristics (Morrow and Tither (4)). The use of precipitation hardening elements such as niobium or vanadium allowed the development of high strength, low alloy (HSLA) steels admirably suited for pipeline use during the 1970s.

Today, the development of on-line, accelerated cooling (OLAC) has allowed the production of very cost-effective steels, with a minimum of alloying additions. The production of these OLAC steels involves laminar cooling of the plate on the runout from the hot mill, computer control allowing properties to be carefully controlled for plate of different thicknesses, different runout speeds, finishing temperatures and so on. Certainly water can be considered to be the most economical alloying agent available!

In order to combat problems of hydrogen pickup and subsequent cracking in sour gas environments, the addition of a small quantity of copper is found to have very beneficial effects. According to Akada et al (5), this occurs because the protective oxide film containing copper suppresses hydrogen entry into the steel. Such copper containing steels are becoming widely used for such critical areas.

TOUGHNESS AND TOUGHNESS ASSESSMENT

The improvement in low temperature toughness through improvements in steel chemistry and microstructure has already been noted. Another very significant advance has been through improvement in steelmaking practice, providing reduction in the quantity and size of inclusions and control of their shape.

The assessment of toughness may be done through the use of Charpy V-notch specimens, pre-cracked Charpy specimens, or Drop Weight Tear Testing (DWTT). Although Charpy specimens are most commonly used, in some cases it is found that Charpy tests cannot adequately characterize the fracture resistance of today's tough linepipe steels. For example, it was commented by the Steel Industry in 1982 that they could not determine valid Charpy toughness measurements using full size specimens at -5°C as required by the specification: the energy absorbed was greater than 80% of the capacity of the impact testing machine, with energy absorption greater than 270J. As a consequence, the test temperature had to be reduced to -20°C to obtain valid impact test results. This indicates just how great the improvement in steelmaking practice has been in recent years.

Thus, with the greatly increased toughness possible, the use of supertough pipe can become part of the original design of a pipeline. The assessment of resistance to ductile fracture can, however, only be made using data from pre-cracked DWTT specimens, and these can be expected to become an industry standard in the future.

Crack arrestors, to stop a running crack, are becoming a part of the initial design. For example, a loose sleeve with insulating grouting between it and the pipe, is used on the Northern Border Line. This restrains the flap opening during a possible running shear fracture, so arresting it. Figure 6 shows the result of such a test on an experimental length of pipe, while Figures 7 and 8 illustrate more clearly the ringing of a full underground test length.

On other isolated lines, crack arrestors with variable spacing may be used, the spacing depending on the economics in terms of time required to undertake a replacement of the damaged length, among other factors.

It should be noted that the higher the pressure and the richer is the gas in the higher hydrocarbons, the greater is the need for arrestors. With lower pressures and leaner gas, the energy release will be insufficient to promote running shear in current linepipe materials.

WELDABILITY

The importance of good weldability, leading to low carbon and low carbon equivalent contents in linepipe steels, has already been noted.

With steel slabs produced by continuous casting procedures, microsegregation of C, Mn and other alloying elements can occur along the centreline. This must be minimized, to reduce the possibility of locally hard spots to a minimum. The use of gas-metal, arc welding (GMAW) is particularly beneficial as this eliminates the possibility of hydrogen being generated to produce hydrogen assisted cracking.

Mechanized welding of pipe sections is becoming of increasing importance, and is almost a "must" on larger diameter, heavier wall pipe, being used extensively in Canada today and to a lesser extent in the U.S.A. For lay barges for offshore pipe laying, mechanized welding has become the normal procedure. Figure 9 illustrates the welding "bugs" running around the outside of a pipe joint, the inside having previously been welded by an internal mechanized procedure.

NEW PROCESSES

A significant development in corrosion prevention in pipelines is the preferred use of epoxy coatings over other coating procedures. These bond much more completely to the surface of properly prepared steel. The cost of cathodic protection of epoxy-coated pipe is reduced, and a pinhole in the coating is found not to be serious, as the corrosion products seal the hole. With other coatings where the coating/metal bond is less intimate, corrosion at a pinhole is serious and spreads out at the interface.

A consequence of the increase in the use of epoxy coatings is the need to have a good thick surface layer of metal free from surface or sub-cutaneous defects. Such a layer is most easily produced by continuous casting practice.

Another significant new development in pipeline fabrication is high impact welding, described by Jamieson et al (6). In this process no filler metal is required, there is no melting, and welding defects are effectively eliminated. The process involves the use of explosive charges to produce a bond, as shown in Figures 10 and 11. The more remote the pipeline and the larger its diameter, the more favoured is the method. For example on a 1220 mm line, five passes of automatic welding would be required, whereas it can be completed with a single high impact welding procedure. Including the post-welding heat treatment to provide stress relief and to alleviate the extreme local hardness produced, a total cycle time of 6 minutes per joint is required for 1068 mm diameter pipe.

NON-DESTRUCTIVE EVALUATION

With the change is field welding process to automatic GMAW, the welding defect that is found most frequently is lack of sidewall fusion. Because of the narrow form of the weld preparation vee, with an angle of 5° only, detection of this defect requires ultrasonic inspection, or else a true radial X-ray beam. Figure 12 illustrates the use of ultrasonics to detect the defect, while Figure 13 shows the applicability of true radial beam X-ray techniques. In the future, however, ultrasonic techniques may become the preferred method for inspecting automatic welds.

New developments in radiographic inspection of pipelines include better crawlers which are battery powered and can run through the line some 15 welded joints only behind the welder. These can run for some 3 km on one battery pack. With improved X-ray generators and the use of a true radial beam the reliability of flaw detection of the lack of sidewall fusion type is excellent. Development is also underway of digital techniques for image enhancement.

The Canadian Standards Association Standard Z184-M1979, "Gas Pipeline Systems", allows an engineering critical assessment to be undertaken of a defect found after the original acceptance of a weld. This involves the application of fracture mechanics principles, and a defect may be allowed even though it exceeds the limits for acceptance after welding. This commonsense approach is particularly valuable when considering the case of offshore pipelines which would be difficult and very costly to repair. Certainly, when there is not a risk of sudden failure taking place, based on fracture mechanics principles, there should be no need for further action.

Acoustic holographic techniques, while of interest for nuclear pressure vessels, are as yet non-starters for pipeline inspection. Present limitations of this technique for pipeline welds relate to the problems inherent in the discrimination of irregular weld profiles in thin walled vessels.

Acoustic emission techniques, however, have proved to be of considerable value in checking for SCC in pipelines. After a SCC failure, acoustic emission may be useful when hydrostatically testing the repaired pipe. Additional SCC activity may be detected by this means.

HYDROSTATIC TESTING

As a means of preventing fracture, proof testing of pipelines at the specified minimum yield strength makes good sense. There is no significant plastic strain in the pipeline, and TransCanada PipeLines consider this to be an integral part of the total program of fracture prevention in pipelines.

Such tests also provide a leak test for sub-critical defects which pass through the wall.

PIPELINE MONITORING

Again, this is an important aspect of assessing the integrity of a pipeline system. Such techniques can detect dents, which often contain gouges, caused by rocks, machinery crossing the line, and so on. On-line electronic inspection tools ("pigs") are now available which pass through the pipe, and using electromagnetic techniques with a flux leakage type of sensor, dents and gouges can be detected. "Pigs" are also available to detect external corrosion, TransCanada PipeLines, for example, having developed such a device with good signal-to-noise ratio.

Similar developments have been reported by British Gas, and some such equipment is now available commercially.

SUMMARY

The foregoing survey has attempted to show that fracture prevention in pipelines is an important and active activity. It involves consideration of the metallurgy and processing of the pipeline material, the use of the latest techniques in welding and NDE, and the application of fracture mechanics principles to minimize risk to the public.

REFERENCES

1. Abe, H., Suzuki, T., and Towawa, F., 1974, Tetsu-to-Hagané, 60, 217.

2. Justice, J.T., 1983, "Defects Need Not Be Buried", Int. Conf. on Pipeline Inspection, Edmonton, Alberta, Canada. (In press.)

3. Strong Tough Structural Steels, 1967, Publn. 104, Iron and Steel Institute, London.

4. Morrow, J.W., and Tither, G., 1977, "High-Strength Coiled Strip for Line Pipe and Structural Applications", Effects of Melting and Processing Variables on the Mechanical Properties of Steel, G.V. Smith, Editor, ASME, New York.

5. Okada, H., Sekino, S., Hosoi, Y., and Murata, T., 1982, "Copper-Containing Structural Steels", Copper in Iron and Steel, I. Le May and L. McD. Schetky, Editors, Wiley-Interscience, New York.

6. Jamieson, R.M., Loyer, A., and Houser, W.D., 1983,"High Impact Girth Welds in Large Diameter Pipe", Steels for Line Pipe and Pipeline Fittings, The Metals Society, London.

Figure 1 Running brittle failure in 760 mm diameter natural gas pipeline in Northern Ontario, Canada. The fracture ran some 650 m

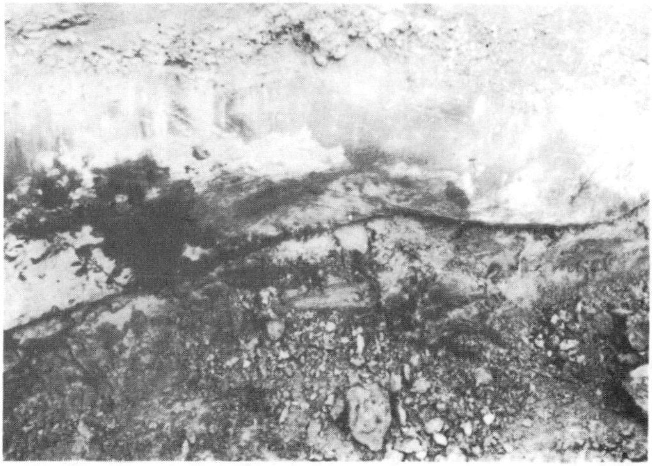

Figure 2 Fracture initiation region of failure shown in Figure 1. The crack started from this area which had been gouged and dented during construction

Figure 3 Pipeline which failed by SCC after 20 years of service

Figure 4 Localized SCC attack in the steel underlying the imperfectly applied asphalt coating of the pipeline shown in Figure 3

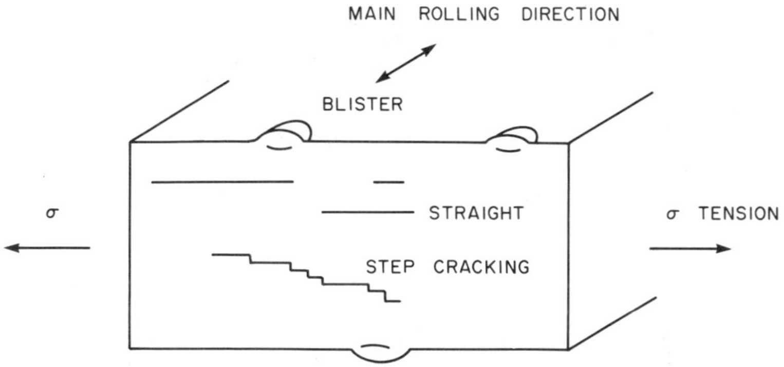

Figure 5 Schematic illustration of hydrogen induced cracking in a transverse section of steel plate

Figure 6 Experimental length of pipe after running shear fracture. The fracture has been arrested at the loose sleeve

Figure 7 Underground test length of pipe after running shear fracture. The fracture terminated at a crack arrestor

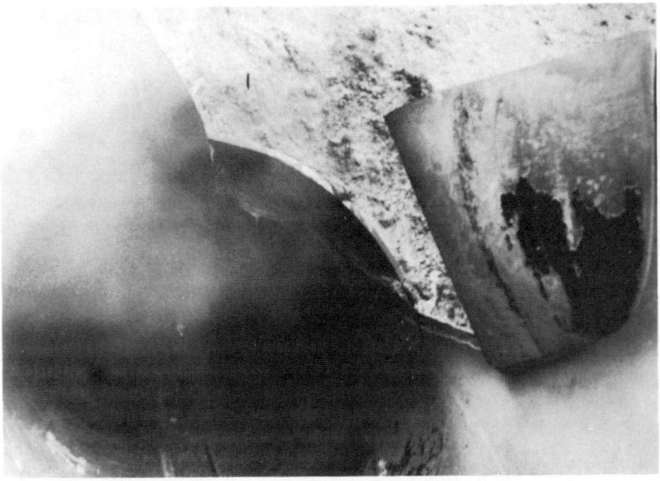

Figure 8 Close-up view of fracture termination at the arrestor in the pipe shown in Figure 7

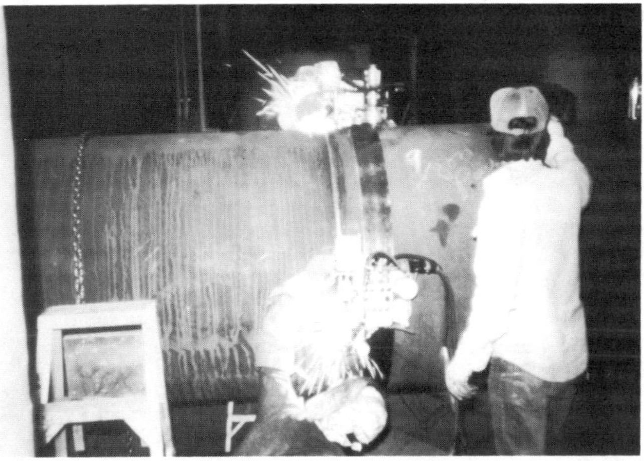

Figure 9 Welding "bugs" running around the outside of a pipe joint

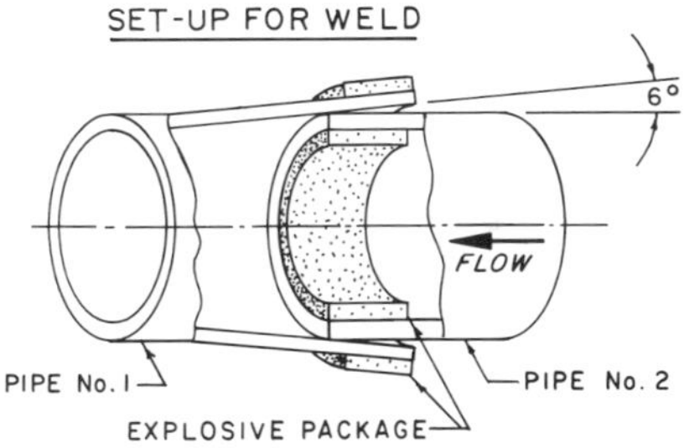

Figure 10 Set-up for high impact welding to joint pipe sections

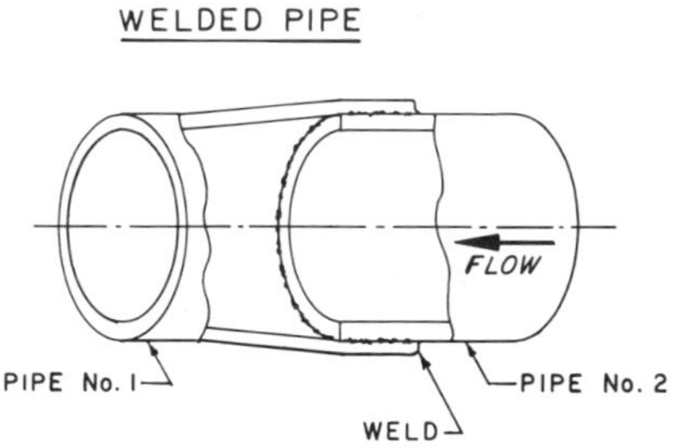

Figure 11 Completed high impact weld

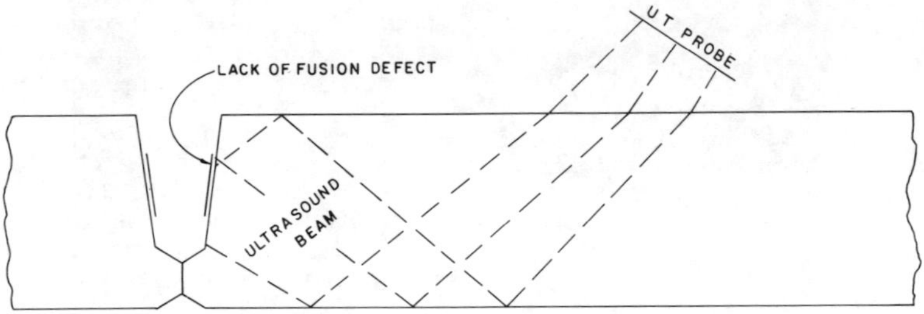

Figure 12 Ultrasonic inspection used to detect lack of sidewall fusion in automatic GMAW field welding

(a)

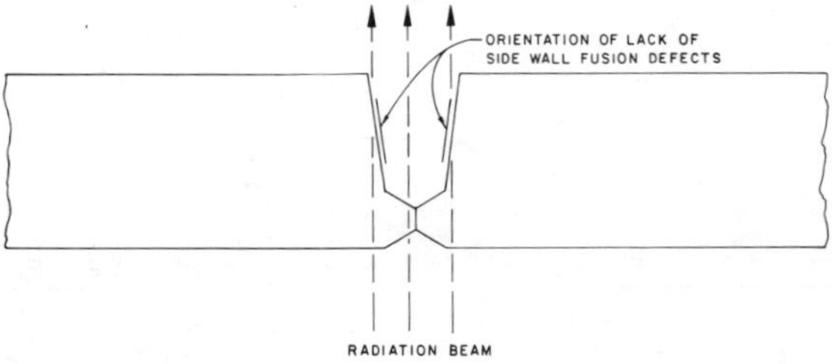

(b)

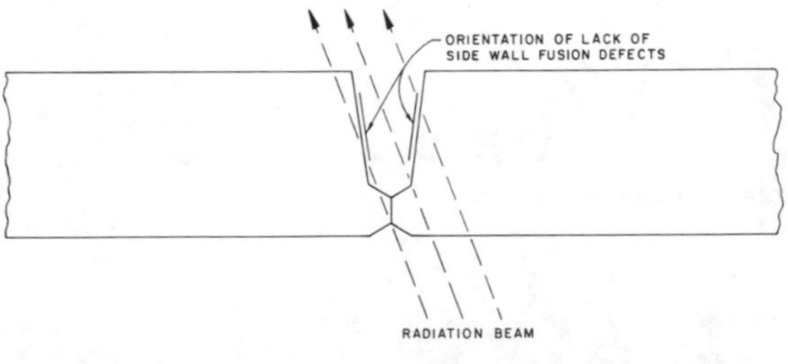

Figure 13 The detection of lack of sidewall fusion using true radial beam X-ray techniques (a). The defects are not detected if the beam is not truly radial, and traditional radiographic equipment is used (b)

FATIGUE AND FRACTURE ASSOCIATED WITH SURFACE AND SUB-SURFACE DEFECTS IN RAILS

S. Marich*

Rail fatigue is one of the main mechanisms controlling rail life and hence operational costs, particularly in high axle load, unit train operations. The paper examines the problems associated with fatigue initiation, growth and final fracture in rails from both surface and sub-surface defects. Fracture mechanics principles are used together with the fatigue properties of the material to determine acceptable size limits for such imperfections. The theoretical predictions have been verified by laboratory experimentation.

INTRODUCTION

The replacement of rails is a major source of operating expenditure and potential loss of revenue incurred by high axle load, unit train operations.

Rail wear, plastic deformation and fatigue are the main mechanisms controlling rail life. Both wear and deformation being longer term cumulative processes, can be readily monitored by track maintenance personnel and hence suitably incorporated in rail replacement strategies. Rail fatigue, however, is a major cause of concern because: (a) fatigue defects on reaching critical size can lead to complete fracture of the rail section and hence become potential sites for derailments; (b) the detection of such defects relies on frequent and expensive ultrasonic inspection of the track; (c) replacements of defective rails leads to considerable maintenance costs and interference to operating schedules, and (d) the amount of wear which a rail can tolerate is directly influenced by the fatigue characteristics of the material. Furthermore, in recent years, the relative importance of fatigue as a rail life controlling mechanism has increased with the introduction of high strength rails, improved lubrication practices and modified wheel/rail interaction characteristics, all of which have led to a marked reduction in the wear and deformation of rails, particularly in curved track as reported by Mutton et al (1), Epp and Okey (2) and Longson and Lamson (3).

In any structural material, and rails are no exception, it is often not technically nor economically possible to prevent the occurrence of defects or small cracks. It is therefore essential to have a means of assessing their behaviour and effect. Fracture mechanics provides an accepted basis for quantifying the characteristics of cracks in structures during their initiation, growth and final failure phases. This paper describes how

* BHP Melbourne Research Laboratories, Australia.

fracture mechanics principles can be used together with the fatigue properties of the material and metallurgical observations to provide guidelines which can be used for realistic manufacturing and design purposes. Since, in high axle load operations the majority of fatigue problems are confined to the rail head, emphasis has been placed on two types of fatigue phenomena, namely those associated with surface and sub-surface defects. In particular, the work examines in detail the initiation and early crack growth stages of fatigue from such defects.

FATIGUE FROM SURFACE DEFECTS

General Concepts

Rail surface defects have generally not received detailed attention, to the extent that current standards either generalise on the requirements or specify limits which are at best based on historical observations. The primary objective of this work was to determine the nucleation and initial growth behaviour of surface defects in the head of rails and relate such behaviour to the applied stress.

The equation relating the stress intensity factor range to the applied stress range ($\Delta\sigma = \sigma_{max} - \sigma_{min}$) and the depth of a surface crack is:

$$\Delta K = Q\,\Delta\sigma\,\sqrt{\pi a} \tag{1}$$

Since this study concentrates on the nucleation of fatigue cracks, use can be made of the above equation rewritten in the form:

$$a_{th} = \frac{1}{\pi}\left(\frac{\Delta K_{th}}{Q\Delta\sigma}\right)^2 \tag{2}$$

where a_{th} is the maximum surface crack depth which can be tolerated without causing fatigue crack growth.

The procedures for determining the parameter Q have been summarised by Rooke and Cartwright (4) for a wide variety of crack geometries. For semi-elliptical surface cracks in a slab subjected to a uniform uniaxial tensile stress, at a crack depth to slab thickness ratio of less than 0.1, and for cracks of depth to half width (c) ratios of 0.4 and 0.5, the values of Q are 0.94 and 0.88 respectively. Therefore equation (2) becomes:

$$a_{th} = 0.36\left(\frac{\Delta K_{th}}{\Delta\sigma}\right)^2 \quad \text{for } a/c = 0.4 \tag{3a}$$

and

$$a_{th} = 0.41\left(\frac{\Delta K_{th}}{\Delta\sigma}\right)^2 \quad \text{for } a/c = 0.5 \tag{3(b)}$$

Fig. 1 shows the fatigue crack growth characteristics of A.R.E.A. standard carbon rails, determined in a previous study using compact tension specimens. It can be seen that the measured value of ΔK_{th} is in the range 13 to 15 $MPa\sqrt{m}$. With this information acting as a guideline, equation (3) can be used to obtain the relationship between a_{th} and $\Delta\sigma$ for various values of ΔK_{th} (the values chosen are at the lower end of the measured range), as shown in Fig. 2. Thus, if the above concept is valid, at a particular $\Delta\sigma$ value cracks with depths below the graphs are not expected to exhibit growth. The experiments described below aim to verify, or otherwise, such a concept.

Experimental Procedure

The fracture mechanics approach is based on the analysis of sharp cracks. The methodology therefore is very conservative in nature since the majority of surface defects which may be introduced during rail manufacture, such as scale and handling marks, are relatively blunt. Nevertheless, to be consistent with the approach, sharp notches of varying depths were machined by means of spark cutting at several locations on the head of the rail specimens, as shown schematically in Fig. 3. Copper discs of various diameters were used for the operation such that for a particular crack depth, the resultant a/c ratio was in the range 0.4 to 0.5. Along the rail length, the notches were no less than 50 mm apart to limit the influence of one notch on the stress intensity factor at the tip of the adjoining notch to less than 2%.

Examples of notches produced using the above procedure are shown in Fig. 4(a), while Fig. 4(b) illustrates in more detail the morphology of the notch tip which had a radius of about 0.06 mm. The spark cutting operation also produced a thin layer of martensite on the surface of the notch which enhanced the severity of the test procedure.

The notched rail samples were subjected to fatigue loading conditions using a rolling load machine which has been described in detail previously by Marich et al (5). The samples were assembled in the machine on a baseplate canted at 6° from the vertical (Fig. 3) to simulate uneven loading of the rail section and hence any torsional affects. All tests were conducted at a vertical applied load of 150 kN, equivalent to a nominal axle load of 30 tonnes. As illustrated in Fig. 3, the wheel segment travelled a distance of 300 mm over the rail running surface, subjecting both the supported and cantilevered sections of the rail to loading conditions. The rate of loading was four complete wheel cycles (back and forth) per second.

Some of the specimens were also fitted with a rail tensioning rig, designed to apply constant longitudinal tensile stresses equivalent to those generated by thermal contraction of the rail at temperatures below the stress free temperature of rail welds. In this study, the rails were subjected to a stress of 80 MPa, i.e. equivalent to 35°C below stress free temperature.

To quantify the stresses applied to the rails during fatigue loading, strain gauge rosettes were applied at numerous locations on the rail cross section, as shown schematically in Fig. 5, and at three positions along the length of the rail, namely at the cantilever point and at 50 mm on either side of this point. Strain readings from the gauges were recorded as the rolling load travelled over a complete cycle.

Examples of the variation in the longitudinal stress measured at three locations on the rail cross section at the cantilever point are shown in Fig. 6. It is of interest to note that on the top and side of the rail head the maximum tensile stress is obtained when the wheel segment is at the end of its travel on the unsupported rail section, i.e. maximum bending. At the bottom of the rail head, on the other hand, the maximum tensile stress occurs when the wheel segment is directly above the measuring point, i.e. the resultant stress is due to the bending of the rail head on the web. Because of this bending, compressive longitudinal stresses are also obtained at the top of the rail head. Pretensioning of the rail results in an overall increase in the tensile stress.

Crack growth, if any, was measured using a Krautkramer d.c. potential drop meter which exhibited a proven accuracy of ± 0.2 mm for total crack depths in the range 2 to 15 mm. The specimens in which crack growth was small or could not be detected were subjected to 1 million stress cycles, i.e. an equivalent of about 40 million gross tonnes of traffic. These samples were subsequently sectioned and examined metallographically.

Results and Discussion

The early stage of fatigue crack growth from one of the machined notches is illustrated by the longitudinal section in Fig. 7(a). Fig. 7(b) shows a rail section in which the fatigue crack has reached critical size and led to failure of the rail. The figure also shows the initial notch and the wheel/rail contact band on the left side of the rail top surface. In all tests, the crack propagation occurred on a transverse plane, indicating that the major stress was essentially uniaxial in nature and acting in the longitudinal direction, as assumed in the fracture analysis.

Figure 8 summarises the results obtained in the form of crack growth/no-growth as a function of initial crack depth and measured stress range. Each point on the graph represents an individual initial machined notch. The graphs relating threshold crack depth to stress range obtained from equation (3) for a ΔK_{th} value of 12.5 MPa $\sqrt{m}$ and for a/c values of 0.4 and 0.5 are also shown in the figure. It is evident that the results validate the fracture mechanics concept, i.e. at a particular $\Delta\sigma$ value cracks with depths below the graphs do not exhibit growth.

In achieving the validation, three aspects related to the results require comment:

1. As shown in Fig. 6, notches on the side and bottom of the rail head in non-tensioned rails were subjected to a stress cycle with $R = 0$. The respective $\Delta\sigma$ values indicated in Fig. 8 were therefore equivalen to σ_{max}.

2. Notches in tensioned rails were subjected to positive R values. For these, the stress values plotted in Fig. 8 were also equivalent to σ_{max} (and not $\Delta\sigma$). This may be justified as follows:

   Cooke and Beevers (6, 7) have shown that in rail steels the relationship between ΔK_{th} and positive R values can be approximated by the equation

$$\Delta K_{thR} = \Delta K_{th} (1 - R) \tag{4}$$

   where ΔK_{thR} is the threshold at a given R ratio and ΔK_{th} is the threshold for $R = 0$, i.e. the value obtained experimentally and used in this study.

   Equation (2) therefore can be rewritten as

$$a_{thR} = \frac{1}{\pi} \left(\frac{\Delta K_{th} (1 - R)}{Q \, \Delta\sigma} \right)^2 \tag{5}$$

   where a_{thR} is the threshold crack depth at a given R ratio.

   Since $R = \sigma_{min}/\sigma_{max}$ and $\Delta\sigma = \sigma_{max} - \sigma_{min}$, equation (5) becomes

$$a_{thR} = \frac{1}{\pi}\left(\frac{\Delta K_{th}}{Q\ \sigma_{max}}\right)^2 \qquad (6)$$

The use of σ_{max} values in plotting the data, therefore, accounts for the influence of R on a_{th}.

3. Notches located on the top of the rail head in non-tensioned rails were subjected to negative R values. For these, the stress values plotted in Fig. 8 are equivalent to the total $\Delta\sigma$, i.e. both positive and negative stresses. The results therefore indicate that an applied compressive stress does have an adverse effect on the fatigue initiation characteristics of the material. The compression portion of a cyclic load is generally not considered in fatigue analysis since the common assumption is that cracks do not grow appreciably whilst in compression. However, Stephens et al (8) have shown that the fatigue life of a material is decreased substantially at negative R values, even under constant amplitude loading. Indeed, Reid et al (9) have observed crack initiation and growth under totally compressive applied loads by applying a relatively high initial compressive load which is thought to produce a plastic zone near the notch tip. On relaxing the load, residual tensile stresses develop in the vicinity of the plastic zone and enhance the fatigue process. The current data support such findings.

The practical application of the analysis is illustrated in the following example:

Laboratory experiments have shown that the maximum longitudinal tensile stresses due to bending and torsion of a rail are obtained at the field lower corner of the rail head (point A in Fig. 9). The graphs in Fig. 9 show measured stresses at various lateral to vertical (L/V) force ratios (V = 150 kN) and percent rail head losses, for a 68 kg/m rail section and central rail loading. From Fig. 8 it can be seen that a 1 mm deep sharp notch will not exhibit fatigue growth at a stress level of 240 MPa. Thus, for jointed railway track, in which thermal stresses are not significant, the data in Fig. 9 indicates that at a L/V ratio of 0.3 (typical of 600 to 800 m radius curves) a rail head loss limit of just under 55% (point B) would be acceptable in terms of fatigue performance. In welded rail, longitudinal tensile thermal stresses have to be considered. For a thermal stress of 80 MPa (equivalent to a rail temperature of 35°C below the stress free temperature), the allowable head wear limit is 40% (point C). Both of these values are considerably greater than what is currently accepted and consequently their adoption would lead to substantial cost savings by deferment of rail replacement.

FATIGUE FROM SUBSURFACE DEFECTS

General Fracture Characteristics of Defects

Fig. 10 illustrates the general appearance of the subsurface nucleated defects which can develop under high axle load operations. Previous fractographic studies by Marich et al (5) and Chipperfield and Skinner (10) revealed that the initiation and early growth of the defects consisted of the following stages (summarised schematically in Fig. 11):

1. Nucleation at a depth of 5 to 10 mm from the gauge corner of the rail in a region just inside the deformed and work hardened layer, which can extend to a depth of 10 mm. The nucleation site is generally an elongated

step which forms by cracking associated with non metallic inclusions (complex silicates or aluminates), typically matrix separation at inclusion edges followed by coalescence of the cracks from closely spaced neighbouring inclusions until a crack or step of "critical" size is reached. The minimum step width observed has been 80 μm with an aspect ratio of 10:1 or greater, i.e. corresponding to the elongated ellipsoidal inclusion clusters produced during hot rolling of the rails.

2. Initial growth from the step proceeds primarily in the transverse direction at an angle of 50 to 70° to the vertical, to form a small featureless elliptical plateau.

3. Subsequent subsurface growth occurs both longitudinally and transversely to form a defect known as a shell.

4. At some later stage of growth the shell defect may branch and rotate, due to the presence of longitudinal tensile stresses and/or forward shear, to form a transverse defect (TD) which grows predominantly on a transverse plane until a critical size is reached which causes rail failure.

Marich et al (5) observed a white etching phase on the fracture surfaces of shells and TD's in their early stages of growth. The formation of this hard phase is due to localised friction at the rubbing surfaces of the cracks and indicates the presence of high shear stresses.

Fracture Mechanics Analysis

The metallographic observations summarised above are used as a guide to the development and as a means of assessing the adequacy of the fracture analysis procedure.

The first stage of the procedure consists of estimating the stresses acting at the nucleation zone of the defects. For this estimation, an elastic stress analysis, based on the theory of Hertz, is performed as described by Chipperfield and Skinner (10). Residual stresses, wheel/rail contact normal and shear forces, thermal and rail bending stresses are all taken into account to compute total axial and total shear stresses as a function of wheel contact position (X) along the rail, subsurface depth (Z) and as a function of axes rotation angle (θ), i.e. for the coordinate axes system x, $\acute{y}$, $\acute{z}$ as shown in Fig. 12. Typical shear stress (τ) distributions calculated for a 150 kN wheel load, 45 kN transverse and longitudinal surface frictional forces, with $\theta = 0$, directly beneath the centre of contact between new wheel and new rail are also shown in Fig. 12.

It is recognised that the elastic stress analysis is a simplification of the true loading situation which involves significant plastic flow and contact near the gauge corner rather than on top of the rail. Further work is being done to improve the accuracy of the analysis. Nevertheless such further work could be justified only if the preliminary analysis shows potential.

The relatively small amount of information available on crack tip opening by Mode I (pure tensile), Mode II (shearing) and Mode III (tearing) mechanisms suggests that an appropriate criterion for the avoidance of fatigue damage is:

$$\Delta K = \Delta K_I + \Delta K_{II} + \Delta K_{III} \leqslant \Delta K_{th} \approx 10 \text{ MPa} \sqrt{m} \quad (7)$$

where 10 MPa $\sqrt{m}$ is the lowest value of ΔK_{th} measured in rail steels using compact tension specimens.

An inclusion or inclusion cluster of diameter 2c and length 2ℓ, situated at a subsurface depth z directly beneath the wheel/rail contact, is equivalent to an elliptical flaw of minor axis 2c and major axis 2ℓ. To calculate the threshold flaw size and preferred angle of propagation, stresses analogous to those shown in Fig. 12 are calculated on the new set of axes x, $\acute{y}$, $\acute{z}$ at various values of θ. Assuming that shear modes dominate the shell initiation event, the total ΔK may be calculated for an elongated defect ($c/\ell \leqslant 0.1$) using data from Rooke and Carthwright (4) as follows:

$$\Delta K_{II} + \Delta K_{III} = (\Delta\tau_{\acute{y}\acute{z}} + \Delta\tau_{\acute{y}x})\sqrt{\pi c} \qquad (8)$$

for the ends of the minor axis, and

$$\Delta K_{II} + \Delta K_{III} = (0.22\,\Delta\tau_{\acute{y}\acute{z}} + 0.44\,\Delta\tau_{\acute{y}x})\sqrt{\pi c} \qquad (9)$$

for the ends of the major axis.

It is therefore evident that the fatigue sensitivity is dependent principally on the diameter (2c) of a subsurface defect. In addition a comparison of the relative magnitudes of equations (8) and (9) confirms that, if the inclusion diameter is sufficiently large to promote fatigue initiation, growth will proceed initially at the end of the minor rather than the major axis, as is indeed observed, i.e. as shown in Fig. 11 lateral growth from Y to B and X to D occurs prior to extension at points A and C.

Threshold defect sizes, calculated using equations (7) and (8), as a function of axes rotation angle θ are shown in Fig. 13. It is evident that at the subsurface depths typical of shell defect development (5-10 mm), the minimum sizes of 70 to 100 µm are obtained at an angle θ of 50-60°. Initial growth on this plane would consequently be preferred. Both threshold defect sizes and plane of growth are in good agreement with the metallographic observations.

The only aspect which is not explained by the "simple" model is the preferred subsurface depth of shell nucleation (2 to 5 mm predicted compared with 5-10 mm observed). However, as proposed recently by Leis and Rice (11), this could be due to the development of high compressive residual stresses near the surface of the rail which would tend to inhibit fatigue nucleation and initial growth.

Discussion

The analysis described above appears to provide a reasonably accurate description of rail head fatigue both in its ability to define the inclusion sizes which are susceptible to fatigue initiation and the topography of subsequent fatigue growth. The procedure, therefore, can be used to assess the influence of various operating and manufacturing parameters on the fatigue performance of rails. For example; it can be shown that an increase in axle load of 33%, from 300 kN to 400 kN, will decrease the minimum threshold defect diameter by 17%. With a knowledge of the statistical inclusion size distribution in the rail, this information can be used to quantify the increased number of fatigue defects which would be expected to occur. The analysis also highlights the importance of contact stresses associated with wheel/rail geometry and interaction and material characteristics, in particular cleanliness and threshold stress intensity factor.

CONCLUSIONS

The preceding discussion has illustrated, by examining two specific examples, how fracture mechanics concepts can be utilised together with material properties and appropriate stress analysis procedures to provide guidelines which can be followed by both railway components manufacturers and users. Similar procedures may be adopted for all railway components, including wheels, couplers, axles, bogies and rail fasteners.

The procedure allows the design of components to be made on a technical basis rather than on historical experience which, although important, is at best qualitative in nature. The procedure can also be used by management as a tool to quantify some of the consequences related to changes in operating practices.

The judicious adoption and use of such concepts will result in improved cost effectiveness of railway operations.

REFERENCES

1. Mutton, P., Epp, C., and Marich, S., 1982 "Rail Assessment", A.A.R. Conference Proceedings "Second International Heavy Haul Conf.", Colorado Springs, U.S.A., Session 30.

2. Epp, C., and Okey, R., 1982 "The Influence of Wheel/Rail Interaction on System Performance", Ibid., Session 31A.

3. Longson, B.H., and Lamson, S.T., 1982 "Development of Rail Profile Grinding at Hamersley Iron", Ibid., Session 33.

4. Rooke, D.P., and Cartwright, D.J., 1976 "Compendium of Stress Intensity Factors", Her Majesty's Stationery Office, London, England.

5. Marich, S., Cottam, J.W., and Curcio, P., 1978 "Laboratory Investigation of Transverse Defects in Rails", The I.E. Aust. Conference Proceedings "Heavy Haul Railways Conf.", Perth, Australia, Session 303.

6. Cooke, R.J., and Beevers, C.J., 1973, Eng. Fract. Mech. 5, 1061.

7. Beevers, C.J., 1977, Met. Sc. 11, 362.

8. Stephens, R.I., Sheets, E.C., and Njus, G.O., 1977 "Fatigue Crack Growth and Life Predictions in Man-Ten Steel Subjected to Single and Intermittent Tensile Overloads", ASTM STP 637, "Cyclic Stress-Strain and Plastic Deformation Aspects of Fatigue Crack Growth", 176.

9. Reid, C.N., Williams, K., and Hermann, R., 1979, Fatigue Eng. Mat. Struct. 1, 267.

10. Chipperfield, C.G., and Skinner, D.H., 1981 "A Study of Subsurface Fatigue in Rails", The I.E. Aust. Conference Proceedings "Track and Vehicle Dynamics", Sydney, Australia, 12.

11. Leis, B.N., and Rice, R.C., 1982 "Rail Fatigue Resistance - Increased Tonnage and Other Factors of Consequence", AAR Conference Proceedings "Second International Heavy Haul Conf.", Colorado Springs, U.S.A., Session 12.

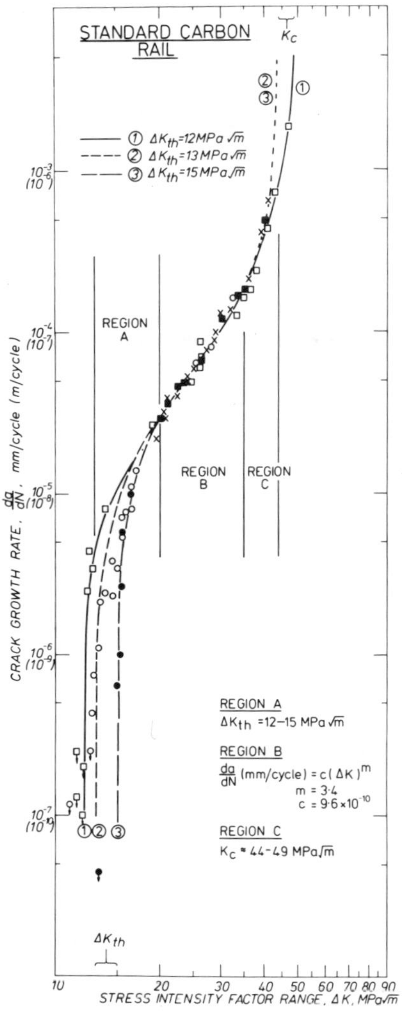

Figure 1: Fatigue properties of standard rail

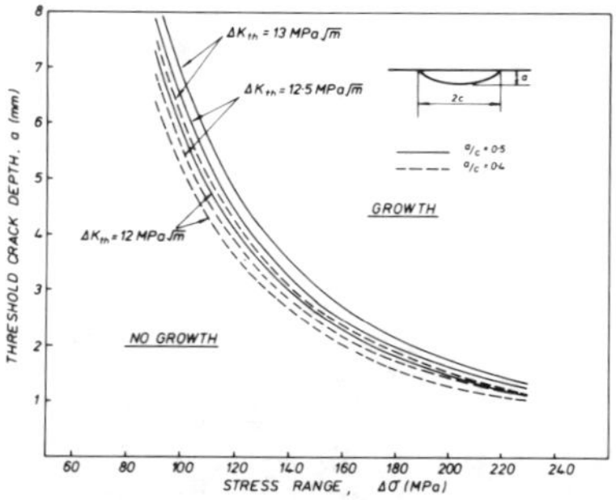

Figure 2: Predicted relationship between a_{th} and $\Delta\sigma$

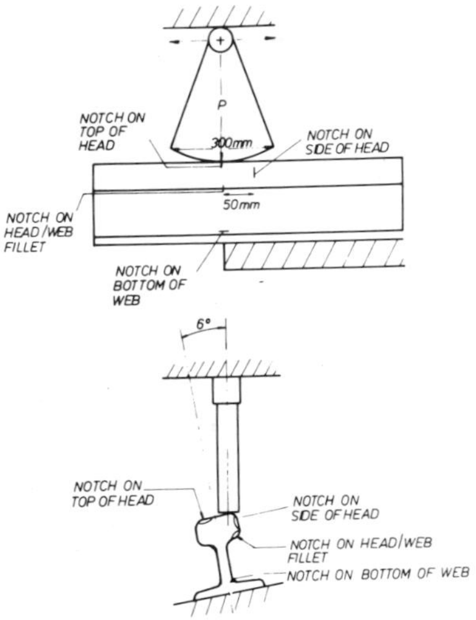

Figure 3: Details of rail loading rig

Figure 4(a): Machined notches in rail

Figure 4(b): Detail of notch tip

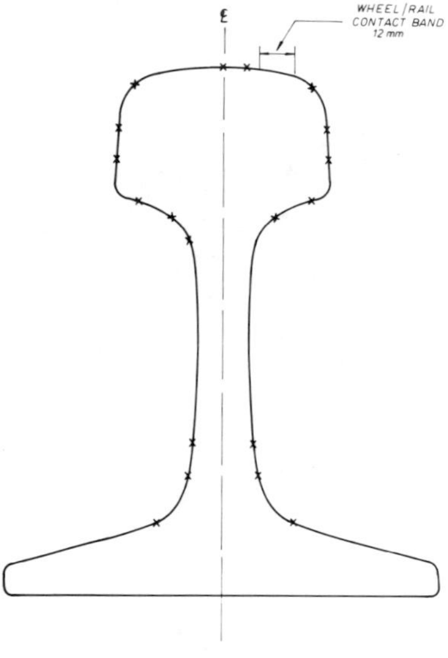

Figure 5: Locations of strain gauges

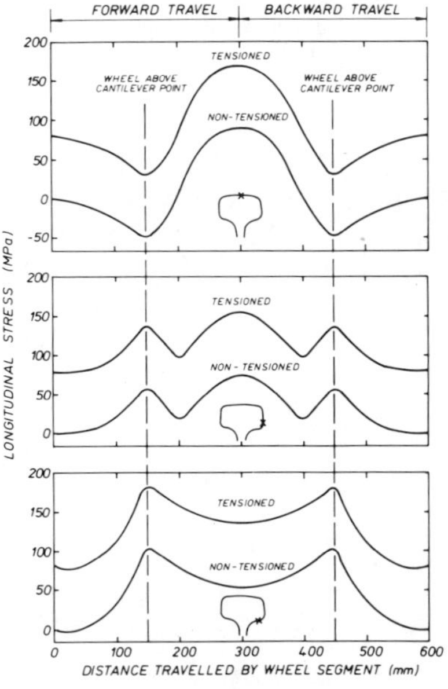

Figure 6: Longitudinal stress cycles

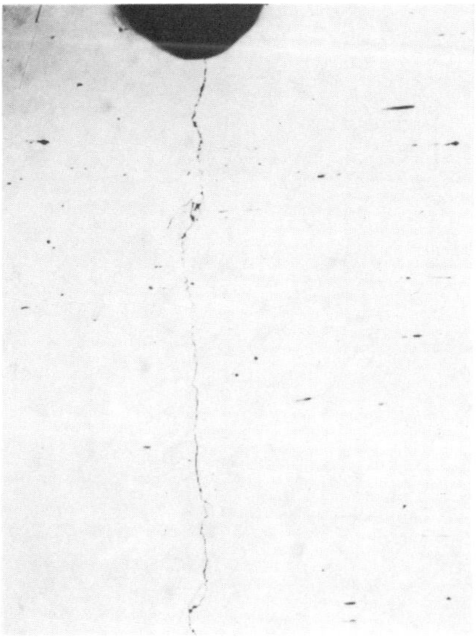

Figure 7(a): Crack growth from notch tip

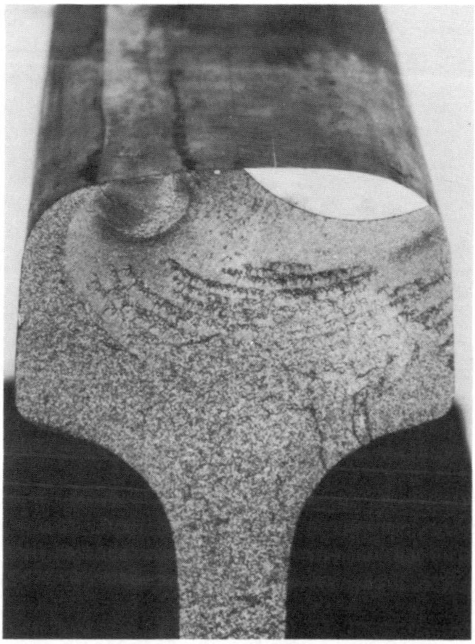

Figure 7(b): Rail in which fatigue crack has reached critical size

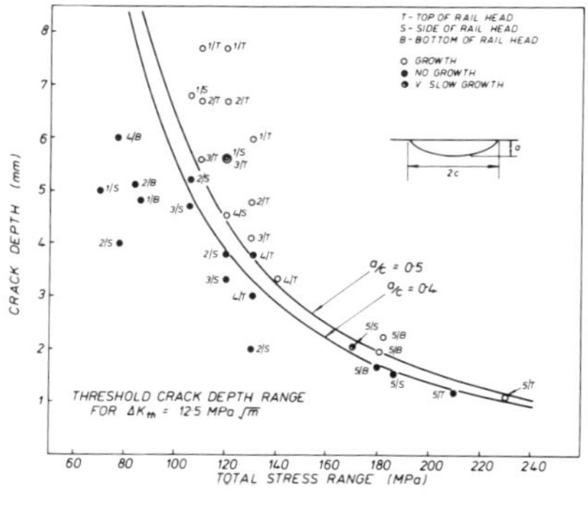

Figure 8: Test results

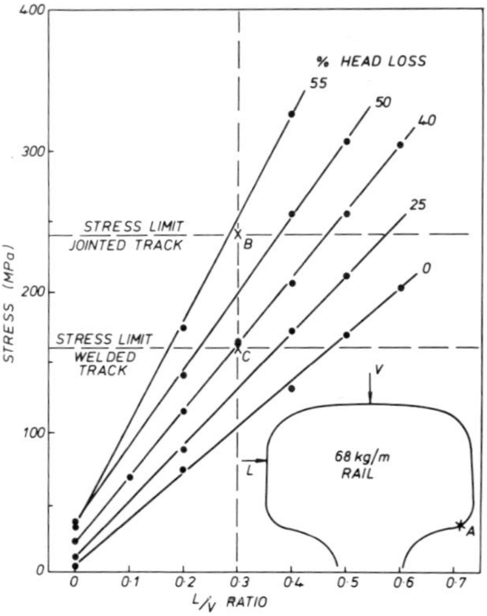

Figure 9: Influence of rail head loss on stress

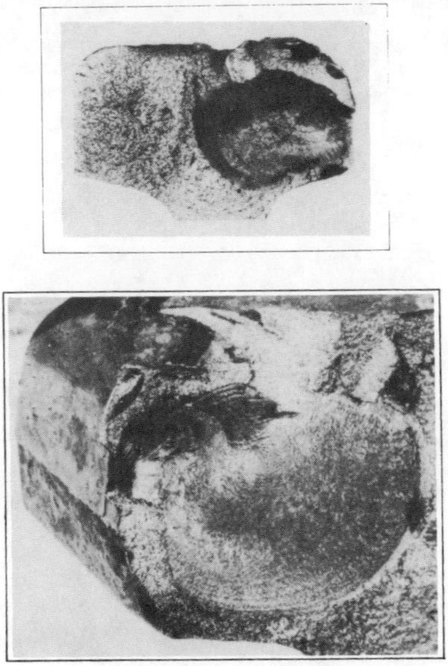

Figure 10: Transverse defect in rail

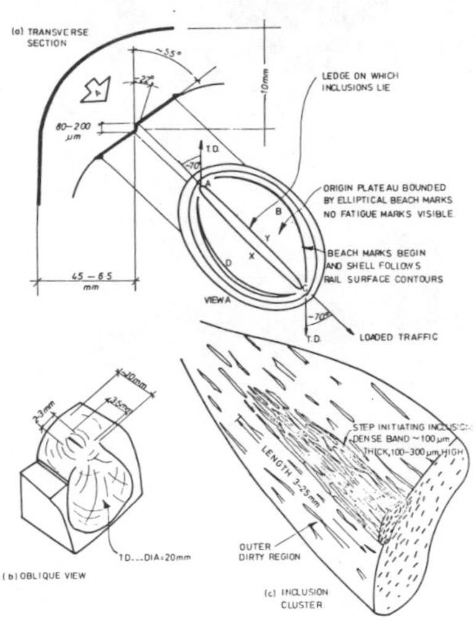

Figure 11: Stages in transverse defect development

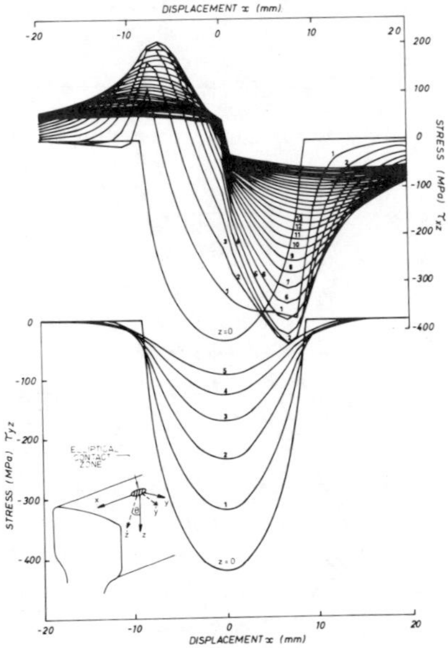

Figure 12: Shear stresses in rail due to wheel/rail contact

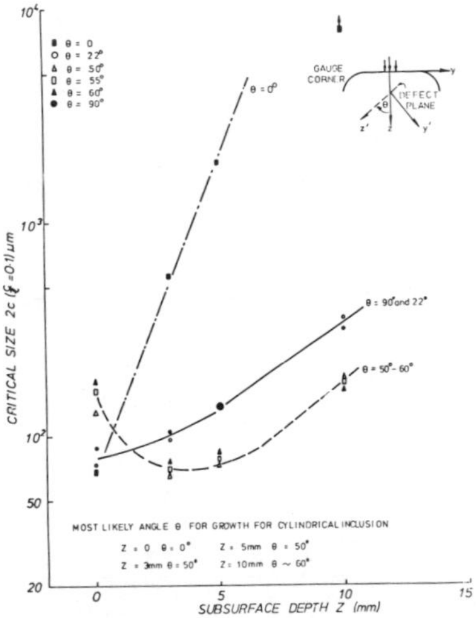

Figure 13: Predicted threshold crack sizes

FRACTURE PREVENTION IN PETRO-CHEMICAL SYSTEMS

J. D. Harrison*

The paper reviews the pressure vessel and storage tank codes used by the petro-chemical industry with respect to fracture prevention. Case histories dealing with failure investigations, and with the application of fracture mechanics to weld defect acceptance are described. It is concluded that, whilst the incidence of failure is not excessive, there are aspects of existing practices which require review. The most important is that the exemption from fracture consideration for plant operating at above 0°C should cease. Adequate toughness must be demonstrated at the minimum temperature at which the plant will be pressurised. Other areas for concern are attachments to vessels and tanks, repair welding, particularly of older tanks and mechanisms of sub-critical crack growth, particularly stress corrosion cracking.

INTRODUCTION

Failures by fracture in the petro-chemical industry are fortunately rare; but when they do occur their consequences can be severe both in terms of loss of life and of economics. This severity will increase in the future as the size and complexity of installations increase and for this reason the industry must be constantly vigilant in learning from past failures and in studying the possible effects of changes in technology on fracture risks.

An illustration of the sizes of modern installations can be got from the following information on storage tanks sizes.

Crude oil up to 1.25 million barrel capacity 110m dia. x 21m high.
LNG and LPG up to 1 million barrel capacity.
Anhydrous ammonia over 35,000 tonne capacity.

Indications of the consequences and hazards are that the brittle fracture of a large LPG storage tank in Qatar led to the loss of seven lives and the destruction of the entire facility including one other LPG tank, two butane tanks and two gasolene tanks (1). (It is believed that a brittle crack propagated the height of the tank). Current lawsuits concerning this failure run to over $533M (2). The author was recently involved in a study of the cause of failure of a pressure vessel in an LNG plant. The plant closure resulting from the failure was reputed to be costing the owner about $3M/day due to lost production. In 1973 the failure of an ammonia storage vessel led to the release of some 38 tonnes of ammonia (c.f. the 35,000 tonne capacity of some installations) and caused the deaths of 22 people (3). An earlier disaster was the failure at Cleveland, Ohio in 1944 of an approximately 20m dia. toro-segmental tank containing about 17,000 barrels of LNG (c.f. current tank sizes up to 1 million barrels). This led to the failure of other tanks with liquid gas spreading into the streets and sewers. Many fires started and 128 people were killed (4).

* Head of Engineering Research, The Welding Institute, Abington, Cambridge, England.

There are many components of petro-chemical plant which can fail by fracture; pressure vessels (there are about 4,000 in a refinery), storage tanks, piping systems, valve bodies, etc., but the present paper restricts discussion to the first two. The paper first sets out the provisions of some selected codes with regard to toughness. It then describes some case histories, firstly concerning failures and secondly concerning the application of fitness for purpose concepts to weld discontinuity acceptance.

CURRENT CODES

The intention of current pressure vessel and storage tank codes is to prevent brittle fracture initiation. Such initiation requires the coincident presence of a tensile stress, a defect perpendicular to this stress, and a susceptible microstructure at the defect tip. Welding is crucial with respect to all these aspects. Welds occur at nozzles, changes in cross-section, etc., and are thus often at points of stress concentration. They also contribute to the acting stresses by the introduction of residual stresses. Defects in rolled plates and forged sections tend to be parallel to the direction of stress flow but those in welds are often transverse to it. Finally, welding can contribute to local embrittlement.The way in which the codes aim to achieve fracture control is described below. The codes reviewed are the AD Merkblatt (5), ASME (6,7) and a British (8) Pressure Vessel Codes and the API (9-12) and British tank codes (13-15).

The Stress

The nominal design stresses permitted by the codes vary quite widely and may be based on a factor on ultimate tensile strength as in Section VIII, Division 1 of the ASME Boiler and Pressure Vessel Code (6,7) or on yield strength as in most other codes. For a steel with a yield strength of $350N/mm^2$ and a tensile strength of $500N/mm^2$, nominal design stresses for the codes reviewed would range from $125N/mm^2$ for ASME VIII, Division 1, to $233N/mm^2$ for A.D. Merkblatt (5) and for the British Codes (8, 13-15). However, because of stress concentrations at nozzles, catalyst trays, stiffeners, etc., and particularly because of tensile residual stresses at welds, the nominal design stress is relatively unimportant and fracture prevention is not greatly dependent on the limitation of stress.

The Defect

The codes all require some level of non-destructive examination (NDE) of welds. The requirements are summarised in Table 1*. It should be noted that there tends to be a concentration on radiographic inspection of the main seams. Other forms of inspection and other welds (nozzles, fillet welded attachments, etc.) receive less emphasis. Two comments are appropriate here. Firstly, radiography is good at finding relatively harmless discontinuities such as pores and slag inclusions. It is much less sensitive to the potentially more serious planar defects (cracks, lack of fusion, etc). Thus, when failures have occurred from defeects in main seams, it has often been from defects which were virtually undetectable by radiography. However, the second point is that more failures initiate from attachments, nozzles, etc., than from main seams. The writer would urge that greater emphasis should be given in all codes to surface crack detection methods for all welds. Even so, many service failures indicate that they would not have been avoided however carefully the NDE had been conducted within practical limits.

---

*Note that the code requirements summarised in Tables 1-3 are much abbreviated. Most codes have many qualifications and special cases. The reader should always refer to the original for specific information.

The Material

Since it is impossible to avoid relatively high stresses at welds and since NDE cannot be relied on as the prime means of defence, the main defence must lie in careful material selection.

Parent steel. Under given circumstances, all the codes require Charpy Impact testing of the parent steels. The requirements are given in Tables 2(a) and (b) for vessels and tanks respectively.

All codes except those for cryogenic storage tanks give exemptions from impact testing under certain conditions. In most cases impact testing is not required for Design Minimum Temperatures (DMT) above 0°C. Pressure vessels built to ASME VIII, Division 1 (6) are exempt down to -29°C and Tanks to API 620 (10) down to -37°C.

The present author believes that this is one of the most important subjects for review. Steels commonly used for pressure vessels and ambient temperature storage tanks are by no means exempt from fracture at temperatures above 0°C. Surveys by Smith and Warwick (16) and by Phillips and Warwick (17) have shown that most vessel failures occur during the hydrostatic test when the temperatures will have been about +10°C. Thus, not only should consideration be given to raising the exemption limits, but an important criterion in material selection should be the avoidance of fracture during the hydrostatic test itself.

Referring to Table 2, it will be seen that there is a notable difference between the requirements of British Standards BS5500 (8) and BS2654 (13) and the remaining codes. The latter (with minor exceptions) all require the Charpy tests to be performed at the DMT or lower. However, in BS5500 and BS2654 the Charpy test temperatures (known in these codes as Material Reference Temperatures (MRT)) vary widely dependent on DMT, thickness, and (in BS5500) on whether the vessel is post weld heat treated (PWHT). For PWHT vessels and for thin as-welded vessels and tanks the MRT can be signficantly above the DMT, whilst for thicker as-welded vessels the MRT can be below the DMT. Figure 1 giving the requirements from BS5500, illustrates this point.

There is no a priori reason why the Charpy tests should be carried out at the service temperature. This test does not provide a true direct measure of toughness and there is a trade off between the effects of thickness, strain rate and notch acuity. The basis for the BS5500 and BS2654 requirements are correlations between the results of about 60 notched and welded wide plate tests carried out in the 1960s (18) and the Charpy transition curves for the base materials used. The correlation adopted was that between the temperature at which a wide plate test could withstand a total applied strain of 4 x yield strain ($4\sigma_Y/E$) and the temperatures at which the Charpy energy was 27 Joules (J) or 40J (depending on whether the tensile strength is less or greater than $450N/mm^2$). In BS 5500 and BS 2654 the Charpy requirements become significantly more onerous with increasing thickness and this is in recognition of the harmful effect of increasing triaxial constraint. None of the other codes have this feature.

An analysis in 1978 (19) of a much larger database comprising over 1,000 wide plate tests has indicated that the approach in these British Standards is reasonable. One gap was a paucity of data for very thin plates (5-10mm) for which the standards permit Charpy testing at temperatures considerably higher than the DMT. Five further wide plate tests have now been conducted which partially fill this gap, and suggest that the approach is still reasonable, although some minor reduction in the Charpy test temperatures for vessels or tanks less than 10mm thick is recommended.

The present author is not aware of the precise justifications for the Charpy requirements in the other codes; but it is presumed that they rest on studies on many of the early ship fractures (20) which showed that the plates in which initiations occurred, generally had Charpy energies of less than 20J.

Weldments. The weldment toughness requirements are summarised in Table 3. All the codes require Charpy Impact tests to be conducted on weld procedure test plates, with the exception of API 620 which gives no explicit requirements with regard to weldment toughness. In most of the codes the weldment requirements are similar to those for base plate. The British Codes only require testing of the weld metals whereas all the remaining codes (except API 620) also require the heat affected zone (HAZ) to be tested. The rationale behind exempting the HAZ from testing in the British Codes is that the Wide Plate - Charpy correlations were for welded wide plates in which the effects of any local degredation will have been accounted for. Because of the very variable response of steels to welding, this philosophy is now questioned and Charpy testing of the HAZ is now recommended.

General Experience with Coded Pressure Vessels and Tanks

Pressure vessels. Whilst the service history for coded pressure vessels is, on the whole good, there have been a number of brittle failures. As previously stated, many have occurred during hydro-test and it can be argued that this shows that the test is performing its function in removing from the population a number of potentially dangerous vessels.

Details of some of the failures have been published. See for example Refs 21-23. Some specific additional cases involving the author's organisation will be discussed later. The main aspects to which attention may be drawn are:-

(a) The importance of toughness at the hydro-test temperature.

(b) The significance of fillet welded attachments (catalyst trays, baffles, etc). There have been a number of service failures, one is described by Cracknell (24), in which failure has initiated at a defective butt weld in an apparently unimportant attachment to the main shell (in Cracknell's case the attachment was a catalyst grid support ring). Fracture can then propagate through the fillet welds fixing the ring to the shell and continue into the shell. There have also been cases of fracture initiating from defects at the toes of the fillet welds themselves.

(c) The importance of taking into account any possible mechanisms for crack growth during the hydro-test or in service by fatigue, hydrogen induced cracking in service, creep, etc.

Oil storage tanks. The failure of oil storage tanks at the Esso Refinery at Fawley in England in 1952 (25) highlighted the potential for brittle fracture in tanks and led to the use of plates and weld metals of improved notch ductility. Their use has now virtually eliminated this risk (26). Three cases of failures since 1955 are known to the author, one being described by Le May (27) and the other two being from confidential files. The failures occurred in 1970, 1972 and 1980 but the tanks were built in 1959, 1946 and 1953 respectively. Since then considerable improvements have taken place in steels, welding consumables, inspection methods, etc. Thus, the available evidence is that existing standards lead to safe installations. Two potential problem areas which the failures have highlighted are the care that needs to be exercised in repair welding and also the possibility that failure may occur when an old tank is put to a new use. Whilst the present situation is satisfactory, care should be taken in adopting new materials such as high strength quenched and tempered steels for the bottom strakes of high rise tanks.

Liquefied gas storage tanks. The, so far, unexplained brittle failure from top to bottom of the LPG tank at Qatar and the consequences of failure of tanks storing large amounts of liquefied gases has given rise to some doubts concerning the adequacy of existing codes which depend on providing resistance to crack initiation. Various solutions are being explored, including the provision of double integrity by means of a concrete wall outside the main tank with or without a surrounding earth bank or alternatively the use of steels for the main tank which are capable of arresting a crack running out of some unknown region whose resistance to crack initiation was insufficient. There is as yet no concensus on the length of crack to be arrested or on the method of measuring crack arrest properties. "Short" crack arrest refers to a crack running through a brittle circumferential weld; "Long" crack arrest, to a crack running the height of one strake in the weld metal or HAZ of a vertical weld. "Short" crack arrest at -50°C has been demonstrated in improved carbon manganese steels, whilst 2½% and 3½% Ni steels are now offered giving "long" crack arrest properties at -50°C, these being demonstrated by means of very large wide plate tests (3m x 3m).

Although the problem of failure of cryogenic tanks was highlighted by the Qatar LPG tank, the largest research programme currently in hand concerns crack arrest in 9% Ni steels for LNG storage at -162°C. This programme is funded by the US Gas Research Institute and is being carried out in laboratories in the USA, Japan and the UK. It is hoped that a detailed and generally applicable crack arrest methodology will arise from this major study.

Finally, it is worth mentioning that tank bottoms are often treated as being unstressed. This is fundamentally wrong, since welding residual stressess, thermal stresses and settlement stresses are often significant, and in some instances are known to have contributed to cracking in tank bottoms.

CASE HISTORIES

It will have been seen above that fracture mechanics as yet plays little part in fracture prevention in the general run of vessels and tanks for the petro chemical industry in contrast to the nuclear industry. However, fracture mechanics comes into its own in failure investigations and in fitness-for-purpose assessments of imperfections. The Welding Institute has been involved in a number of such cases from which there are useful lessons to learn.

Failure Investigations

A vertical refinery vessel. In the winter of 1981 a refinery vessel failed by brittle fracture during a revalidation hydro-test. The tower had been in operation for 13 years. The revalidation test was called for because two new nozzles had been added. Under normal operating conditions the contents of the vessel were at 450°C; but the water for the hydro-test was at approximately 8°C. Failure initiated at a weld between the main vessel cylinder and a smaller diameter "boot". At this position a compensating doubler plate was also attached.

The weld metal had a low initiation toughness at the hydro-test temperature. (CTOD approximately 0.019mm. Estimated K_{Ic} approximately 1750N.mm$^{-3/2}$). This combined with a locally high hoop stress under hydro-test and an unusually high residual stress (for a PWHT vessel) was the cause of fracture initiation. The base plates had low Charpy properties at 8°C (7 to 29J) so that crack arrest was unlikely.

The initiating defect, which was clearly visible on the fracture surface, was a fabrication induced transverse weld metal hydrogen crack which had propagated by a creep mechanism under the high applied and residual stresses to become a surface breaking crack 38mm deep x 55mm long. Failure from a defect of this size was reasonably predicted by linear elastic fracture mechanics.

Lessons to be learnt from this failure are:

a) The hydro-test promoted failure. Brittle fracture in normal service would be impossible. However, the defect could have continued to grow by creep to leakage.

Thus, if leakage of the contents of the vessel in service would have created a serious hazard, the hydro-test performed a useful function in removing the vessel from service by causing it to fail.

b) This failure, like many others under hydro-test, occurred at a temperature at which none of the codes require any consideration of fracture.

c) There is little likelihood that the original defect could have been reliably detected by any form of NDE. Thus in this as in most other cases, the toughness of the material lay at the root of the problem.

Failure of a spherical catalytic reforming reactor vessel This disruptive brittle failure is described in detail by Merrick and Ciuffreda (28). The failed carbon steel vessel was 4.3m diameter and 41mm wall thickness. Fracture occurred when the vessel was on stand-by at 75% of normal operating pressure and when the vessel wall was at about +5°C (the lowest temperature which the vessel had experienced when at pressure). The fracture initiated from the root of a weld attaching an 8mm thick carbon steel ring to the inside of the vessel, this ring being required to support a stainless steel shroud or baffle. The shroud support ring had been replaced at least twice in the 20 year life of the vessel. There had been no heat treatment after this repair because the welds were so small. CTOD tests on the base plate gave high toughness results (0.47mm) but tests in which a saw-cut notch was welded over as described by Burdekin (28) gave exceptionally low CTODs (0.03mm) indicating the susceptibility of the steel to dynamic strain ageing embrittlement. It was evident that the shroud support ring had introduced the following effects:

a) strain ageing damage due to the repeated re-welding,

b) residual stresses transverse to the weld of at least yield magnitude on the inside surface of the vessel,

c) small multiple cracks 1 to 3mm deep caused by the repeated re-welding and

d) a stress concentration factor of about 1.6.

Taking account of these aspects the failure could be predicted by a fracture mechanics analysis using the CTOD approach.

The authors conclude that ASME VIII Division 1 does not provide sufficient safety. Charpy testing should be required for all vessels and the requirements should relate to the lowest pressurisation temperature. The required Charpy energy should increase with increasing thickness and yield strength.

Whilst most modern steels are not so susceptible to strain age damage, there are many vessels in existence made from steels which are. Repairs or alterations to such vessels should be approached with caution. PWHT is beneficial in reducing this form of embrittlement and in lowering residual stresses and should be adhered to even for minor repairs to vessels where any risk of embrittlement exists.

Stress corrosion cracking in ammonia storage tanks and vessels. There is a generic problem of stress corrosion cracking in vessels, etc. used for storing anhydrous ammonia. For example a recent survey showed that over half of the 72 spheres included in the survey contained stress corrosion cracks. There is a considerable volume of literature on this topic and the subject can only be treated very briefly here. Towers has recently written a comprehensive survey (30).

The only apparently reliable methods of preventing SCC are the use of low strength steels combined with low temperature storage (-33.5^{o}C) at atmospheric pressure. Or alternatively, the use of low strength steels with full stress relief prior to service. It had been thought that the addition of 0.2% water to the ammonia was effective; but now SCC has been found in the upper parts of tanks where the ammonia is present in the vapour space and the water concentration is depleted. An important aspect of fracture prevention in situations where freedom from SCC cannot be certain is the need for steels which are tough enough not to fail by brittle fracture from an SC crack. When SC cracks are found, their depth can be assessed by grinding. Fracture mechanics analysis can then be used to assess the risk of failure from cracks of similar depth which have escaped detection. An important point here is that ASME VIII Division 1 would permit a vessel to be built for the storage of ammonia down to -29°C without requiring any impact tests on the steel. Clearly, in the light of present knowledge, this is unwise.

The Application of Fracture Mechanics to the Assessment of Weld Discontinuities

Weld discontinuities which lie outside the requirements of the NDE clauses in the vessel and tank codes are not necessarily deleterious. These requirements are based on normal good workmanship and can be looked on as a means of quality control. However, it can often be very advantageous economically to re-assess the significance of defects on a fitness-for-purpose basis with a view if possible to obviating unnecessary repair or to deferring repair to a later more convenient date. The present author has shown the very large savings which can often occur when advantage is taken of such and approach (31). Furthermore, there are sound safety reasons for avoiding repairs if possible. BS 5500 (8) has a crucial clause permitting this procedure to be adopted by agreement betwen the contracting parties and a British Standard Published Document, PD 6493 (32), provides the basis for such agreement. With regard to fracture the method uses the CTOD design curve as described in reference 33.

PD 6493 has been extensively used in the petro chemical industry. One major company advised the author that the document is applied in a routine manner almost weekly to make major decisions often concerned with the timing of repair. One such case of a CO_2 absorber vessel is described by Dunmore and Parlane (34). Here the fact that repair was deemed unnecessary saved the company concerned some $9M. A further case from the petro chemical industry may be described in more detail.

Process plant pressure vessels. During overhaul, cracks were found in longitudinal seams and at nozzle crotch corners in three 4m diameter x 40mm thick pressure vessels made from carbon-manganese steel. These were attributed to stress corrosion cracking. Assuming that the causes of this cracking could be eliminated by changing the operating environment, could continued operation be validated?

Two possible start-up regimes were under consideration.

1. Pressurise to 7 bar and raise temperature from 20° to 90°C, raise pressure to the 28 bar operating level, and finally bring temperature to operating level of approximately 110°C.

2. As above but maintain pressure at a higher level of 24 bar during heat-up from 20° to 90°C.

The nozzles and the longitudinal seams were considered separately. It transpired that decisions hinged on the nozzle cracks. A typical detail is shown in Fig. 2. Clearly, with this configuration, measurement of crack depth was difficult. However, no cracks could be deeper than shown in the figure, because otherwise leakage would have occurred into the space between the doubler plate and the vessel wall. There were 'tell-tale' holes through the doubler plates and no leakage had been detected at these.

No weld material from the nozzle welds was available, but a sample of a longitudinal seam with representative plate material on either side was extracted from one vessel. Because of the uncertainty surrounding the nozzle weldment toughness, it was assumed that a brittle crack might initiate in this material. The arrest toughness of the parent steel was estimated from dynamic tests as being at least $2200N.mm^{-3/2}$ at -20°C. Reference 35 was used to estimate the stress intensity factor for cracks emanating from the nozzle region and it was found that the critical crack lengths for arrest were: 500mm for an applied pressure of 7 bar and 30mm for an applied pressure of 24 bar.

Because it could not be assumed that a 30mm crack would be completely outside the weldment, a start-up pressure of 24 bar was too high and the lower start-up pressure was recommended. The safety of the vessels with regard to nozzle cracks for this regime was confirmed by Pellini drop weight tests which gave a nil-ductility temperature of -16°C. This also gave confidence in pressurisation at full pressure at 90°C.

The cracks in the longitudinal seams were assessed using the methods of reference 32. Minimum CTOD values for the weldment were 0.03 and 0.22mm at 20° and 90°C respectively. For the 7 bar/20°C start-up condition long surface cracks 14mm deep were tolerable, and this increased somewhat at 28 bar/90°C. It was decided that these values gave sufficient confidence for the vessels to continue in service so that replacement vessels were not required. There were two factors to be put on the debit side in this decision. Firstly, the reduced start-up pressure extended the time to reach operating conditions. Secondly, it was decided to increase the frequency of in-service inspection (two-yearly instead of six-yearly) which involves stripping out and replacing catalyst trays for each inspection. However, these debits were considerably outweighed by the credit which was that three replacement vessels estimated to cost at least $1.5M a piece were not required.

CONCLUDING REMARKS

1. Whilst adherence to existing pressure vessel and tank codes provides a reasonable measure of fracture prevention it could be improved. The following are areas of concern to the author and his colleagues.

   a. The Charpy properties should be determined appropriate to the minimum temperature of pressurisation be this hydro-test or service. Waivers should certainly not be granted in codes simply because this temperature exceeds 0°C.

   b. Charpy requirements should reflect the need for greater toughness with increasing thickness and yield strength.

   c. Butt welds to internals which are themselves welded to the shell should be treated as rigorously as butt welds in the shell.

   d. All welds should be subject to surface crack detection, especially fillet welds.

   e. Repairs and alterations particularly to older equipment should be approached with caution and the possibility of strain age damage resulting from repairs should be borne in mind. Post weld heat treatment of repairs should be considered.

   f. Where the possibility exists of sub-critical crack growth by stress corrosion cracking, consideration should be given to the use of fracture mechanics to assess safe operation.

2. The provision of an enabling clause in standards, which permits contracting parties to assess weld defects on a fitness-for-purpose basis as opposed to the existing arbitrary requirements, is very valuable.

3. Consideration could be given to reducing the amount of radiographic inspection but at the same time paying increased attention to ultrasonic and surface crack detection methods, these being more sensitive to potentially harmful defects.

4. Research into the crack arrest approach for large liquefied gas storage tanks will continue. Whilst some might argue that there has been a tendency to over react to the failure of the Qatar LPG tank, it does seem that steels capable of "long" crack arrest should be available at relatively little extra cost, and these will be adopted for the extra security which they confer.

ACKNOWLEDGEMENTS

The author is grateful to his colleagues at The Welding Institute, particularly Drs. Dawes and Garwood, and also Mr. Towers for helpful suggestions concerning the contents of this paper.

REFERENCES

1. The Times, 2 September 1977, London.

2. The Financial Times, 13 May 1983, London.

3. Lonsdale, H., Symposium on Safety in Ammonia Plant and Related Facilities, Proc. AIChE 17, 126-131.

4. Elliott, M. W., Seibel, C. W., Brown, F. W. Artz, R. T. and Berger, L. B., 1944, "Report on investigation of the fire at the liquefaction, storage and refrigeration plant of the East Ohio Gas Company, Cleveland, Ohio", US Department of the Interior, Bureau of Mines, R.I. 3867.

5. AD-Merkblätter, "Technical Rules for Pressure Vessels".

6. ASME Boiler and Pressure Vessel Code, Section VIII Pressure Vessels, Division 1.

7. Ibid, Division 2, Alternative Rules.

8. BS 5500:1982, "Unfired fusion welded pressure vessels".

9. API 650, "Welded steel tanks for oil storage".

10. API 620, "Recommended rules for design and construction of large, welded, low pressure storage tanks".

11. Ibid, Appendix R, "Low-pressure storage tanks for refrigerated products".

12. Ibid, Appendix Q, "Low-pressure storage tanks for liquefied hydrocarbon products".

13. BS 2654:1973, "Vertical cylindrical welded storage tanks with butt welded shells for the petroleum industry".

14. BS 4741:1971, "Vertical cylindrical welded steel storage tanks for low temperature service: single wall tanks for temperatures down to -50°C".

15. BS 5387:1976, "Vertical cylindrical welded storage tanks for low temperature service: double-wall tanks for temperatures down to -196°C".

16. Smith, T. A. and Warwick, R. G. Int.J. of Pres. Ves. and Piping 2, 283-322.

17. Phillips, C. A. G. and Warwick, R. G. "A survey of defects in pressure vessels built to high standards of construction and its relevance to nuclear primary envelopes", UKAEA Health and Safety Branch Report No. AHSB(S)R 162.

18. Woodley, C. C., Burdekin, F. M. and Wells, A. A., Brit.Weld.J. 11, 123-136.

19. Dawes, M. G. and Denys, R., 1984 "BS 5500 Appendix D: An assessment based on wide plate brittle fracture test data", to be published in Int.J.of Press.Ves. and Piping.

20. Hodgson, J. and Boyd, G. M., Trans. Royal Instn. of Naval Architects 100, 141-180.

21. Conference on Failures in Large Steel Structures, 1968, West of Scotland Iron and Steel Institute, (A number of papers describe vessel and tank failures).

22. Banks, B. Welding and Metal Fab. 41, 4-12.

23. Moisio, T., Metal Construction 4, 3-10.

24. Cracknell, A., "Ammonia plant safety", Proc. AIChE 13, 57-59.

25. Feely, F. J. and Northup, M. S., Welding J 34 Part II, 596s-607s.

26. Clarke, J. S., 1969 "Survey of oil storage tank failures", Belgian Petroleum Institute, Brussels.

27. Le May, I.. Metal Progress 122, No. 3, 35-37.

28. Merrick, R. D. and Ciufredda, A. R., 1983, "Brittle fracture of a pressure vessel - study results and recommendations", 48th Mid-year refining meeting, API.

29. Burdekin, F. M., Brit.Weld.J. 14, 81-83.

30. Towers, O. L., 1984, "History of stress corrosion cracking in anhydrous ammonia storage vessels and implications with respect to vessel integrity", to be published in Metal Construction.

31. Harrison, J. D., 1981, "The economics of a fitness-for-purpose approach to weld defect acceptance", Conference on fitness-for-purpose validation of welded constructions, The Welding Institute.

32. BS PD 6493, 1980, "Guidance on some methods for the derivation of acceptance levels for defects in fusion welded joints".

33. Harrison, J. D., Dawes, M. G., Archer, G. L. and Kamath, M. S., 1979, "The CTOD approach and its application to welded structures", ASTM STP 668, 606-31.

34. Dunmore, O. J. and Parlane, A. J. A., 1981, "Fracture mechanics analysis of a fillet welded attachment in a pressure vessel", Conference on fitness-for-purpose Validation of Welded Constructions, The Welding Institute.

35. "PVRC recommendations on toughness requirements from ferritic materials", 1972, Welding Research Council Bulletin, 175.

Standard	Butt Welds		
	Longitudinal+	Circumferential	Nozzle and Fillet Welds
A.D. Merkblatt Ref. 5	100% RT* or UT*	25-100% RT or UT for large dia. nozzles	10-100% SCD*. UT or RT
ASME VIII Div.1. Ref. 6	100% RT	Partial RT	No specific requirements
ASME VIII Div.2. Ref. 7	100% RT	100% RT	100% SCD or RT or UT
BS5500 Ref. 8	100% RT or UT	100% RT or UT	100% SCD
API 650 Ref. 9	100% RT for thickness greater than 25mm - Spot RT otherwise	Spot RT	Visual
API 620 Ref. 10	100% RT for thickness greater than 31mm - Spot RT otherwise	Spot RT	No specific requirement
BS2654. Ref 13	½% to 10% RT	½% to 2% RT	Visual
API 620 Appendix R Ref. 11	100% RT	Spot RT	100% SCD if not RT
BS4741 Ref. 14	100% RT	5% RT	Visual
API 620 Appendix Q Ref. 12	100% RT	Spot RT	100% LP* if not RT
BS5387 Ref. 15	100% RT	5% RT	Visual

\+ (or vertical in cylindrical storage tanks)
* RT = Radiographic testing. UT = Ultrasonic testing.
SCD = Surface crack detection. LP = Liquid penetrant testing.

TABLE 1 - NDE Requirements in Standards.

Standard	Maximum thickness for as-welded construction, mm	Exemption from impact testing	Temperature for Charpy testing	Required Charpy energy, J
AD-Merkblatt (5) W10	30	If DMT>-10°C	DMT for usual design stress (stress category 1). For lower design stresses (stress categories II and III). DMT +50°C to DMT +80°C.	47J longitudinal 27J transverse
ASME VIII Division 1 (6)	38	If DMT>-29°C	DMT	18J for UTS<448N/mm^2 20J for 448<UTS<517N/mm^2 27J for 517<UTS<655N/mm^2 0.38mm lateral expansion for UTS >655N/mm^2
ASME VIII Division 2 (7)	38	Varies according to steel grade and thickness	DMT	As ASME VIII Division 1
BS 5500 (8)	38	If DMT>0°C	Varies according to thickness, DMT and whether or not vessel is PWHT and can be significantly above or significantly below the DMT, see Fig. 1.	27J for UTS<450N/mm^2 40J for UTS>450N/mm^2

TABLE 2 - Base Metal Toughness Requirements in Standards.

a) Pressure Vessels.

Standard	Products	Temperatures	Exemption from impact testing	Temperature for Charpy testing	Required Charpy energy
API 650 (9)	Oil	Ambient. Map of North America shows lowest one day mean isotherms. DMT is 8°C above this	Varies with DMT, thickness and steel type	DMT	Varies with steel type and thickness from 21J for low strength as-rolled steels to 58J for higher strength Q and T or normalised steels with the maximum permitted shell thickness of 44mm.
API 620 (10)	General with pressure in gas or vapour space greater than API 650	As API 650	Impact testing is required for cases where thicknesses >25mm and DMT <-37°C	DMT	Varies with steel type and thickness (values are given in Appendix R).
BS 2654 (13)	For ambient temperature storage of crude, gasoline, etc.	DMT is 5°C above lowest mean daily temperature	For thicknesses less than 12.5mm and steels with UTS less than $500N/mm^2$ and for combinations of thickness and DMT defined graphically	Depends on thickness and DMT. Defined graphically similar to BS 5500. Scales are given for the hydro-test condition and for service (less conservative)	27J for specified UTS<$430N/mm^2$ 41J for specified UTS>$430N/mm^2$
API 620 (11) Appendix R	Refrigerated products giving DMTs of -51 to +4°C	Temperature of product	Varies with DMT, thickness and steel type	DMT	See API 620

b) Storage tanks. Cont'd...

Standard	Products	Temperatures	Exemption from impact testing	Temperature for Charpy testing	Required Charpy energy
BS 4741 (14)	Refrigerated products down to -50°C	Temperature of product	-	DMT for t<20mm (DMT -10°C) for 20 <t <30mm (DMT -20°C) for 30<t<40mm	27J for specified UTS<450N/mm^2 41J for specified UTS>450N/mm^2
API 620 (12) Appendix Q	Liquefied ethane, ethylene and methane	-168 to -51°C	Austenitic stainless steels and aluminium alloys are exempt	-196°C (-140°C may be used for ethane and ethylene)	27J for plates 34J for sections, forgings and piping (all in 9% and 5% Ni steel) and a lateral expansion of 0.38mm
BS 5387 (15)	Liquefied ethylene, ethane, methane, oxygen and nitrogen	Temperature of product	Only aluminium alloys, austenitic stainless and 9% Ni steels may be used. Charpy tests are required for the latter	-196°C	34J

b) – Storage tanks cont'd...

Standard	Test temperature	Weld metal requirements	HAZ requirements
AD-Merkblatt (5) HP5/2	DMT	As in AD-Merkblatt W10 for base metal, see Table 2(a)	28J
ASME VIII (6,7) Divisions 1 and 2	DMT	As for base metal, see Table 2(a)	
BS 5500 (8)	As for base metal, see Table 1 and Fig. 1	30J if σ_Y of base metal $\leq 300N/mm^2$ 40J if σ_Y of base metal $>300N/mm^2$	No requirements if weld heat input between 1 and 5kJ/mm. If outside this range, to match base metal
API 650 (9)	DMT	Required when Charpy testing of base metal required or when DMT $<+4^oC$. Requirements vary with plate type	As weld metal
API 620 (10)		No stated requirement	
BS 2654 (13)	**As for base metal, see Table 2(b)**	27J	**No tests required**
API 620 R (11)		As for base metal, see Table 2(b)	
BS 4741 (19)	**As for base metal, see Table 2(b)**	**27J**	**No tests required**
API 620 Q (12)		As for base metal, see Table 2(b)	
BS 5387 (15)	As for base metal, see Table 2(b)		No test required

TABLE 3 - Weldment Toughness Requirements.

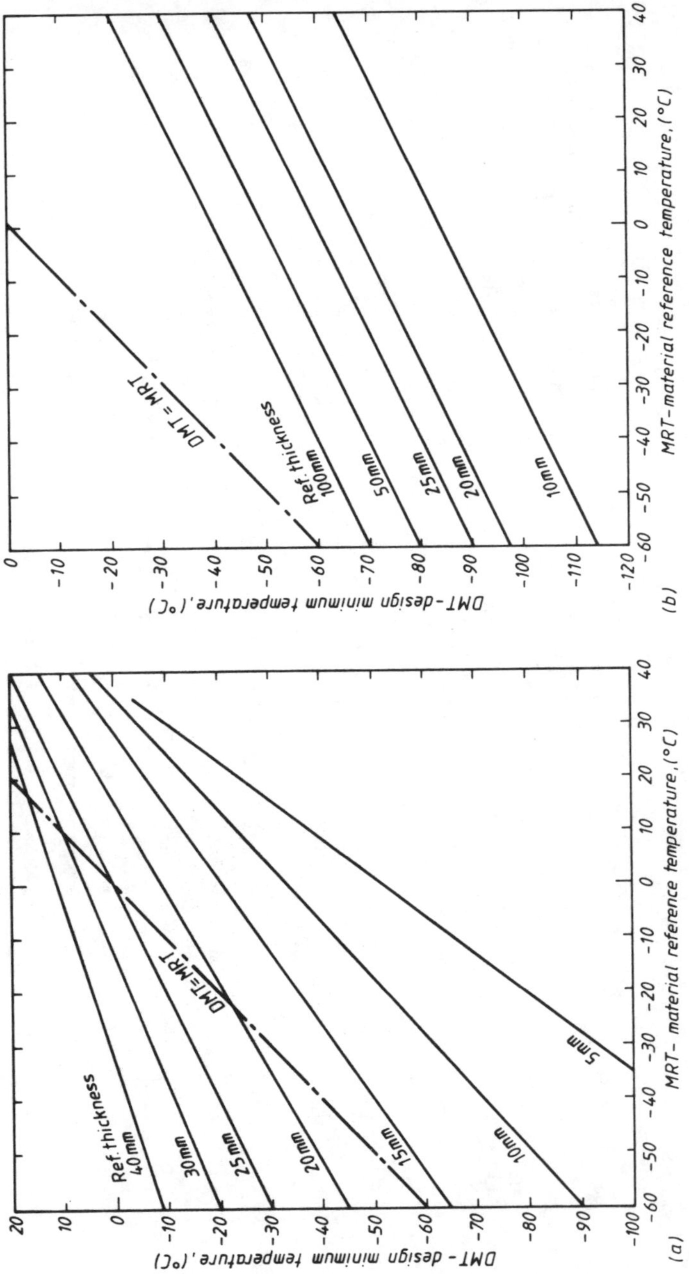

Fig 1 *Permissible design minimum temperature/reference thickness/material reference temperature relationships (BS 5500): (a) as-welded components; (b) postweld heat-treated components*

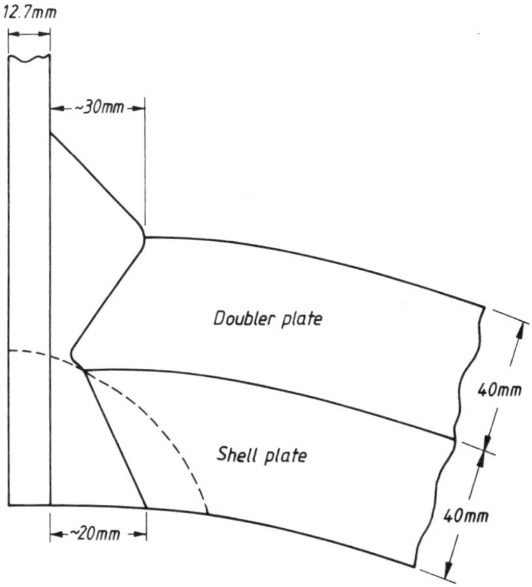

Fig 2 *Nozzle crotch corner detail. Broken curve indicates hypothetical corner crack just causing leakage into spacing between doubler and shell plates*

FATIGUE AND FRACTURE PREVENTION IN THE MOTOR VEHICLE INDUSTRIES

A.J.McEvily*

A brief review of the design procedures involved in fatigue analysis is presented. Topics covered include notch analysis and variable amplitude loading. In addition the conditions for fatigue crack propagation are examined. The empirical expressions for fatigue notch sensitivity and the fatigue size effect are shown to depend upon the extent of crack closure at the tip of a fatigue crack.

INTRODUCTION

The useful lifetime of a ground vehicle is generally limited by the combined effects of fatigue, corrosion, and wear, and with durability being of greater concern than ever before, the design team must make use of the advances of modern technology to avoid product failure. Failure prevention in the motor vehicle industries in large measure entails the avoidance of fatigue during service lifetime. In order to avoid fatigue a knowledge of loading spectra, material response, and the influence on fatigue of design details, manufacturing procedures, and processes such as corrosion and fretting must be available. Major steps are being taken in the modernization of fatigue design as a result of the demand for lightweight vehicles. To meet this demand new approaches to fatigue design are being introduced to supplement traditional procedures which are no longer sufficient to assure a satisfactory design. Traditional fatigue design in the motor vehicle industry has been based on experience gained in the use of more-or-less standardized materials and structural designs, accelerated road testing in test track runs, and user responses. With millions of vehicles being produced each year the failure statistics of such a large sample provided an important feedback which could be analyzed to determine the need for design modifications. On this basis a generally satisfactory design procedure, without detailed knowledge of load induced stresses and strains, had evolved. These procedures are still useful but no longer of themselves satisfactory to insure reliable performance because of the the recent relatively rapid introduction of new designs, new high strength materials, and new manufacturing procedures into the motor vehicle field. Fortunately in the research laboratories new design procedures were being developed what could be used to meet the new demands on fatigue design imposed by these

* Metallurgy Department, University of Connecticut, Storrs, CT 06268, USA.

changes. However, until recently lack of efficient communication between the research engineer and the design community has been a major stumbling block hindering the utilization of the information gathered in the research laboratories. Now this impediment is being removed through the use of interactive computer program modules for the formulation and solution of a wide variety of motor vehicle design problems (Conle and Landgraf (1).

The purpose of the present paper is to highlight the principal considerations involved in modern fatigue design procedures, a topic already which has been given excellent coverage in a number of recent articles which deal with fatigue in ground vehicles (Breen and Wene (2), fundamentals of modern fatigue analysis for design (Mitchell (3), and the control of fatigue in ferrous alloys (Landgraf (4). In addition the conditions for the propagation or non-propagation of fatigue cracks will also be discussed in relation to design considerations.

FATIGUE DESIGN PROCEDURES

An important step in the fatigue design of components such as wheel discs, suspension systems, and steering assemblies which are sensitive to external loads has been the recognition that under the influence of the highest loads experienced in service plastic deformation occurs in localized regions associated with stress raisers. In fact for such components 90% of the fatigue life may be expended in resisting only the highest 10% of all the loads applied. In these cases design approaches based on elastic behavior and the use of the stress-life (S/N) curve are not adequate. Instead new design procedures based on the strain life (ε/N) curve and the influence of plastic deformation on fatigue lifetime have been adopted. It should be pointed out, however, that in designing many other components, e.g. the crankshaft, which are required to withstand millions of cycles of relatively low stress the use of the S/N curve may still be sufficient.

The basic design tools involved in fatigue design based on strain include:

a. the cyclic stress-strain curve for candidate materials and their fatigue lives in terms of elastic and plastic strain.
b. a means for dealing with the effect of notches.
c. a means for relating local strains to applied loads. This may entail finite element analysis or component calibration with strain gages.
d. the loading spectra for both on-road and off-road conditions and for different driver handling characteristics.
e. a method for breaking down the spectra into an assemblage of individual cycles.
f. a method of assessing the interactive effects of the individual cycles to obtain a prediction of the lifetime of a component.
g. an allowance for statistical scatter in load spectra, material characteristics, and manufacturing procedures.
h. an allowance for possible deleterious effects on fatigue such as corrosion and forms of surface damage which may occur in service.

The utilization of the above procedures will enable the designer to select materials and properties for a particular application. Verification of the design can be obtained by laboratory testing of the component under the loading conditions obtained from test runs of prototype vehicles as well as from road test results from the prototype vehicles themselves. Consideration will next be given to some of the individual items listed above.

In the Coffin-Manson approach to fatigue design the fatigue life can be related to either the plastic or elastic strain range or to the sum of the two as indicated in Fig. 1. To facilitate cycle counting under random loading conditions the number of reversals, equal to 2N, are plotted rather than N. $2N_T$ marks the transition life from low to high cycle fatigue. At $2N_t$ the elastic and plastic strains are equal. The total strain amplitude can be expressed as

$$\frac{\Delta\varepsilon}{2} = \frac{\sigma_f'}{\varepsilon} (2N_f)^b + \varepsilon_f' (2N_f)^c \tag{1}$$

However the plastic and elastic strain ranges may not be constant throughout a test. For a given total strain range the plastic strain range for many materials may either initially increase or decrease before reaching a steady state or saturated condition. If it increases the material is said to have cyclically softened; if it decreases the material has cyclically hardened. Cyclic softening is typical of cold worked metals whereas cyclic hardening is associated with annealed metals. Quenched and tempered martensitic steels will often show cyclic softening as the dislocations induced on transformation undergo rearrangement to lower energy configurations during cycling. A cyclic stress strain curve as shown in Fig. 2a drawn through the stabilized hysteresis loops is used to determine the saturated cyclic stress-strain state which can be expressed as

$$\Delta\sigma = k \left(\frac{\Delta\varepsilon_p}{2}\right)^n. \tag{2}$$

Fig. 2b compares the cyclic stress-strain response with monotonic behavior. It is these saturated values of plastic strain and stress which are used in the Coffin-Manson equations. In some cases, particularly at very high strain amplitudes, a material may either harden or soften without reaching a steady-state condition before fatigue failure occurs. In such instances the cyclic properties for analysis are taken to correspond to those developed at 50% of the lifetime. In the ground vehicle industry the cyclic stress-strain properties of materials of interest as well as the strain-cycles to failure plots and the stress-cycles to failure plots are stored in a computer data bank and are available to the designer as an aid in materials selection (1).

Since fatigue cracks generally initiate at stress raisers, fatigue notch analysis is an important aspect of design. One method of dealing with the effect of notches is to use Neuber's Rule which states that the square of the theoretical stress concentration factor, K_T, is equal to the product of the concentration factors on stress, K_σ, and strain K_ε, the distinction between K_σ at K_ε being only significant when plastic deformation is involved. This rule is

$$K_T^2 = K_\sigma K_\varepsilon \tag{3}$$

In the case of localized plastic deformation Eq. (2) can be written as

$$K_T^2 = \frac{\sigma_{\ell p}}{\sigma} \cdot \frac{\varepsilon_{\ell p}}{\varepsilon} \tag{4}$$

which can be rearranged as

$$K_T^2 \, \sigma\varepsilon = \sigma_{\ell p} \, \varepsilon_{\ell p} \quad (5)$$

which is of the form of a hyperbola for fixed values of K_T^2 and σ. This equation may also be used in the form

$$K_T \, \sigma = (\sigma_{\ell p} \, \varepsilon_{\ell p} E)^{1/2} \quad (6)$$

For fatigue analysis the fatigue stress concentration factor, K_F, may be used in place of K_T. K_F will be discussed in a later section.

Fig. 3 shows how the Neuber Rule can be used to estimate the stress-strain state at a notch after yielding has occurred, and it is interesting to note that the local value of R can differ from the applied R as the result of plastic deformation.

In order to estimate the fatigue lifetime of a material part it is assumed that the quantities on the right hand side of Eq. 6 represent those of an unnotched specimen whose fatigue life is known as a function of $\sigma_{\ell p}$ and $\varepsilon_{\ell p}$ (or $\ell\Delta\varepsilon_p/2)^{n+1}$ if the cyclic stress-strain relation is used). Identical numerical values on each side of the equation correspond to equivalent lifetimes. Therefore data obtained with unnotched specimens can be used to predict the fatigue lifetime of notched specimens.

A major concern in fatigue analysis is the effect of variable amplitude loading on the overall fatigue lifetime. By instrumenting test vehicles the loads experienced in service by individual components can be ascertained. Realistic loading spectra are of course important for problems have arisen where design was based on incorrect assessments of the actual loads. Problems can also occur due to poor instrumentation or if the selected test conditions do not truly reflect actual service conditions. In order to analyze a load history for design purposes, a procedure for breaking down this complex history into individual cyclic loads is needed. One such procedure in use is the rain-flow method, which is illustrated in Fig. 4 (5). This method of analysis allows the spectrum to be broken down into a compilation of strain ranges and mean strains. The following rules are used to tranform the strain-time history to cycles:

1. Plot the history so that the largest strain magnitude occurs as the first and last peaks or valleys. This eliminates half cycles when counting.
2. Rainflow is initiated at each peak and allowed to drip down and continue - except that if it initiates at a maximum point (points A,B,D,G) it must stop when it comes opposite a more positve peak than the maximum from which it started. Rainflow dripping from B must stop opposite D because D is more positive than B. The converse rules are also necessary for rainflow initiated at a minimum (points A,C,E,F).
3. Finally, rainflow must stop if it encounters rain from the roof above, as in the event from C to D. (3)

"Black boxes" are now available which can be used to obtain data and to automatically carry out an analysis of the data in terms of the rain-flow method as well as other statistical counting procedures. With the aid of a Goodman diagram, which indicates the effect of mean stress on fatigue life, the ranges can be converted to equivalent fully-reversed ranges. To estimate the fatigue lifetime use is then made of Miner's law which states that

$$\sum_{i=1}^{i=i} \frac{n_i}{N_i} = 1 \qquad (7)$$

In using this simple relation some aspects of the fatigue process are not fully accounted for. For example, stresses below the endurance limit have no effect, yet as shown in Fig. 5 (6) these stress levels can lead to fatigue failure as the result of crack initiation at higher stress levels. In Fig. 5 data are compared for tests performed with no overstrains, with initial cyclic overstrains and with periodic overstrains. The first two conditions result in runouts (no failure) at comparable strain levels. Specimens subjected to periodic overstrains show no runouts at these levels; in fact the data points fall on extrapolations of the finite-life strain curves. This behavior suggests the endurance limits will be lowered, if not eliminated, under spectra loading conditions (4). There is a related problem in the laboratory testing of prototype components, for in order to save on test time the lowest loads which occur with highest frequency are often arbitrarily eliminated for the test program with uncertain effect. Further, load interaction effects are not taken into account. For example, at a notch a beneficial compressive stress will develop on unloading if localized plastic deformation has occurred in tension, whereas the reverse is true for compressive loading. Nevertheless comparison of predicted with experimental results has shown that reasonably good agreement between predicted and experimental lifetimes can be obtained, i.e., with difference between the averages of two values often being less than 2:1. Another consideration in assessing the fatigue lifetime of a component is that cyclic plastic loading may cause the relaxation of a beneficial residual stress induced by processes such as shot peening. At present there is no explicit method for analytically treating such matters.

As materials of higher strength are introduced sensitivity to manufacturing procedures can be expected to increase. For example it may appear desirable to use quenched and tempered steels which have double the yield strength of traditional steels. However, there is a need for caution in the use of these new steels for there have been instances where their use in applications involving welding have proven to be unsatisfactory because of problems arising due to weld defects which led to easy fatigue crack initiation. The strength of conventional steels can be increased by heat treatment to obtain the presence of both martensitic and ferritic phases (dual phase steels). However, more strigent production controls are needed as compared to conventional processing in order to insure that the desired microstructure is obtained. In some instances the scale-up from the laboratory has proven to be difficult.

PROPAGATION OR NON-PROPAGATION OF CRACKS

In the foregoing, lifetime predictions were based on the ε-N or σ-N curves and no distinction was made with respect to the initiation and propagation stages involved in determining the fatigue lifetime. In fact, in contrast to the aero-space industry, fatigue crack propagation is not an important consideration in the motor vehicle industry. For example, in a 1982 SAE Fatigue Conference (7), of 24 papers only three dealt with fracture mechanics. However, it seems significant in view of the widespread use of welding that, as the authors of one paper emphasized, since the fatigue life of a welded structure is spent essentially in crack propagation there is a need to know more of the propagation process. A purpose of the present section is to show that the conditions for the propagation of a crack from a stress raiser figure importantly in establishing allowable stress levels. In contrast to road impact loadings which control low cycle fatigue design the considerations to be discussed are of greater importance in the design of components intended to survive millions of cycles at more or less constant amplitude. First some background.

In studies of fatigue crack growth it has been found that there exists a threshold level for fatigue crack propagation. That is, for a given R value certain combinations of stress amplitude and crack length must be exceeded for fatigue crack propagation to occur. This combination is expressed in terms of the stress intensity factor range ΔK, where ΔK for the case of a small, centrally located crack in a sheet specimen is given by $\Delta K = \Delta\sigma\sqrt{\pi a}$. On a plot of the log of $\Delta\sigma$ against the log of a this relationship plots as a straight line of slope - 1/2 as shown in Fig. 6, for R = -1 loading. In Fig. 6 a is equal to c + ℓ, and the dotted line refers to holes of different radii. This relationship between the stress range and crack length is valid in the macroscopic crack range but, as indicated in Fig. 6, for very small cracks the endurance limit becomes the controlling factor and the line has a slope of zero in the small crack range. It is also known that at the threshold level the process of crack closure importantly affects the threshold level itself. This closure process is due primarily to the roughness of the fracture surface as a result of Mode II and Mode I propagation. Oxidation and corrosion products can also increase closure in the threshold region. If we consider that only the open portion of the cycle, that is $K_{max}-K_{op}$ is effective in propagating the crack, a situation which appears to hold for steels, we can then plot the threshold condition in Fig. 6 in terms of ΔK_{eff}, curve B. When a fatigue crack first forms at a notch or flaw it does so without closure being present. However, the closure process develops rapidly over a distance of approximately 0.5 mm and as a result the stress amplitude must be increased for the crack to continue propagating. For example, in the case of a steel of medium strength as shown in Fig. 7 the stress requirement goes through a maximum and then merges with the propagation requirement for a large crack as indicated by curves C, D and E (8). Because of the stress increase due to increasing closure, non-propagating cracks can develop as indicated by the data points (9) shown on this figure, curves C and D, where the applied stress is sufficient to nucleate a crack at a notch or flaw but not sufficient to overcome the barrier imposed as crack closure develops and crack arrest occurs. Such an arrested crack is often referred to as a non-propagating crack. It is noted that the propagation stress for the medium strength steel under consideration is well above the initiation stress in the case of curves C and D which apply and it appears likely that in fatigue design the non-propagation of cracks rather than their initiation may often be the critical factor. For this reason careful examination of non-failed parts which have undergone extensive cyclic loading may reveal the presence of these arrested cracks.

The closure process is dependent on yield strength and microstructure. It is more important in low strength steels and is less important for carburized or nitrided components. For such materials crack initiation is a more important consideration propagation. Initiation will also be important if the stress-notch size conditions are to the left of curve A where also crack initiation is the critical step.

Another interesting aspect of the closure process is that the terms fatigue notch sensitivity and fatigue notch size effect can be readily understood in terms of the closure behavior as depicted in Fig. 7 (10). For example for the three hole sizes shown 0.2, 0.40 and 4.8 mm each has the same value of K_T, namely 3.0. Yet the predicted value of K_F, the ratio of the fatigue strength of unnotched specimens to those of notched specimens varies as a function of size, as indicated in Fig. 8. This variation is compared with the empirical relationship proposed by Kuhn and Hardrath (11) based on Neuber, and by Peterson (12)

Kuhn-Hardrath $$K_F = \frac{K_T - 1}{1 + \sqrt{\rho'/\rho}} \qquad (8)$$

Peterson $$K_F = \frac{K_T - 1}{1 + a_o/\rho} \qquad (9)$$

The notch sensitivity is often expressed as

$$q = \frac{K_F - 1}{K_T - 1} \quad . \qquad (10)$$

For low strength materials closure is high and K_F is correspondingly low. For high strength materials closure is low and K_F approaches K_T. Therefore the fatigue notch sensitivity of a material can be directly related to closure. Since closure decreases with increase in mean stress, corresponding changes in notch sensitivity should be expected.

It has been proposed that the condition for the threshold for crack propagation from a sharp notch of radius ρ can be expressed (13) for a given material as:

$$\Delta K_I/\sqrt{\rho} = \text{constant} \qquad (11)$$

This expression stems from the Irwin definition of the stress intensity factor:

$$\Delta K_I = \lim_{\rho \to 0} \Delta\sigma_{max} \sqrt{\frac{\pi\rho}{4}} \qquad (12)$$

If the tip radius goes to a small value ρ rather than to the limit of zero, then

$$\frac{2}{\sqrt{\pi}} \frac{\Delta K_I}{\sqrt{\rho}} = \Delta\sigma_{max} \qquad (13)$$

which is equivalent to the expression cited above. For a centrally located ellipse in a sheet this can be written as

$$\frac{\Delta\sigma\sqrt{c}}{\sqrt{\rho}} = \text{constant} \qquad (14)$$

We can examine the implications of this relationship with the aid of Fig. 7. Assume that c = 5 mm and ρ = 0.25 mm, i.e. $\sqrt{c}/\sqrt{\rho} = 14.14$. For this condition from Fig. 7 we expect that a crack would initiate at a stress amplitude of 20 MPa but propagate only if the stress amplitude of 50 MPa. For a longer crack of 35 mm length and for the same ration of c/ρ, the radius of the stress raiser would be 0.175 mm. For this condition the stress amplitude to initiate a crack would still be 20 MPa, and the stress amplitude for propagation would be the same. Therefore it appears that the ratio $\Delta K_T\sqrt{\rho}$ may be constant for crack initiation from a sharp notch but does not correlate with the stress for propagation in the case cited. For values of c larger than 35 mm such cracks should initiate and propagate from an elliptical notch under the conditions that

$$\frac{\Delta\sigma}{2} K_T = \sigma_e \tag{15}$$

which for c>>ρ becomes

$$\frac{\Delta\sigma\sqrt{c}}{\sqrt{\rho}} \alpha \sigma_e \tag{16}$$

or in approximation

$$\frac{\Delta K}{\sqrt{\rho}} \alpha \sigma_e = \text{constant} \tag{17}$$

It is seen that this relationship stems directly from a consideration of stress concentration factors and the endurance limit rather than from stress intensity factors and the threshold. It is also possible to estimate the value of σ_e from the above expression if the stress amplitude required to propagate a crack is known and if the c and $\Delta\sigma/2$ coordinates are to the left of curve A in Fig. 7.

Finally the effects of closure on material selection are indicated in Fig. 9 (10). If components containing flaws above a certain size set by inspection capabilities are kept out of service, those that do see service may have flaws just below the inspection limit. A factor of safety is automatically set since the working range is below the endurance limit. However, note that a material of lower strength may prove to be superior to a material of higher strength in the presence of flaws of the same size. Therefore the influence of flaws and crack closure on fatigue behavior should be considered in the selection of materials, particularly those of higher strength.

CONCLUDING REMARKS

In this brief review it has been pointed out that the pace of technological developments in the ground vehicle field has resulted in the development of attractive design procedures and the rapid transfer of these procedures from the laboratory to the design office. Nevertheless further insight concerning the initiation and propagation of fatigue cracks is still needed to minimize reliance on empirical approaches and to improve resistance to fatigue.

ACKNOWLEDGEMENT

The support for this study provided by the U. S. Air Force Office of Scientific Research is gratefully acknowledged.

REFERENCES

1. Conle,A.,and Landgraf,R.W.,198 ,in "Digital Techniques in Fatigue",to be published by the Society of Environmental Engineers Fatigue Group.
2. Breen,D.H., and Wene,E.M.,1979,in "Fatigue of Microstructure",ASM,Metals Park,Ohio,57-99.
3. Mitchell,M.R.,ibid,385-437.

4. Landgraf,R.W.,ibid,439-466.
5. Landgraf,R.W. and LaPointe,N.R.,1974,"Cyclic Stress-Strain Concepts Applied to Component Fatigue Life Predictions,SAE Paper No. 740280, SAE,Automotive Engineering Congress,Detroit,Mich.
6. Dowling,N.E.,J. Testing and Evaluation 1,1973,271.
7. Proceedings of the SAE Fatigue Conference,p.109,SAE,Warrendale,PA, 1982.
8. McEvily,A.J. and Minakawa,K. to be published in Scripta Met.
9. El Haddad,M.H.,Topper,T.H.,and Smith,K.N.,1979,Eng. Frac. Mech. 11, 573.
10. McEvily,A.J. and Minakawa,K., to be published by AIME.
11. Kuhn,P. and Hardrath,H.F.,1952,NACA Tech. Note. 2805.
12. Peterson,R.E.,1974,Stress Concentration Factors,John Wiley and Sons, New York.
13. Rolfe,S.T. and Barson,J.M.,1977,in Fracture and Fatigue Control in Structures,Prentice-Hall,Inc.,Englewood Cliffs,N.J.

LIST OF SYMBOLS

a = crack length

a_o = material constant

c = semi-major axis of ellipse

c = Coffin-Manson exponent

E = Young's modulus

K_F = Notch fatigue factor

K_T = theoretical stress concentration factor

K_{max} = maximum value of the stress intensity factor

K_{op} = stress intensity factor at opening load

K_σ = stress concentration factor

K_ε = strain concentration factor

ΔK_{eff} = effective range of stress intensity factory ($K_{max} - K_{op}$)

ℓ = crack length measured from tip of stress raiser

n = strain hardening exponent

n_i = number of cycles at i^{th} level

N_i = number of cycles to failure at i^{th} level

R = ratio of maximum to minimum stress in cycle

ε = strain

$\Delta\varepsilon_\rho$ = plastic strain range

$\Delta\varepsilon_e$ = elastic strain range

$\Delta\varepsilon_T$ = total strain range

$\varepsilon_{\ell p}$ = local plastic strain

$\Delta\sigma$ = stress range

$\sigma_{\ell p}$ = local stress in plastic range

ρ' = material constant

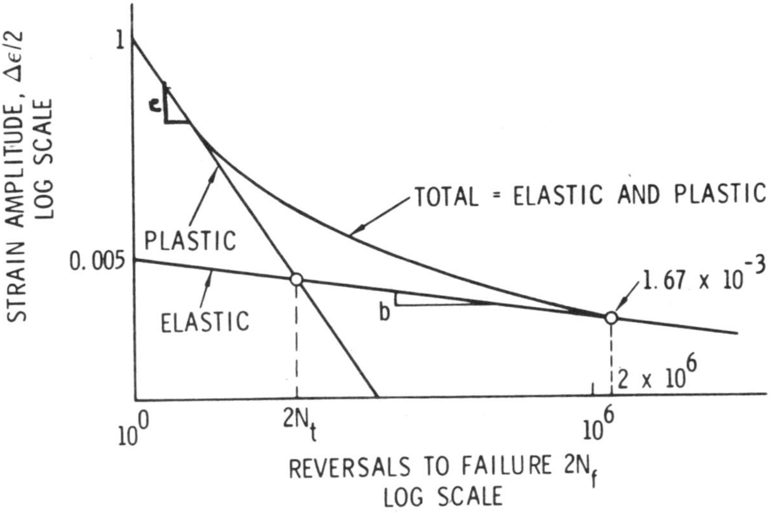

Figure 1 Estimated ε/N plot for a steel (H_B 200) (3).

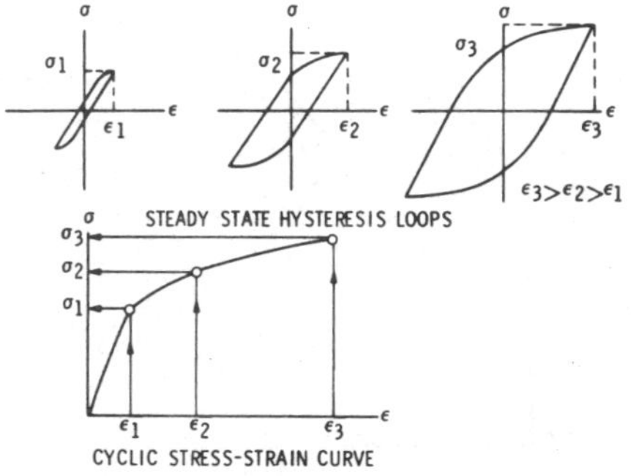

Figure 2 a. Construction of cyclic stress-strain curve by joining tips of stabilized hysteresis loops (3).

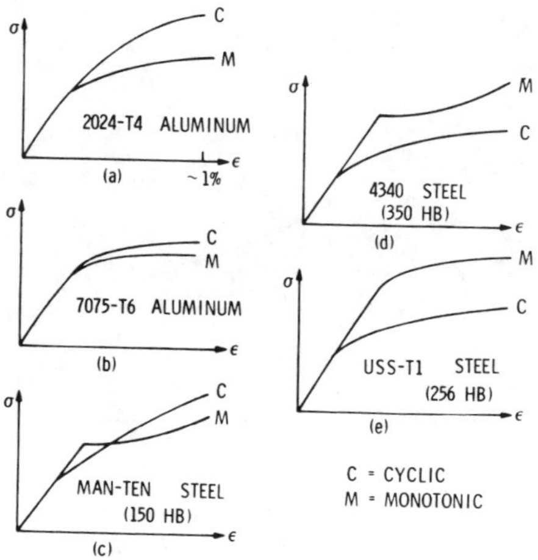

Figure 2 b. Cyclic stress-strain response compared with monotonic behavior to aluminum alloys and low strength steels (3).

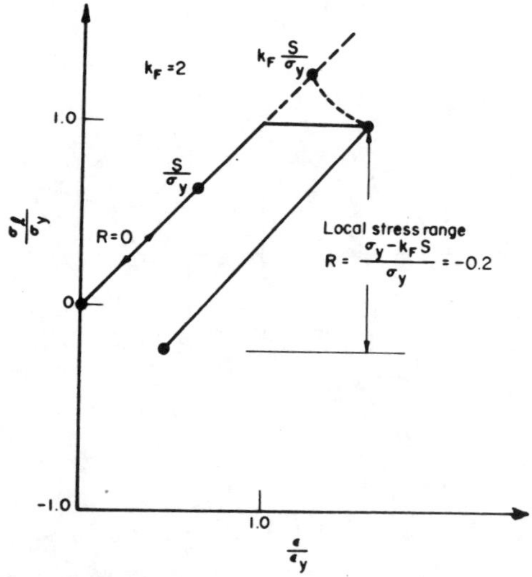

Figure 3 Stress-strain behavior at root of notch, $K_F = 2$ R = 0 loading applied. Applied stress 5/8 of yield stress.

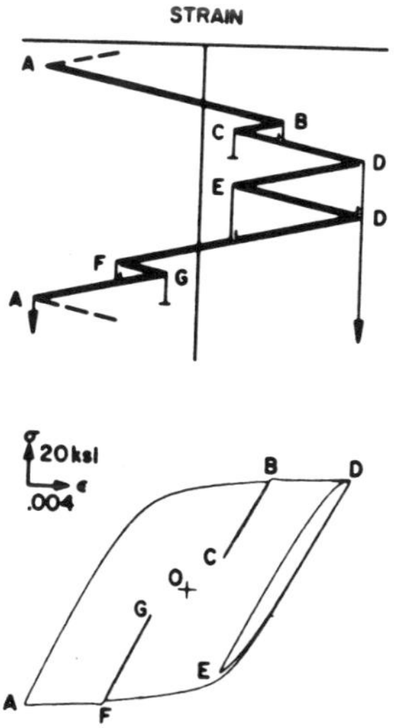

Figure 4 Schematic of rain-flow counting technique (5).

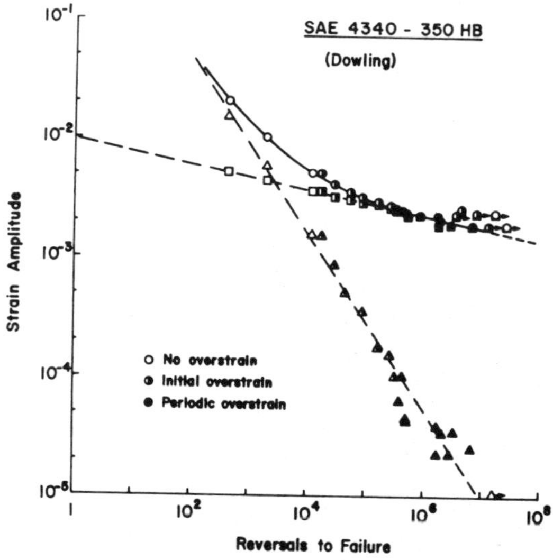

Figure 5 Influence of overstrains on the fatigue life of steel (6).

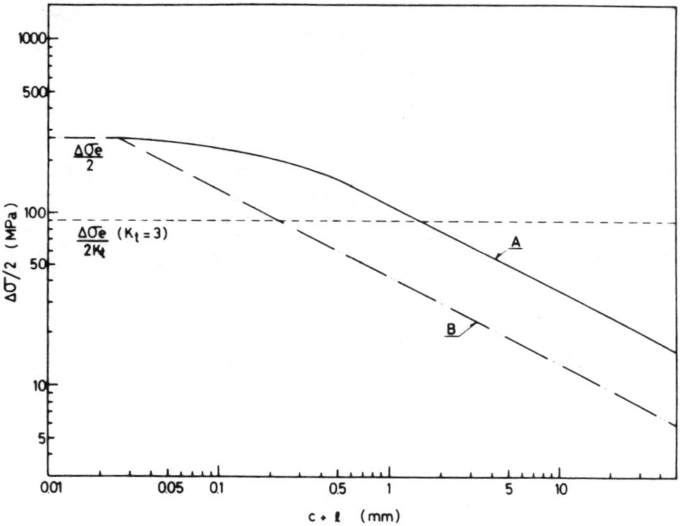

Figure 6 Crack propagation conditions as a function of stress amplitude and total crack length, c + ℓ. (10)

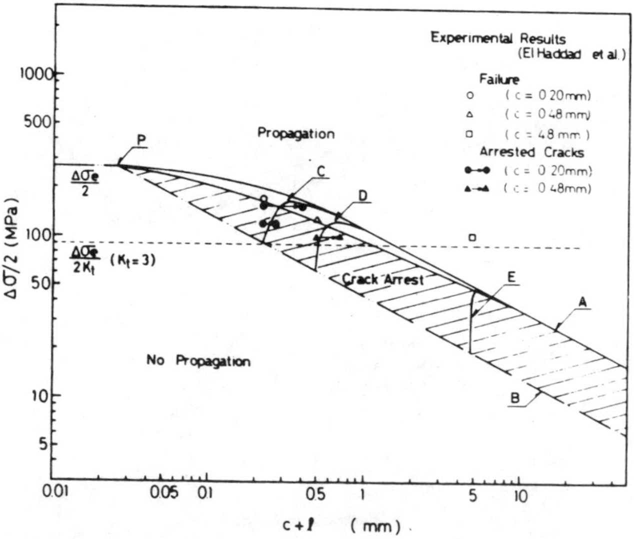

Figure 7 Influence of crack closure on the stress required to propagate fatigue cracks as a function of notch or flaw size. (10)

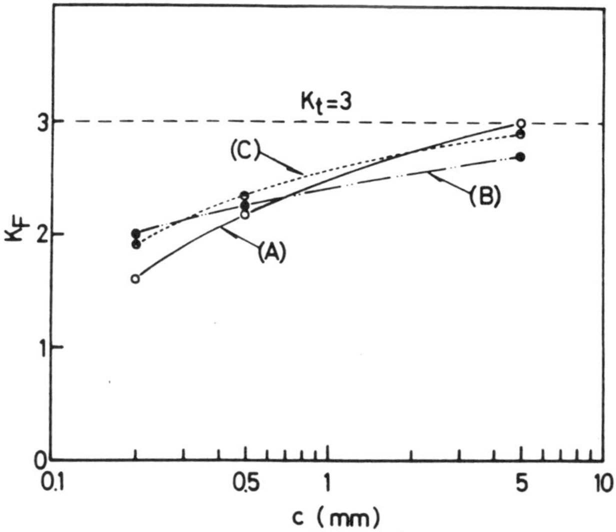

Figure 8 Variation of K_F as a function of hole size for three cases (A) based on Fig. 7; (B) based on Eq 7; and (C) based on Eq. 8 ($\rho' = 0.4$ mm, $a_o = 0.25$ mm) (10).

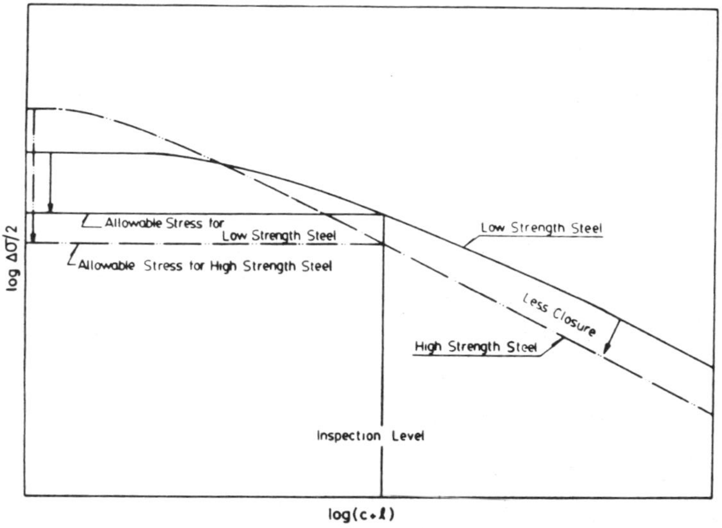

Figure 9 Effect of strength level and crack closure on the allowable stress for non-propagation of a crack as influenced by inspection capability (10).

PREVENTION OF FRACTURE IN PRESSURE VESSELS FOR HIGH TEMPERATURE HYDROGEN APPLICATIONS

Juro Watanabe*

Securing reliability of high temperature-pressure hydrogenation reactor vessels is very important for the industry. Research and experience have led to the understanding of possible fracture modes of the reactors, and the improvements in design, materials, fabrication and inservice inspection successfully prevent the fracture of these vessels.

INTRODUCTION

High temperature-pressure hydrogenation units are being used world-wide. Securing safety of heavy wall reactors in the units is of vital importance. In the past ten years many improvements have been achieved in design, materials, fabrication and inservice inspection of the reactors. In this paper, variables of and counter measures for the failure of the reactors will be discussed.

RELIABILITY OF HEAVY WALL REACTORS

Reliability of pressure containing components of hydrocracking units, especially main reactors, is one of the most important subjects for plant operators.

Service Life of Reactors

Fig. 1 is a schematic presentation of service life of a reactor. The upper line is the defect size allowed to be present in the reactor under its operating conditions. It may decrease during operation because of degradation of materials. The lower line is the size of defect, and it may increase during service. When these two lines cross together a failure of the reactor will occur. Since any failure must be definitely avoided, decision as to the replacement or repair is required when the defect size approaches to the critical one.

* The Japan Steel Works, Ltd., Tokyo Japan

Failure Modes

In order to prevent failure of a structure, it is required to study possible failure modes. Table 1 illustrates possible failure modes in the hydrocracking reactor. Crack initiation and subcritical crack growth occur by either creep, fatigue, stress corrosion cracking, hydrogen attack, hydrogen assisted cracking or their combinations. Final crack growth will lead to a failure, but prior to that subcritical crack growth may proceed.

TABLE-1 Possible Failure Modes in the Hydrocracking Reactor

Failure mode	Crack initiation and subcritical crack growth	Creep
		Fatigue
		Stress corrosion cracking
		Hydrogen attack
		Hydrogen-assisted crack growth
	Fracture	Stable fracture
		Unstable fracture

Among these possible failure modes,

(1) Creep: Heavy wall hydrocracking reactors are usually made of 2 1/4Cr-1Mo steel because of its many advantages including enough high temperature strength and good hydrogen attack resistance (1). Based on the ASME Code Section VIII Division 2 by which many hydrocrackers are built, creep of 2 1/4Cr-1Mo steel does not need to be considered up to 755 K. The highest design temperature of hydrocrackers is around 727 K.

(2) Fatigue: In many hydrocrackers the number of load cycles or shutdowns will be less than 100 during their life, and except in very few cases fatigue analysis of the reactors is not required. At some stress concentrated locations, failure by low cycle fatigue can occur; this will be discussed later.

(3) Stress corrosion cracking: SCC such as polythionic acid corrosion cracking can be avoided by proper operational precautions, and no major SCC problem has been experienced recently.

(4) Hydrogen attack: The first consideration given in the selection of materials for hydrocrackers is the resistance to hydrogen attack. 2 1/4Cr-1Mo is an excellent steel to avoid methane formation under high pressure-temperature hydrogen, because it contains stable carbide formers such as Cr and Mo. When methane forms in steel, it decreases strength and ductility. Selection of steel grades is done based on the Nelson curve, and 2 1/4Cr-1Mo steel has been successfully used for hydrocrackers for many years.

(5) Hydrogen assisted cracking: In the hydrocracker, hydrogen enters the steel during operation when the metal is hot, and when the reactor cools down below around 422 K absorbed hydrogen can cause cracking under certain unfavorable conditions.

Now it has been found that among the above mentioned possible failure modes hydrogen assisted crack growth is the principal concern for the reliability of hydrocrackers.

When defects reach a certain critical size, fracture will occur in a stable or unstable fashion. The hydrocracking reactor vessels are usually designed in accordance with the ASME Code Section VIII Division 2 which gives a safety factor of 3 to tensile strength. Consequently, a stable fracture can hardly occur under foreseeable service conditions.

In recent heavy wall reactor experience, unstable fractures are few, but there are cases that led to the unpleasant consequences (2)(3)(4). Fig. 2 shows the fracture surface of an 8 in. thick hydrocracker that failed during field repair work after about three years of service (3). Contributing factors to the failure were judged as: (1) cracks initiated at incomplete weldments of internal attachments; (2) the crack initiation was attributed to sigma phase and hydrogen embrittlement of Type 347 stainless steel (5)(6) and thermal stress caused by the difference in thermal expansion between austenitic and ferritic steels; (3) subcritical crack growth into base metal by hydrogen assisted crack growth; and (4) severe temper embrittlement during three years of service. In this case, the fracture was triggered by an excessive thermal stress due to unfavorable temperature gradient generated during PWHT.

A burst test of a 100mm thick wall 2 1/4Cr-1Mo steel pressure vessel was carried out (7). In the vessel three precracked specimens with different toughness levels were embedded (Fig. 3 and Table 2). The vessel was hydrostatically pressurized at ambient temperature, 283 K, and brittle fracture occurred from the most brittle sample "A" at the pressure of 51MPa. Since the design pressure of the vessel was 23MPa, the experimentally determined safety factor (burst pressure/design pressure) was 2.2. Table 3 gives a safety factor estimated by the linear fracture mechanics.

TABLE-2 Crack and Material Details of Samples.

Sample	Room Temperature Strength (MPa)		CVN Properties		Crack Size (mm)	
	0.2% Yield Strength	Tensile Strength	Upper Shelf Energy (Joule)	vTr40 (K)	Depth	Length
A	432	623	161	388	50	99
B	446	616	142	339	50	188
C	470	615	182	293	75	206

TABLE-3 Safety Factor for Sample A at Design Pressure 23MPa and 283 K.

Defect Depth, a (mm)		Safety Factor
Actually Present	Allowable Defect Size Calculated by LEFM*	
51	122	2.4

* Linear Elastic Fracture Mechanics

SECURING RELIABILITY

Failure Mechanisms and Counter Measures

Table 4 summarizes the failure mechanisms of hydrocracking reactor vessels and the counter measures established through many years of experience and research in the industry.

Crack Initiation

Cracks can be either defects left out in the fabrication, mostly weld cracks, or low cycle fatigue cracks grown from stress raisers such as gasket groove corners, internal attachment corners and supporting skirt. The former can be controlled by good quality control and workmanship. Weld preparation design to reduce or eliminate weld defects is also important. For the latter, every care must be paid to reduce stress level at the stress concentrated area. Proper design and smooth surface finish are required.

Fig. 4 shows the design changes to avoid the crack initiation at internal support rings. The support ring was made of weld build-up of austenitic stainless steel in the past to obtain enough extrusion, but recently most of its volume is machined out of the shell forging. This design change helps to reduce thermal stress caused by the difference in thermal expansion of ferritic base metal and austenitic stainless steel. Corner radius is made as large as possible to reduce stress concentration, and Type 347 stainless steel is weld overlaid after the final PWHT to avoid sigma phase formation. Adverse effects of sigma formation and hydrogen absorption on tensile ductility are remarkable (Fig. 5), and the severe loss can lead to crack initiation (5)(6).

TABLE-4 Failure Mechanisms and Counter Measures

Subject	Mechanism	Counter Measure
Crack Initiation	• Fabrication defects • Low cycle fatigue cracking from stress raisers	• Quality control during fabrication • Eliminate or decrease stress raisers, such as gasket grooves, internal attachment corners and skirt • Decrease stress levels
Subcritical Crack Growth	• Hydrogen assisted crack growth	• Maintain safe tensile strength level • Maintain safe hydrogen level • Lower stress intensity factor • Decrease temper embrittlement
Fracture	• Brittle fracture from defects	• Improve toughness by suppressing temper embrittlement and increasing metal temperature • Monitor dangerious defects by inservice inspection

Subcritical Crack Growth

When a flawed sample charged with hydrogen is loaded, subcritical crack growth can occur. Crack growth rate depends on stress level or stress intensity factor (K_I) level, and under the critical stress intensity factor the crack does not grow. Kerr and Erwin reported the effect of tensile strength level and hydrogen content on the threshold K_{IT} of 2 1/4Cr-1Mo steel as shown in Fig. 6 (1). It illustrates a strong effect of tensile strength level on K_{IT}, and if the tensile strength is lower than approximately 690MPa K_{IT} is very high. Effect of temper embrittlement, of which detail will be discussed later, is also significant. Fig. 7 shows the relationship between temper embrittlement expressed by CVN (Charpy V-notch) fracture appearance transition temperature versus K_{IH} (equivalent to K_{IT}) of a conventional 2 1/4Cr-1Mo reactor steel (8). With an increase of temper embrittlement, K_{IT} can decrease down to about 31MPa$\sqrt{m}$.

Weld Overlay Debonding

Weld overlay debonding found at the interface between weld overlay and base metal is assumed to be a form of hydrogen assisted subcritical crack growth (9). Hydrogen absorbed in the reactor during high temperature-pressure operation can reach a high concentration at the interface during cooling, and it can lead to the debonding with the help of thermal stress caused by different thermal expansions of weld overlay and base metal. Many efforts are being paid to give more quantitative explanation of the role of many metallurgical and operational variables involved in this phenomenon, and on the other hand welding methods to obtain better resistance to debonding are being developed.

Brittle Fracture

Fig. 8 shows relationship between fracture toughness, applied stress and critical flaw size for brittle fracture of a pressure vessel containing a semi-elliptical surface crack with aspect ratio 1/5. For a tough material with 440MPa$\sqrt{m}$ K_{IC}, the critical crack depth is more than 500mm, but it decreases sharply with drop of K_{IC}. Fig. 9 illustrates CVN energy and K_{IC} transition curves of a temper embrittled and de-embrittled 2 1/4Cr-1Mo steel (10). After about 6 years service, this particular steel lost its toughness because of temper embrittlement to the considerable degree. The embrittlement could be reversed by short de-embrittlement heat treatment (e.g. 923 K for 0.5 h). By temper embrittlement, both CVN and K_{IC} transition curves moved rightward, and the toughness loss at ambient temperature was significant. It can be recognized that at around 373 K, K_{IC} of embrittled and de-embrittled steels is the same level.

Temper Embrittlement

General characteristics of temper embrittlement summarized by C.J. McMahon are as follows (11).

1. Alloy steels such as Ni-Cr, Ni-Cr-Mo, and Cr-Mo steel are susceptible. Carbon steel does not embrittle.
2. The temperature range for the development of temper embrittlement is about 618 to 838 K.
3. Embrittlement is reversible by heating for short times above 838 K
4. Temper embrittlement is manifested by an increase of ductile to brittle transition temperature.
5. The cause of embrittlement is segregation of Mn, Si, P, Sn, Sb and As at the grain boundaries.

Effect of tramp elements such as Mn, Si, P and Sn on temper embrittlement is demonstrated by $\overline{X}$ (12) and J-factor (13)(Fig. 10). The lower the J-factor, the lower is the fracture appearance CVN transition temperature (FATT).

There are several commercially available steel making practices (14) to reduce J-factor, including VCD (vacuum carbon deoxidization) process. VCD does not need silicon for deoxidation of molten steel. The deoxidation is carried out by the reaction between carbon and oxygen during teeming in high vacuum. VCD steel has low silicon content (average 0.025%), and phosphorous and tin are also reduced to obtain low J-factor. Fig. 11 shows chronological change of J-factor during 1970 to 1980 (15), and its average decreased from 229 in 1970 to 102 in 1980.

An API sponsored program "Characterization Study of Temper Embrittlement of Chromium-Molybdenum Steels", generated temper embrittlement data of commercial heats and weldments (16). In its report Shaw proposed a method to estimate very approximate isothermal embrittlement after time t (h).

$$I_{(t)} = 0.67\ (\log_{10}(t) - 0.91) \times (S.C.E.)$$

where $I_{(t)}$: isothermal embrittlement
S.C.E.: step-cooled embrittlement

Step-cooling is a heat treatment to obtain short time test results of temper embrittlement.

Warm Startup and Shutdown

The strong temperature dependance of fracture toughness and critical flaw size was cited earlier. More quantitative analysis on the effect of pressurizing temperature on the safety factor will be discussed here.

Assumptions for the analysis are:

(1) A 25mm deep semi-elliptical surface crack with aspect ratio 1/5. A crack of this depth is seldom found in weld metal or base metal. However, in order to be conservative, the large crack is assumed. Naturally, careful nondestructive examinations will not miss a crack of this size.

(2) Working stress at the crack tip equal to the yield strength of material, 441MPa. This is also a conservative assumption, but because of the high residual stress caused by different thermal expansions of base metal and austenitic weld, this assumption may not be too conservative.

(3) Fracture toughness transition curves shown in Fig. 12. This figure gives the fracture toughness of base metal, SAW (subarc) and SMAW (shield metal arc) weld metals before service and after 100,000 h service. The method to predict the toughness after service is given by Watanabe and Murakami (9). The figure also compares the toughness of typical old vintage reactor materials (built before 1975) and new vintage (built in and after 1982) materials. The new vintage materials have much smaller shifts of transition curves caused by temper embrittlement, and have low transition temperatures.

Based on these assumptions, safety factor (K_{IC}/K_I) versus metal temperature relationships of new and old vintage reactor vessels were obtained (Fig. 13). BSI PD6493 "Guidance on Some Methods for the Derivation of Acceptance Levels for Defects in Fusion Welded Joints" suggests to maintain at least 1.4 safety factor K_{IC}/K_I (17). It is found from Fig. 13 that the old vintage reactor vessel must be heated to temperatures higher than around 333 K to maintain 1.4 safety factor, but the new vintage pressure vessel can be pressurized at any ambient temperature. It clearly demonstrates improvement in and advantage of new vintage reactors, however it does not imply that the vessel can be pressurized at unreasonably low temperatures. Integrity of other pressure containing components of the unit and past experiences must also be studied when startup and shutdown procedures are determined.

INSERVICE INSPECTION AND ASSESSMENT OF ITS RESULTS

Inservice inspection is very important to secure reliability of pressure vessels. Detection, locating and sizing of defects are the basis for the assessment of integrity of a vessel.

Nondestructive Examination Program

Table 5 lists examples of nondestructive examination programs for inservice inspection.

TABLE-5 Examples of Nondestructive Examination Programs for Inservice Inspection

1	2	3	4
• UT from outside on critical areas such as major weld seams and internal attachments • UT for debonding on critical areas	• 1, plus • PT on gasket grooves and internal attachments corners • MT on support skirt corner	• 2, plus if any cracks exist • UT and/or destructive method (griding) for crack depth measurement	• LEFM analysis such as BSI PD6493:1980

UT: Ultrasonic testing PT: Dye-penetrant testing

MT: Magnetic particle testing

1st program: Ultrasonic testing is carried out on critical areas such as major weld seams and internal attachments. Ultrasonic test for debonding is also done on critical areas such as behind internal skirts and rings.

2nd program: In addition to the first program, dye-pentrant tests on gasket grooves and internal attachment welds and also magnetic particle tests on support skirt are performed.

3rd program: When any crack is found by the first or second program, precise locating and sizing must be tried. Ultrasonic test is an useful tool, and sometimes careful grinding is carried out to determine the crack depth.

It must be emphasized that the past experience shows that no nondestructive testing can be fully reliable, and the techniques are still being improved. Reliability depends on examination skill, accessibility to the defect, alloted time and other variables such as surface preparation, type of defects etc. NDE program including frequency of inservice examination must be selected based on the information as to the original materials, design and fabrication history, operational history and past inspection results of the pressure vessel to be inspected.

Assessment by LEFM

The assessment of nondestructive examination results can be done by LEFM (Linear Elastic Fracture Mechanics) which gives, by calculation, the safety factor K_{IC}/K_I of the inspected pressure vessel. K_{IC} of 2 1/4Cr-1Mo steels and K_I at the crack tip were discussed earlier. Linear elastic fracture mechanics assumes elastic behavior at the crack tip, but in many structural components some plastic deformation proceeds prior to the brittle fracture. Hence complete elastic brittle fracture seldom occurs and the critical load (pressure) predicted by LEFM is a conservative estimation.

Table 6 compares actual burst pressure (51MPa) and the pressure predicted by LEFM (36MPa) in the burst test described earlier (Fig. 3). The actual burst pressure was 1.42 times the predicted one. Scanning electron microscopy revealed a stable crack in front of the crack tip, providing evidence of some plastic deformation.

TABLE-6 Comparison of LEFM assessment with burst test result.

Sample	Crack Size, mm		K_{IC} at 10°C ($MPa\sqrt{m}$)	Calculated Burst Pressure (MPa)
	Depth	Length		
A	51	99	72.2	36.2*
B	51	187	143.2	54.5
C	63	205	221.0	78.0

*The test vessel failed from sample A at the internal pressure 51MPa

Fig. 14 is an example of the assessment. Assume a crack at internal ring weld, and its growth into base metal,10mm deep. Actually it is very difficult to determine the crack depth of this size ultrasonically, and improvement of the ultrasonic technique is being tried. Grinding off method may be required to determine the depth. Assuming a penny shaped crack and working stress 440MPa, K_I is obtained as $82.5MPa\sqrt{m}$. K_{IC} versus temperature curve was calculated for an old vintage material after 100,000 h (Fig. 12), and the safety factor K_{IC}/K_I versus temperature curve was obtained. In order to keep 1.4 safety factor, warming the reactor vessel up to around 293 K is required.

SUMMARY AND CONCLUSIONS

Prevention of fracture in high temperature-pressure hydrogenation reactor vessels was discussed. It may be summarized as follows.

1) Many improvements have been accomplished in the design, materials and fabrication of the reactor vessels such as,
   (1) design change to minimize stress concentration,
   (2) suppressing temper embrittlement susceptibility of 2 1/4Cr-1Mo steel, thus maintaining high toughness after long term service, and
   (3) improvement in the resistance to weld overlay debonding.

2) Through these improvements, reliability of new vintage reactor vessels has been much increased with,
   (1) less possibility of crack initiation,
   (2) slower subcritical crack growth rate, and
   (3) higher resistance to brittle fracture.

3) Importance of inservice inspection was emphasized especially for old vintage reactor vessels.
   (1) Skilled and well planned nondestructive examination is most recommendable,
   (2) Results of inservice inspection can be assessed by linear elastic fracture mechanics, and its procedure was briefly introduced.

REFERENCES

1. Erwin, W. E. and Kerr, J. G., 1982, "The Use of Quenched and Tempered 2 1/4Cr-1Mo Steel for Thick Wall Reactor Vessels in Petroleum Refinery Processes: An Interpretive Review of 25 Years of Research and Application", WRC Bulletin 275.
2. Rosenfield, A. R. and Reid, C. N., 1977, "Explosion of an Ammonia Pressure Vessel", Army Material and Mechanics Research Center, U.S., Report No. AMMRC MS77-5, June.
3. Watanabe, J., Shindo, Y., Ohnuma, H., Ishigaki, S., Kawakami, K. and McGuire, W. J., 1976, "Investigation in a Failure of a Direct Desulfurization Reactor During Its Field Repair Work", Proceedings of International Joint Pressure Vessel and Petroleum Mechanical Engineering Conference, Mexico City.
4. Yorizane, M. et al, 1980, High Pressure Gas. 17, 622.
5. Johnson, E. W. and Hudak, S. J., 1978, "Hydrogen Embrittlement of Austenitic Stainless Steel Weld Metal with Special Consideration Given to the Effects of Sigma Phase", WRC Bulletin 240, Aug.

6. Watanabe, J., Ohnishi, K., Murai, M. and Chiba, R., 1977, "On the Cracks in Stainless Steel Internal Attachment Welds for High Temperature, High Pressure Hydrogen Services", CORROSION/77, Paper No. 104.

7. Watanabe, J., Ohnishi, K., Saikudo, R., Yamamoto, S., Tsukikawa, T., Nakao, M. and Ueyama, H., 1979, "Acoustic Emission Testing of Pressure Vessels Made of 2 1/4Cr-1Mo Steel", Proceeding of the API Midyear Meeting, U.S.

8. Murakami, Y., Nomura, T. and Ohnishi, K., 1983, "Hydrogen Embrittlement Behavior in Temper Embrittled Cr-Mo Steels", The Japan Pressure Vessel Research Council, Final Report of Task Group II, MHE - 9, 135.

9. Watanabe, J. and Murakami, Y., 1983, "Startup and Shutdown Procedures of Hydrocracking and Hydrodesulfurizing Reactors", The Japan Steel Works, Ltd. File No. R(PV)83-003.

10. Iwadate, T., Karaushi, T. and Watanabe, J., 1979, "Fracture Toughness of Temper Embrittled 2 1/4Cr-1Mo and 3.5Ni-Cr-Mo-V Steels", Presented at the Joint USA - Japan Seminar, Hayama, Japan.

11. McMahon, C. J. Jr., 1968, "Temper Brittleness - An Interpretive Review in Temper Embrittlement of Steel", ASTM STP 407, 126.

12. Bruscato, R, 1970, Welding Journal, 49, 148 - s.

13. Murakami, Y., Nomura, T. and Watanabe, J., 1982, "Heavy Section 2 1/4Cr-1Mo Steel for Hydrogenation Reactors", ASTM STP755, 129.

14. Sangdahl/Semchyshen, Editors, "Application of 2 1/4Cr-1Mo Steel for Thick-wall Pressure Vessels", ASTM STP755, ASTM 1982,

15. Watanabe, J. and Murakami, Y., 1981, "Prevenation of Temper Embrittlement of Chromium-Molybdenum Steel Vessels by Use of Low-Silicon Forged Shells", Proceedings of the API Midyear Meeting, U.S.

16. Shaw, B. J., 1982, "Characterization Study of Temper Embrittlement of Chromium and Molybdenum Steels", API Publication 959.

17. PD6493, 1980, "Guidance on Some Methods for the Derivation of Acceptance Levels for Defects in Fusion Welded Joints", British Standards Institution.

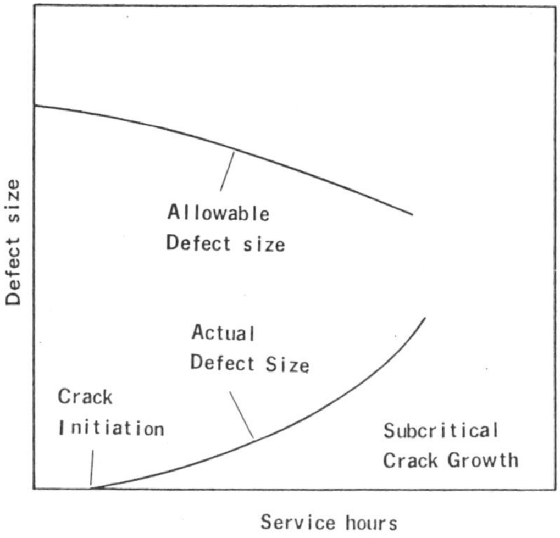

Figure 1   Allowable defect size versus actual defect size

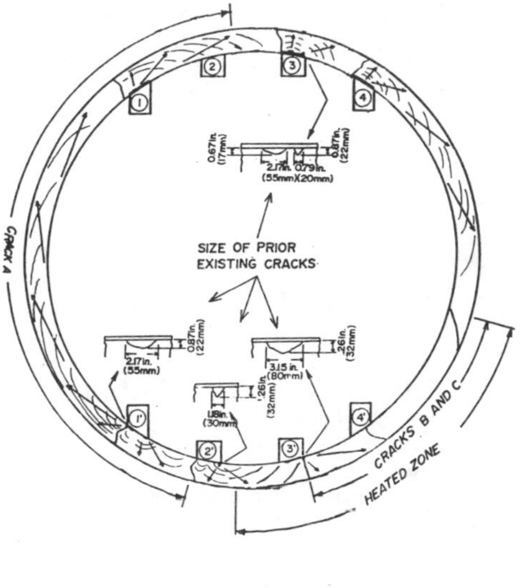

Figure 2   Sketch of the fracture surface of a hydrodesulfurization reactor

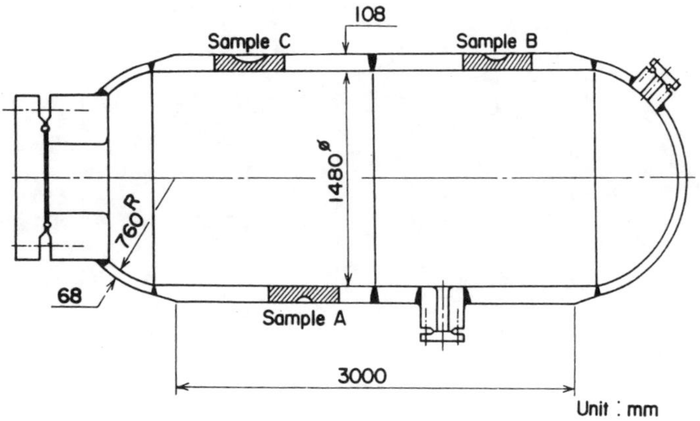

Figure 3 Dimensions of test vessel

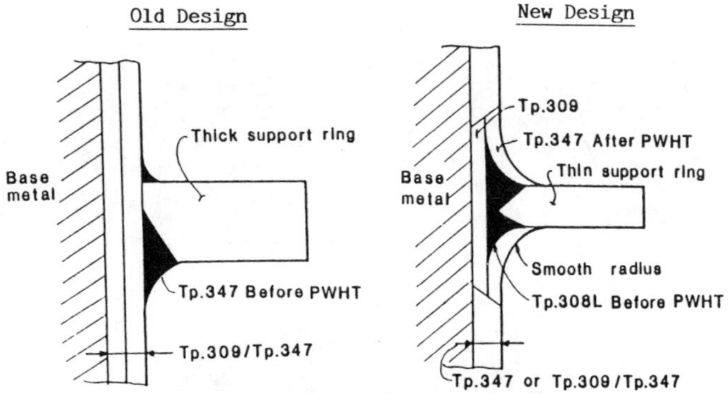

- Low thermal stress
- Low stress concentration
- Low susceptibility to hydrogen embrittlement cracking

Figure 4 Design changes of internal support ring to avoid crack initiation

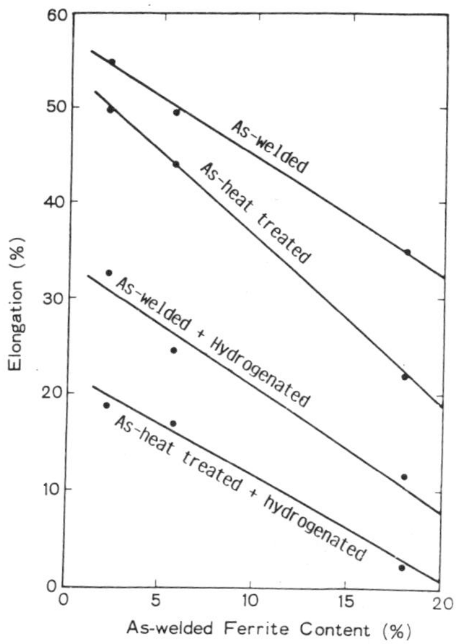

Figure 5 Influence of heat treatment and hydrogenation on the ductility of Type 347 weld metal

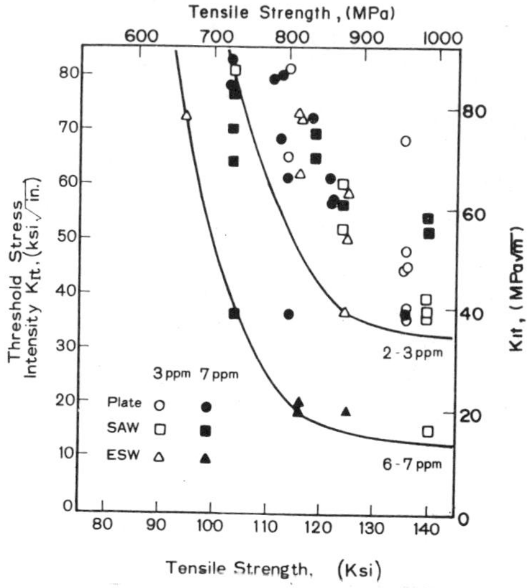

Figure 6 Threshold stress intensity, K_{IT}, versus tensile strength for delayed cracking of hydrogen charged 2 1/4Cr-1Mo steel (Data from the work at Chevron and Battelle)

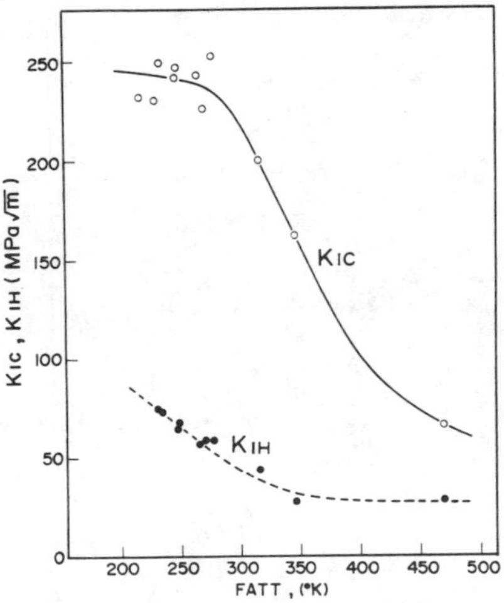

Figure 7 Room Temperature K_{IC} and K_{IH} versus FATT for 2 1/4Cr-1Mo steel

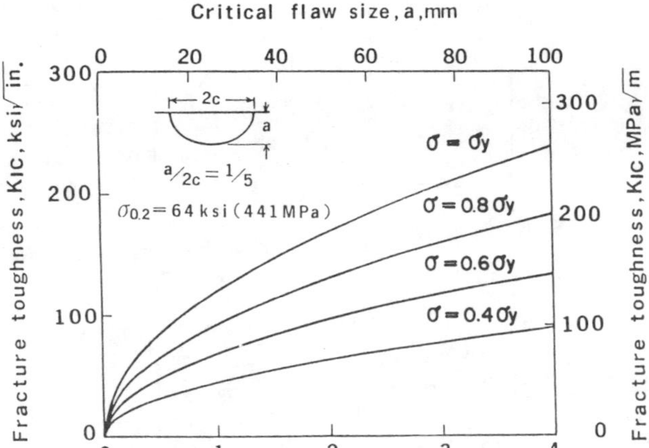

Figure 8 Relationship between fracture toughness K_{IC} and critical flaw size

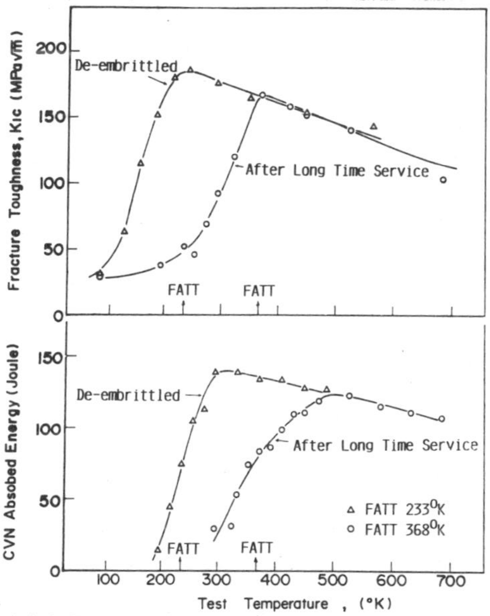

Figure 9 Examples of K_{IC} and CVN energy-temperature relationships for 2 1/4Cr-1Mo steel

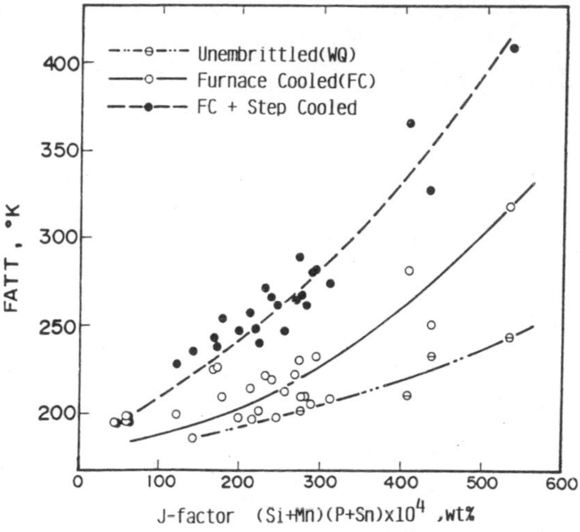

Figure 10 FATT of 2 1/4Cr-1Mo steel as a function of J-factor

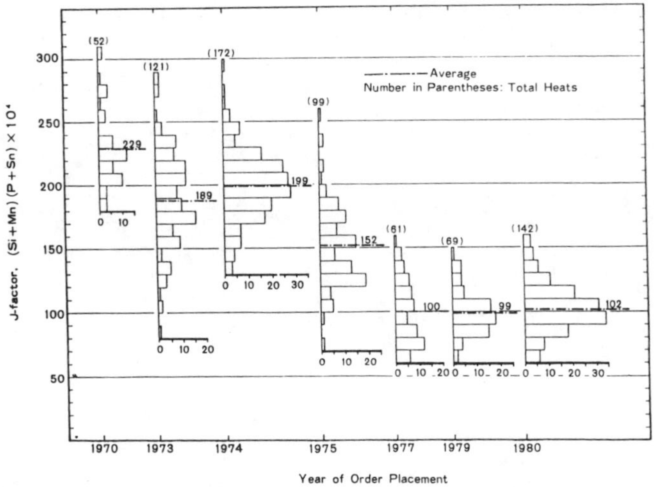

Figure 11 Chronological improvement in the sensitivity of 2 1/4Cr-1Mo steel to temper embrittlement as described by J-factor

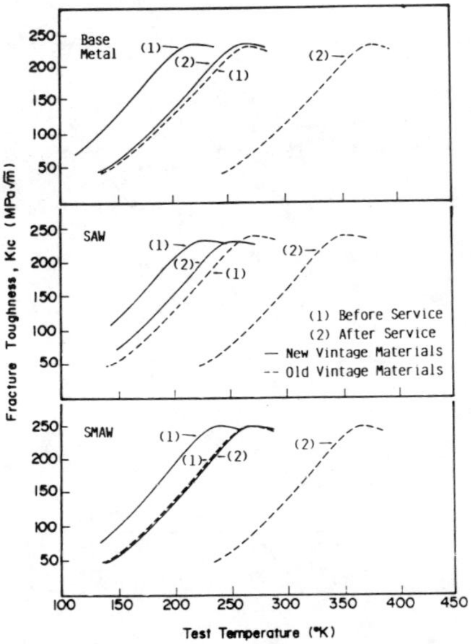

Figure 12 Comparison of estimated fracture toughness for new and old vintage 2 1/4Cr-1Mo steels

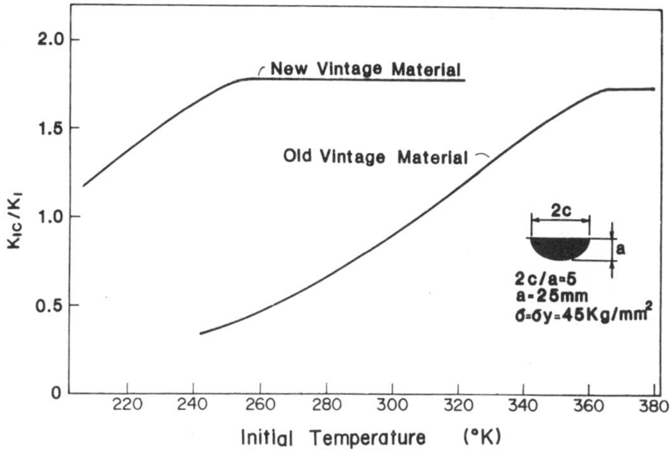

Figure 13 Safety factor K_{IC}/K_I-temperature relationship for new and old vintage reactors

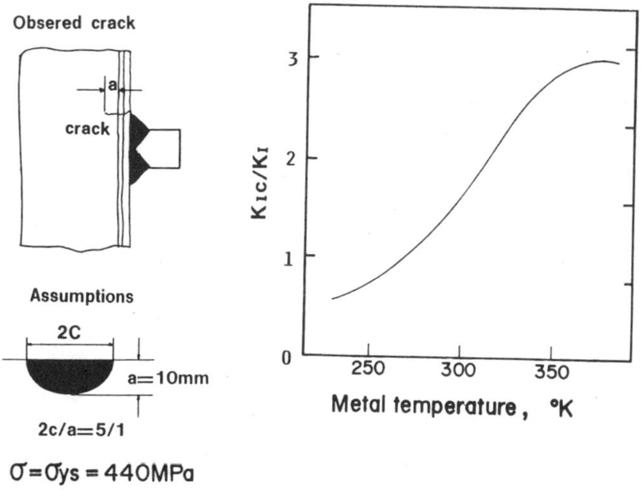

Figure 14 An example of fracture safe assessment for 2 1/4Cr-1Mo reactor (K_{IC} is estimated for an old vintage steel after 100,000 hour service)

FRACTURE PROBLEMS IN OFFSHORE STRUCTURES

Jerrell M. Thomas*

Some of the fracture problems facing U.S. designers, fabricators, and operators of offshore structures are discussed. Based upon recent experience, interviews, and literature surveys, suggestions are made for addressing these problems. Suggestions for immediate implementation and for further research consideration are presented.

INTRODUCTION

In the Spring and Summer of 1982, Failure Analysis Associates undertook two major fracture-related surveys to determine the state of the art in fracture mechanics techniques. These surveys, together with recent experiences in analyzing several offshore incidents, form the basis of this review of fracture problems in offshore structures. A "Fracture Mechanics Life Technology" review was performed for the National Aeronautics and Space Administration's (NASA's) Marshall Space Flight Center [Besuner, et al. (1)] and focuses on current fracture mechanics technology for the prediction of the lifetime of structural components subjected to cyclic loads. Since it was a concurrent effort, and since one of the project's central objectives was to recommend development of fracture mechanics-based analytical tools for modeling and forecasting subcritical fatigue crack growth in structures, the NASA study contributed much to the second survey, "Fracture Control for Fixed Offshore Structures" [Besuner, et al. (2)], sponsored by the Ship Structures Committee of the National Research Council. While both U.S. and European practices were considered in the study, the survey and recommendations do reflect a U.S. focus. However, many of the companies and individuals interviewed for the survey have experience with European operating environments and regulations, and the draft report was sent to various European operating and regulating bodies for review and verification of design, construction, inspection, and repair procedures.

CURRENT PRACTICES AND PROBLEMS

At present, designers, fabricators, operators, and regulators work toward the

*Failure Analysis Associates, 2225 E. Bayshore Road, Palo Alto, California 94303

common goal of controlling fracture in offshore structures--from the planning stages on through to the monitoring and maintenance of an operating structure. While these separate activities have a unifying philosophy (i.e., to: prevent cracks when possible, contain or tolerate growth of those cracks not prevented, and contain a fracture within a part or tolerate the loss of the part if a crack should grow critically), they are not always approached in a unified way. The adoption of more systematic measures for integrated fracture control seems inevitable as platforms become larger and more expensive to design, build, and maintain.

The lack of unified measures is is due in part to an industry reluctance to acknowledge that cracks exist in these structures. In fact, cracks and crack-like defects do exist in any weld or heat-affected zone of any steel structure and may initiate during construction, transport, installation, operation, or even repair procedures.

Defects in the original material (porous region in a steel plate or nonmetallic inclusion or lamination) can slip by; poor weldability of materials can leave large crack-like defects in welds; certain joint configurations lead to heavy weld restraint, resulting in high residual stresses and perhaps cracking; or joints may be overloaded during construction or after a severe environmental loading.

The essence of cost-effective fracture control is to prevent or discover and eliminate those defects which are dangerous, while not spending valuable resources dealing with those which are innocuous. With good design and welding practice, and proper controls, most defects will be prevented or caught and rejected or repaired before the structure goes into operation. Improved and special welding procedures can alleviate problems with weld-embrittled material, and the use of material with special through-thickness ductility in critical locations can reduce the chance of fracture by lamellar tearing and of brittle crack extension in the rolling-plane of leg and brace walls subjected to significant out-of-plane loads.

Still, a number of problems remain, even with the improved materials and advanced equipment and techniques available to the designer/operator. Many powerful tools and voluminous materials data now exist, and the current technology is capable of providing adequate results under many circumstances. However, conflicting theories and inconsistent data have been reported, and there is an obvious need for both additional materials data and a better understanding of underlying phenomena.

Thus, in the offshore industry, as in others, there are two classes of problems to overcome in establishing effective fracture control. The first class is lack of integration, or failure to apply existing technology in an effective manner. The second class of problems is unavailability of proven methods or data to deal effectively with problems that arise.

The first problem (integration) is most easily corrected. It requires, primarily, a willingness to apply the resources necessary to achieve fracture control. For example, grinding the weld-toe at critical locations will improve a structure's fatigue life <u>if</u> the weld is also then cathodically protected. Without the second step (cathodic protection), corrosive action could pit the weld surface and negate most of the benefits of the grinding. All decisions to "improve" a design at one level must be carried over and evaluated on other levels as well, to integrate the effects of one change over the various phases of the platform's existence. To accomplish the necessary integration requires a knowledgeable staff with sufficient authority and budget.

The second problem relates to new technology or new frontier areas. For example, much research is still needed to reliably define and "prove" what is now assumed about fatigue and wave histories, and current methods for measuring and calculating these. As experience is gained with one design in one environment, problems (such as weldability of new materials, lamellar tearing in thick plates, and fatigue in early North Sea platforms) diminish in later designs. By the third generation in a frontier area, most of the problems have been worked out, but this is an expensive and dangerous way to learn.

In view of this background, current practices and problems will be briefly reviewed in terms of four major activities that affect fracture control of offshore structures: material selection, design, construction and operation. Only a few of the most important problems are discussed.

Material Selection

Of the four major activities related to fracture control, material selection and control practices exhibit the most variation in the industry, primarily due to widespread disagreement over the material properties necessary to control fracture. The variables include the properties to be selected (and why), the method of specification, and the tests performed to ensure that the desired properties are present.

As an example, the central point of material selection controversies is often the test chosen to determine toughness -- a value used for quality assurance, as part of fracture control -- and for detailed fracture assessment calculations. One example of this disagreement arises with the Charpy V-Notch and Drop-Weight Test (DWT) requirements, the purpose of which is to assure that the nil-ductility transition temperature of the material is below the required value determined from the Fracture Analysis Diagram (FAD).

First: The test results are not related to applied stress and strain (except indirectly*), and therefore the results are not directly usable for design purposes or for fitness-for-purpose evaluations.

Second: The small Charpy samples are not necessarily representative of the heavy sections actually used in tubular joints. For this reason, most specialists in material toughness evaluations prefer DWT and Crack-Tip Opening Displacement (COD) tests.

Third: Testing at only one temperature does not define the entire toughness versus temperature transition curve. There is much scatter in test results, even for one piece of material.

Partially due to these arguments, there is a trend toward COD testing. Of the various fracture mechanics fracture toughness measures, COD has the most immediate potential, although there are still questions about what properties are needed. The COD test is static. The loading of a tubular joint can be more dynamic. There is a disagreement among materials experts in the industry on whether a static toughness measure is enough, or if a dynamic measure is also needed. Under dynamic loading a material's strength increases, preventing plastic flow around a crack or a notch, and thus adding constraint. This constraint makes the material more susceptible to brittle fracture. Therefore, with increased strain rate, the toughness of the material decreases. This is

*Empirical correlations do exist with such stress-related parameters as K_{IC} and COD.

especially true of low strength steels, and less true of high strength steels. Since critical crack extension in and some loadings of a tubular joint are dynamic, many experts are reluctant to give up the dynamic tests, Charpy and Drop-Weight.

Design

Unlike the variations in material specifications, the nominal design practices used in the U.S. (i.e., the Gulf of Mexico) are fairly uniform throughout the offshore industry. The API RP-2A recommendations [American Petroleum Institute (3)] form the backbone of the practice, with each major design office implementing and executing the API provisions with its own procedures, analysis methods, and computer programs. There are still, however, some incompletely understood design problems that bear discussion.

Tubular joint design. API RP-2A, paragraph 4.1.3c., "Joint Details for Shielded Metal Arc Welding," describes the highly controversial "improved" weld profile. Those who use the improved profile are rewarded with a special S-N (stress versus number of cycles) design curve, the X; those who do not improve the profile are penalized with the X' S-N curve. The controversy rages over whether or not the profile is indeed an improvement, and if so, is the cost justified.

The ideal profile depicted in the API recommended practice is difficult to achieve without grinding and the addition of cap and butter passes. The purpose of the improved profile is to reduce the notch effect of the weld, and the additional benefits of the grinding (which removes the last, and presumably worst, weld bead) include the probable removal of material containing the worst defects, microstructure properties, and post-weld residual stresses.

Detrimental effects of the grinding include the possibility of surface damage and the significant loss of area in load-carrying cross-sections. The effect of weld profiling on cracks growing in regions of large plastic deformation is an area of ongoing research in analytical and experimental fracture mechanics.

Fatigue analysis. Fatigue analyses have so many inherent uncertainties that they are interpreted by experts only in a relative sense. Among the dominant contributors to the uncertainty of the analysis are the prediction of the long-term sea state distribution (which may include a 100 year forecast made from two years of data), the calculation of wave forces in a given sea state (using Morrison's equation, which is the best approach available but gives a poor estimate of local wave forces on individual members), and the computation of hot spot stresses given that the various stress concentration factor formulas do not agree with one another.

Another fatigue problem that is relatively new to U.S. operators is that of plate thickness effects, which are thought to be tied to the notch size effect of the weld as well as to other effects. One direction of European research is to use fracture mechanics approaches to understand these phenomena, and as American practice moves to deeper water, it becomes yet another problem awaiting resolution for U.S. operators.

Fracture mechanics approaches hold out hope of someday being able to derive S-N curves or similar design aides reliably, with a minimum number of fatigue tests of specimens or full-scale structural details. Of course, all of the uncertainties associated with loads, hot spot stresses, and subsurface stress distributions will impinge upon the fracture mechanics analysis. To increase the viability of this approach, the industry must turn in earnest to further reseach calibration with in-service observations of fatigue crack growth, and the elimination of many geometrical and load and stress distribution parameters associated with fracture mechanics models at their best.

Construction (Fabrication, Installation, Inspection)

Fracture control in the fabrication phase is primarily a matter of quality assurance for the incoming material and welding procedures during construction. Offshore construction technology is changing rapidly. The introduction of flux cored welding and ultrasonic testing have significantly advanced the state of the art. Yet the introduction in 1980 of the API RP-2X recommended practice for ultrasonic testing [American Petroleum Institute (4)] stirred a major controversy over weld root defect acceptance criteria. There is also a current trend in U.S. practice toward longer tows from the fabrication yard to the installation site. Fatigue during transport has thus become a concern.

Weld root defect acceptance criteria. Before the API RP-2X, guidance on the acceptable size of defects in the root of tubular joint welds came mainly from the AWS D1.1 [American Welding Society (5)]. Two levels of reject criteria are specified by the AWS D1.1: strict reject criteria (applied originally to bridges) and more relaxed criteria (applied originally to buildings). Recognizing that tubular joints in offshore structures are, loosely expressed, somewhere between bridges and buildings with respect to fatigue, the AWS D1.1 leaves the specific criteria up to the operator.

The API RP-2X was introduced to fill the gap in specifications and quantify the acceptable defect sizes in tubular joint welds for the operator. The criteria are based on experience with Gulf of Mexico type design and construction. The controversial aspect is the greatly relaxed criteria applied to defects in the weld root. For example, outside of the root a planar defect is acceptable if it is less than 1/8" wide and 1/2" long; but, in the root area a 1/8" wide defect may be up to 2" long (i.e., 1/8" x 1/2" versus 1/8" x 2").

Since stresses in the root area are less than elsewhere in the weld, since residual stresses at the root tend to be compressive, and since fatigue tests have shown that, as long as the root defect is not so gross as to significantly affect the overall weld area and stresses, root defects do not control the fatigue strength of tubular joints (fatigue cracks usually start in the weld toe), the relaxation of criteria appears to be justified.

There are two points to the controversy. First, there has been criticism that experience alone is not enough justification for relaxing the root defect acceptance criteria; these criteria should be backed up by further testing and analysis. Second, there is a feeling that these criteria were designed to protect the status quo in fabrication practices. Specifically, the criteria are based on typical quality levels achievable using the frame method of fabrication prevalent in Gulf of Mexico practice. In the frame method, tubular joint welds must be made from one side, the outside, with no backing. Since this is very difficult to do, weld root defects might be expected to occur rather frequently. In fact, the difficulty is so great that, should the weld be repaired, the repair weld may be no better.

An important question to be asked here, which must be answered in the future, is how suitable are these relaxed criteria outside of the Gulf of Mexico? Certain assumptions about the structure, its operation, and its environment have been made. Thus, built into these criteria are assumptions regarding acceptable risk levels, the "purpose" part of fitness-for-purpose, and other aspects of fracture control which may not be suitable for areas outside of the Gulf of Mexico.

Transport and inspection. There is a current trend in construction practices toward longer tows to the installation site, especially for frontier areas, thereby exposing the structure to greater fracture risk.

In the past, transport received roughly the same design treatment as other construction loads, such as launch. Repeated loads, causing fatigue damage, were not considered. With the trend toward longer tows, this attitude is changing and transport is being recognized as an additional mission for the structure.

During transport, the fracture control attention has been directed toward the sea fastenings tying the structure to the barge, rather than toward the structure itself. After transport, generally more attention is paid to the installation equipment carried aboard the structure, such as hydraulic lines, valves, and instrumentation. And after it has been launched, the speed of the rest of installation is so important that an inspection for fracture control is "impossible" until installation is complete. So it is not until well after a series of potentially severe loadings; load out, transport, and launch, that the next inspection for fracture control can take place. And then such an inspection is likely to be only a quick visual check to see if the structure is intact.

It is time that a full design treatment be routinely given to the transport aspects of the structure, including fatigue analysis.

Operation (Including Inspection and Repair)

Some of the issues raised by recent reconsideration of operating practices bring into question some long-held tenets which formed the bases of many fracture control activities.

Repair. The evaluation of a crack's impact on the joint and on structural integrity is often based on experience and rules of thumb, not analysis. And the decision to repair is influenced by "external" factors -- the influence of regualtions, insurance, liability, and litigation. Some regulators seem especially prone to reflex reactions to cracks; they require repair regardless of the crack's significance. In terms of liability and litigation, it seems likely that a court would find the operator more liable for an accident involving a structure with a known crack, than one without. This contributes to a decision-making environment which heavily favors the automatic repair of any crack as a remedial measure, and poor decisions are often the result. Not only are repairs made when other remedial actions (e.g., non-routine operation) might be more economical, but the total risk picture might be worse with the repair than with other actions. The answers to these questions require careful treatment in each instance.

The sad truth is that few cases see full analytical treatments.

As for the fitness-for-purpose analysis, its newness and industry's lack of experience with it are partly responsible for its lack of popularity. As experience is gained, more of a trend toward its use is expected. A more serious drawback is the uncertainty of the calculations, which makes interpretation of the results difficult. The technology is currently unsuccessful at predicting the ductile failure and ultimate strength of a cracked tubular joint. The fracture toughness (COD) of the materials is not specified or inspected for, adding to the uncertainty. And the growth of cracks in tubular joints is not yet understood. So, the fracture potential and fatigue life calculations for cracked tubular joints are basically educated guesses at this time and are, therefore, difficult to interpret properly. These guesses can be improved with more research and this area is currently being studied.

Inspection. There are two periodic inspection philosophies, designated here as the "fine-toothed comb" and "broad brush" approaches. Since the introduction of ultrasonic techniques for underwater inspection, there has been a trend toward the "fine" approach, inspecting for small cracks, and away from the traditional approaches, from which the "broad" approach is derived. The success of the "fine" approach depends on the ability of the operator to correctly predict where cracks are likely to initiate at any given time. Recent experience has demonstrated that operators are not very successful at making these predictions.

Under normal operating conditions cracks often form where they are not anticipated. (Had they been anticipated, some way would likely have been found to design them out of the structure.) "Fine" inspections either catch these unanticipated cracks after they are already large or not at all. Some operators are therefore reconsidering the use of such inspections. Instead of concentrating the inspection on only a few joints each time, they reason, it would be better to look for the larger, more easily detectable cracks over the entire structure. If large cracks are at least temporarily tolerable, then would not a "broad" inspection, which would find the unanticipated cracks, be preferable? A blend of the two approaches would seem most appropriate: "fine" inspections for locations identified as "fracture critical," and "broad" inspections for the rest of the structure.

SUGGESTIONS AND DIRECTIONS FOR IMPROVEMENT

Expanding Existing Technology

The NASA survey (1) pointed out that fracture mechanics analyses of crack growth often involve consideration of fatigue and fracture under extreme conditions of temperature and/or aggressive environment, as is the case with many deep water platforms. Therefore, aside from errors outside the fracture mechanics analysis (such as load estimation errors), inaccuracies in predicting component lifetime will be dominated by inaccuracies in environmental and fatigue crack growth relations, stress intensity factor solutions, and methods used to model given loads and stresses.

One of the recommendations made in that study was to put some research effort into expanding, and filling the gap in, existing technology in an effort to reduce these inaccuracies. Suggestions included development of improved models of subcritical crack growth (for estimating fatigue crack growth under aggressive environments and predicting crack growth under variable amplitude and cyclic loadings, incorporating a better understanding of the influence of the environment and previous load history on crack thresholds), and research efforts aimed at better characterizing residual and assembly stresses that can be introduced during fabrication. Research toward extending the current most popular methods for analysis of elastic/plastic effects (COD and J. Integral) should be performed. In particular, use of these methods in areas of high stress gradients may be achievable but has not been demonstrated. Specialists in fatigue and fracture of offshore structures will recognize that these are the same developments needed for their own applications.

Some suggestions for expanding existing technology, categorized as to probability of success, are summarized in Table 1.

TABLE 1 - Suggestions for further research and development.

High Probability of Success	Moderate to Low Probability of Success
Develop guidelines for the use of available techniques for improving welded joints where fatigue performance is marginal or inadequate.	Set up a "devils advocate" testing program to evaluate fracture criteria (i.e., shed light on the Charpy V-notch vs. DWT vs. COD controversies).
Collect reliable fracture data to be matched up with offshore needs in order to produce recommended programs for closing the "data gap."	Determine the feasibility of determining appoximate effects of stress gradients in estimating elastic-plastic crack tip stress parameters.
Develop algorithms for the problem of contained plasticity in notches.	Develop a data base of service and repair histories.
Develop deterministic design and fitness-for-purpose approaches for routine analysis of significance of defects and for development of examples and guidelines.	Develop a probabilistic fracture mechanics approach for routine crack analysis.
Define stress gradients and other characteristics of the subsurface stress distribution.	Study methods for determining hot spot stresses and tubular joint behavior outside the standard case.
Develop accurate, versatile, automated crack growth analysis methods.	Develop additional design data for steel "shell" components.
Start a materials data base for all important measured fracture parameters of offshore structural steels.	Study wave loading and associated phenomena more closely and develop guidelines for application.
Further develop monitoring systems to be portable, be discriminating, minimize the use of divers, and have an acceptable rate of false alarms.	Consider redundancy more quantitatively in undertaking risk-based remedial actions.
Undertake large-scale component testing of the effectiveness of ways to improve weld toe fatigue performance.	Conduct quantitative toughness testing using specimens which simulate the physical characteristics at the crack border of typical structures.
Develop accurate stress intensity factor solutions for all stress fields and crack geometries of concern. Include evaluation of displacement control exhibited by most tubular joint crack geometries. In addition, develop a handbook or software library of stress intensity factor solutions for often occurring geo-	Study effects of soil-structure interaction and, particularly, long-term foundation degradation.
	Develop a more accurate finite element program for the global analysis of structures using both joint and member elements.
	Build improved structural reliability models capable of calibrating to and

TABLE 1 - Continued

High Probability of Success	Moderate to Low Probability of Success
metries and load cases.	extrapolating from field experience.
Survey industries using more formal fracture control documents than does the offshore industry.	Expand the range of tubular joints tested and used to set S-N curves.
Evaluate the neglect of larger wave periods in fatigue analyses.	Build a data base of failure, accident, and success experience for feedback to those who influence fracture control.
Prove that Charpy tests are meaningful for new situations.	Consider the effect of greater-than-predicted wave loadings upon the fatigue life of structures.
Define applications suitable for use of higher-order-average alternating-stress methods for life prediction.	Formalize the statistical approach to defining the variability of S-N and sub-critical crack growth data.
Determine the accuracy of "identical wave" dynamic amplification factors in variable wave spectrums.	Estimate the effect of multiple crack-site origins at the weld toe.
Define and execute an experimental program to evaluate constant amplitude fatigue, overload, and underload effects upon crack growth. Ensure that an adequate range of crack propagation rates is covered.	Establish design loads for and protection against impact damage (collisions, explosions, etc.).
	Assess effects of uncertain hot spot stresses and incorporate into a probabilistic fracture mechanics model.

Using Current Technology

Current technology could find more extensive use if easily used and widely accessible software were available. While numerous computer codes for automated fracture mechanics analysis are available, none of these fully utilize today's technology and, for the most part, are not easy to use and are not available to a wide range of users. Suggested software development includes:

1. A widely accessible software package for the determination of stress intensity factors for a wide range of crack configurations and loadings. This software package could include items 2, 3, and 4 below.

2. Software for treating contained plasticity due to notches and other local stress-raisers.

3. Current publicly available codes, merged to form one package for the automated analysis of flaw growth.

4. Software for predicting critical flaw sizes for various typical crack configurations.

5. Improvements to current codes and procedures for generation of stress intensity factors for two-dimensional configurations and cracked three-dimensional bodies to make them more accessible and user-oriented.

6. Automation of the failure assessment diagram for easy application.

To assist in the transfer of technology to the day-to-day fracture mechanics practitioner, several approaches are recommended at present, recognizing that the development of widely available and user-friendly software such as that described above would greatly reduce the necessity for such approaches. The recommendations are to identify typical critical geometries for which existing stress intensity factor solutions are inadequate, and generate such solutions for future use; exercise these solutions for both hypothetical and practical problems which encompass most geometries, stress, material, and environmental combinations expected in the field, creating modeling examples and guidelines.

Another problem that is crippling the use of current technology is that, without appropriate test data, even the most powerful tools for the prediction of crack growth are limited and their results are necessarily inaccurate. Suggestions for the generation of additional test data to complement current technology include:

1. Identify key material/environment combinations of relevance to offshore structures for which adequate fatigue crack growth data is unavailable. Perform tests to characterize the subcritical crack growth of the material.

2. Test to discriminate between various proposed models of crack growth under variable amplitude loading.

3. Perform limited testing aimed at a clearer understanding of the transition behavior of part-through cracks.

4. Generate J-resistance curves for ductile materials at temperatures for which critical crack lengths have an important influence on predicted lifetimes.

5. Test J-resistance curves for use in analysis of part-through cracks.

6. Test to better understand crack growth under mixed mode cyclic loading.

7. Perform tests to confirm procedures for analyzing the growth of part-through cracks under complex stress conditions.

Integration of the various fracture control technologies and activities seems to some to be an inevitable step in the direction of achieving some of the goals just outlined. Aside from some feeling that API RP-2A, the ABS Rules [American Bureau of Shipping (6)], portions of the OCS Platform Verification Program [United States Geological Survey (7)], and other more specialized references [Bristol, P. (8); McClelland, B. (9); Pellini, W. S. (10); Rolfe, S. T., and Barson, J. M. (11); McHenry, H. I., and Rolfe, S. T. (12)] provide an excellent start to documenting some of the elements of fracture control, only one U. S. entity, a major oil company, appears to have an explicit written fracture control plan. However, the elements of integrated fracture control exist implicitly within the offshore industry through two media:

1. Use of experienced, competent engineers who may be called fracture control generalists.

2. Team efforts of engineers in the various fracture control sub-specialties responsible for ensuring that all aspects of their specialties are considered in the context of the other technical elements of the overall fracture control plan.

Although the participants in these media may come from the operator, designer, or fabricator, a key factor in how vigorously fracture control is pursued appears to be the attitude of the operator (who eventually bears the cost).

Only a minority of engineers in the offshore industry want to immediately create a written integrated fracture control plan for general usage. Many in the industry are averse to any sort of official fracture control document in the form of a regulation or binding recommended practice. This aversion is due to their fear that the document would not contain sufficient generality and freedom for competent structural engineers to optimize all aspects of their structures including safety and fracture control. In spite of this reluctance and aversion, there is a general feeling in the offshore engineering community that some additional commonality in integration of the subspecialties of fracture control is necessary and desirable.

An operator who wishes to take immediate positive steps toward more uniform fracture control could do so by using a fracture control checklist such as the one devised in Appendix B of Reference 2. The purpose of a checklist is to make guidelines available to the fracture control specialist so that for each fracture control activity (material selection, design, construction, and operation) there is a relatively comprehensive list to select from in determining what to emphasize in a particular fracture control check. This, combined with careful documentation, should make it easier to ensure that any modifications to an existing design or technology are integrated over all of the disciplines, so that a material improvement (for example), or new welding technique, will not compromise the design's integrity.

Some further, more specific suggestions for making better use of existing technology are summarized in Table 2.

TABLE 2 - Suggestions for changes and procedures that could be implemented using existing technologies.

Relatively Easy to Implement	Moderate to Difficult to Impelement
Make routine and extensive use of simplified analysis procedures, such as the Failure Assessment Diagram.	Use first-order bounding fracture mechanics models to determine relative effects of toughness and fatigue-design control.
Encourage Fracture Control Integration.	Supplement S-N curves with deterministic fracture mechanics approaches.
Survey the entire structure for critical elements.	Use a calibrated fracture mechanics

TABLE 2 - Continued

Relatively Easy to Implement	Moderate to Difficult to Impelement
Document the effects of every major structural decision or change upon all fracture control elements.	model to address tough fatigue and fracture problems.
Modify punching shear criteria to prevent other failure modes.	Employ natural load shedding and displacement control features to help design crack arrest features.
Tailor the inspection procedures to the intended application.	Apply structural reliability models to optimize design and operational decisions.
Combine independent inspection methods.	Model size/shape of crack and transition behavior in brace or leg.
Reduce the human error factor through education and minor modification of the USGS Design Verification Program.	Establish the level of cathodic protection necessary at all fatigue-critical welded joints.
Ensure that divers, platform operators, and inspection personnel are adequately trained.	Determine the suitability of proof testing as an inspection procedure for joints known to have seen stresses at or near their design envelope.
Determine the condition of the weld root before improving the weld toe performance.	Spell out available crack repair schemes in operation, emphasizing their effects on fracture control and safety risk.

CONCLUSION

Results of the concurrent surveys of experts, the open literature, and direct participation in solving fracture problems have revealed that the more advanced fracture control methods used in the United States offshore industry closely parallel those used by other high-technology industries such as aerospace. Sophistication of the best methods used considerably surpasses analysis requirements of typical codes used in several other industries (e.g., nuclear power). However, the best methods do not appear to be as uniformly applied and/or documented as they should be. Thus, it appears that emphasis for the foreseeable future should be placed first on more widespread and uniform use of the best existing methods and second on steady improvements in the methods. The first emphasis should be accomplished voluntarily under leadership of the platform operators. (The survey revealed that typically, designers and constructors look to the operators for guidance.) The second emphasis should be addressed by research organizations.

There are still numerous problems to be solved before catastrophic fracture is virtually eliminated as a threat to offshore structures, but there is much that can be done, even at present, to greatly reduce the incidence of fracture and failure.

REFERENCES

1. Besuner, P. M., Harris, D. O., and Thomas, J. M., 1983, "A Review of Fracture Mechanics Life Technology," NASA Report, Contract NAS8-34756, Failure Analysis Associates, FaAA-83-3-11, Palo Alto, CA.

2. Besuner, P. M., Ortiz, K., Thomas, J., and Adams, S. D., 1983, "Fracture Control for Fixed Offshore Structures, " Ship Structures Committee, National Resarch Council Report No. SR-1288, Failure Analysis Associates, FaAA-83-6-2, Palo Alto, CA.

3. American Petroleum Institute, 1982, "API Recommended Practice for Planning, Designing, and Constructing Fixed Offshore Platforms," API RP-2A, Thirteenth Edition, Dallas, Texas.

4. American Petroleum Institute, 1980, "API Recomended Practice for Ultrasonic Examination of Offshore Structural Fabrication and Guidelines for Qualification of Ultrasonic Technicians," API RP-2X, American Petroleum Institute, Dallas, Texas.

5. American Welding Society, 1979, "Structural Welding Code - Steel," AWS D1.1-79, Third Edition, American Welding Society, Inc., Miami, Florida.

6. American Bureau of Shipping, 1983, "Rules for Building and Classing Offshore Installations," Special Committee on Offshore Installations, New York.

7. United States Geological Survey, Conservation Division, 1979, "OCS Platform Verification Program," Department of the Interior, Washington, D.C.

8. Bristoll, P., 1978, "A Review of the Fracture Mechanics Approach to the Problems of Design, Quality Assurance, Maintenance, and Repair of Offshore Structures," Proceedings of the European Offshore Steels Research Seminar, Welding Institute, Abington, Cambridge.

9. McClelland, B. (ed.), 1982, The Design of Fixed Offshore Structures, with specific reference to Chapters 18 and 19 ("Tubular Joint Design" and "Steel Selection for Fracture Control") by Peter Marshall, and Chapter 27 ("Welding and Inspection") by P. W. Marshall, H. F. Cricks, and P. T. Marks, to be published by van Nostrand Reinhold, New York.

10. Pellini, W. S., 1972, "Criteria for Fracture Control Plans," Naval Research Laboratory, NRL Report 7405.

11. Rolfe, S. T. and J. M. Barsom, 1977, Fracture and Fatigue Control in Structures, Chapters 14 and 15, Prentice-Hall, Inc., New Jersey.

12. McHenry, H. I., and S. T. Rolfe, 1980, Fracture Control Practices for Metal Structures, National Bureau of Standards IR79-1623.

FRACTURE PREVENTION IN THE HYDRO AND THERMAL ELECTRICITY INDUSTRIES

W. A. Mannheimer[1]

The paper describes some of the problems of fracture in the electricity industry, for the specific case of Brazil. The emphasis on hydroelectric power generation is noted, and it is suggested that the absence of spectacular failures in generation and transmission facilities indicates the less critical conditions within the Brazilian industry or the efficient application of fracture prevention techniques. Some details are also presented concerning the facilities and activities of CEPEL, the Electrical Energy Research Centre, which has responsibilities for fracture prevention programs.

INTRODUCTION

The electricity industry, like other branches of modern engineering, is concerned with the problem of fracture.

It is proposed to discuss this problem for the particular case of Brazil, where this International Conference on Fracture Prevention in Energy and Transport Systems is being held. Brazil has a large territorial area of about 8,500,000 km^2, and possesses an estimated 213,000 MW of hydroelectric reserves. Currently, of these about 27,000 MW are in use, and 20,000 MW additional are scheduled to be put into service by the end of the decade. This would indicate that only about 25% of hydro reserves will have been tapped. It should be noted, however, that the population and industrial distribution of the country are largely coastal and situated in the southeastern and southern regions, so that power consumption is not uniform throughout the country. As a consequence most important hydroelectric sites in the more heavily populated areas have been explored, and Brazil will be faced in the near future with the task of transporting large blocks of electric power over long transmission lines, including in the future the very large reserves available from the tributaries of the Amazon river.

Because of this scenario Brazil is to a very large extent a hydroelectric country, this source supplying about 90% of the country's electrical needs. There is a small amount of fossil fuel thermal generation and an incipient nuclear generation industry.

Brazil and Paraguay are currently engaged in building the largest hydroelectric complex in the world, of which the first of eighteen turbines will be commissioned in 1984 and providing, after conclusion towards the end of the decade, a total generation capacity of 12,600 MW. In this project some of the

[1] Head, Materials Department, CEPEL - Electrical Energy Research Centre, 21941 Rio de Janeiro, Brazil; Adj. Professor, Federal University of Rio de Janeiro.

largest hydroelectric generators ever built are being installed (700 MW units), with the corresponding scale of mechanical and fracture considerations. It might be interesting to scan the whole series of equipment from generation to utilization, and point out some of the potential areas for fracture.

Hydroelectric dams include components that are large welded structures, mainly gates and penstocks, that are subjected to a high level of stress. Some classical cases of fracture have been reported worldwide for penstocks, but in most cases it has been possible to show that the problems can be adequately met by conventional application of high strength steel, utilizing conventional welding design and technology. In the case of hydroelectric generators some problems have been encountered in the field, with cracking due to residual weld stresses in turbine rotors and stay-vanes, as well as a result of vibration and resonance during critical stages of operation. In this particular case, adequate techniques have been developed to study the vibration behaviour of such large machines and, either by modification of design to include proper hydrodynamic treatment of the profiles of turbine elements, or by proper operational practice to avoid critical stages of operation, it has been possible in general to control the problem.

High voltage, high power transmission is largely based on steel towers, both self supporting and guyed, and aluminum (generally steel core reinforced) electrical cables. It seems that in the few reported tower failures, no fractures were involved that could be related to materials problems, or to fracture-mechanical origin; however, cables very often suffer fatigue failure when subjected to wind induced vibrations.

Worldwide, some spectacular fatigue failures have been reported associated with steam turbogenerator rotors. In Brazil we have no direct experience of such occurrences, because of the lack up to now of such large thermal machines.

We are, perhaps, fortunate in that the lack of recent spectacular failures may indicate less critical conditions for the Brazilian generating system or, hopefully, efficient application of fracture prevention techniques.

CEPEL - RESEARCH FACILITIES AND PROGRAMS

At CEPEL - Electrical Energy Research Centre, Rio de Janeiro, Brazil, programs are underway to provide technical information and support services to assist in the prevention of fracture in critical components in the Brazilian electrical industry. Some of the areas of investigation and facilities are indicated in the remaining part of this paper.

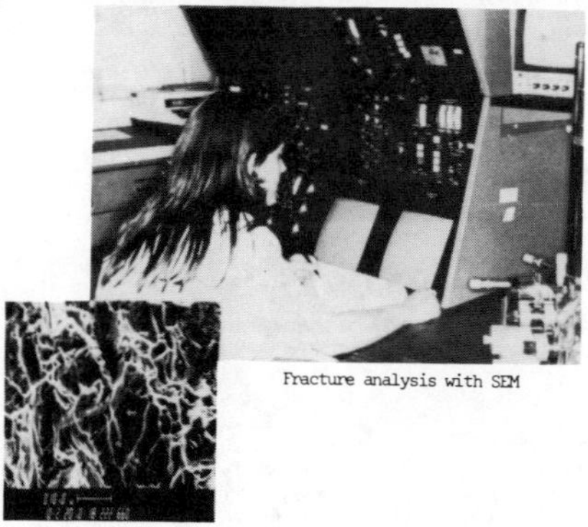

Fracture analysis with SEM

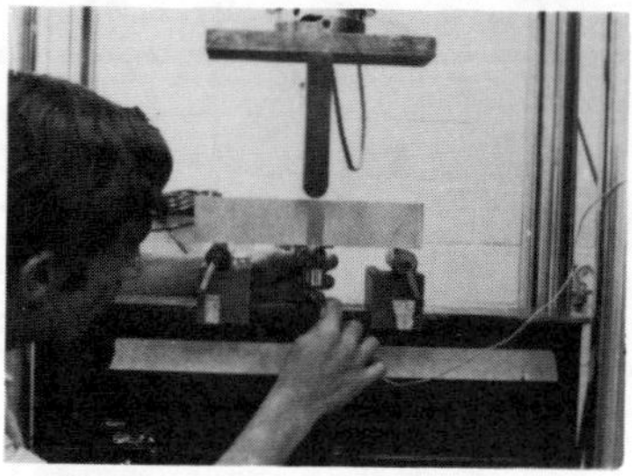

COD test

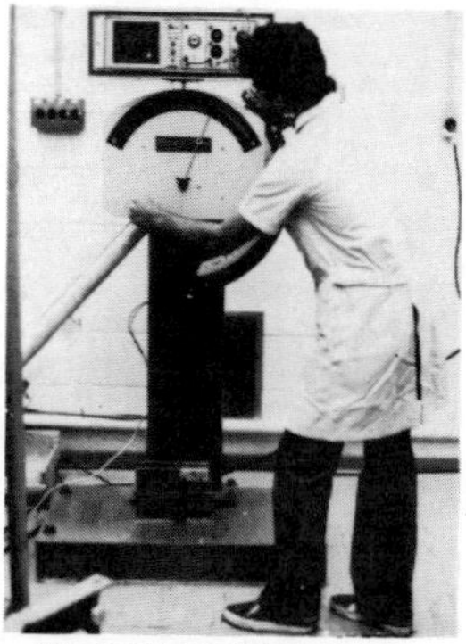

Instrumented impact test for K_{ID} determination

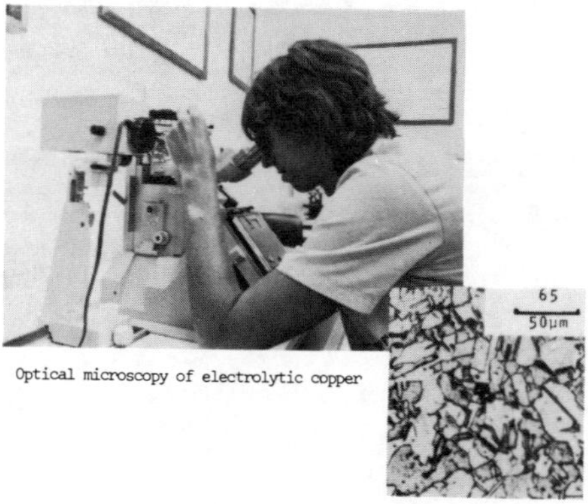

Optical microscopy of electrolytic copper

Cepel
Centro de Pesquisas de Energia Elétrica

Mailing Address
CEPEL
Caixa Postal 2754
CEP 20001
Rio de Janeiro, RJ - Brasil

Cable Address
CEPELETRO
Rio de Janeiro, RJ - Brasil

Telex
(021)21035 - CEPE BR

Head Office and Electrical Systems Laboratory
Cidade Universitária —
Ilha do Fundão
Rio de Janeiro, RJ — Brasil
Telephone (021) 270-0112

Electrical Equipment Laboratory
Adrianópolis
Nova Iguaçu, RJ - Brasil
Telephones (021) 767-9079 and 767-9821

RADIATION DAMAGE SURVEILLANCE: IMPLICATIONS FOR FAILURE PREVENTION IN LIGHT WATER REACTORS

L. E. Steele*

Experience in the USA has shown that radiation embrittlement of reactor pressure vessels may be significant. Assessment of the degree of embrittlement must be accomplished using fracture specimens of the vessel steel which has been exposed to simulate the vessel exposure. A review of results has shown that such simulation, called surveillance is vital to the assurance of continuing ductility of the vessel. The level of ductility of course must be analyzed from small irradiated specimens and such analyses extended to the full vessel under all conditions of service even abnormal conditions which may result in emergency core cooling. This review highlights the merits and limitation of "surveillance".

INTRODUCTION

Nuclear steam supply plants for the generation of electric power have gained a significant fraction of the base load in several nations especially those with limited domestic fossil fuel resources though the impetus for nuclear power has diminished because of a world-wide abundance of fossil fuels. Nevertheless, there are many nuclear plants in operation, for example, some seventy-five operating or licensed plants in the USA. Those who support nuclear power as a clean and effective long-term alternative to fossil fuels, which are admitted to be finite in availability and of great value as a reservoir of basic organic chemicals, are duly concerned that nuclear technologists assure safe operation of nuclear plants. Similar concerns are presented by those who oppose nuclear power. For both, the most deadly scenario is one in which the primary containment vessel ruptures catastrophically and dangerous radioisotopes are released so as to endanger public health. For these reasons dedicated programs of research and experimentation have sought answers to enhance our assurance of reactor vessel integrity. One such program is called "reactor vessel embrittlement surveillance," often simply called vessel "surveillance."

This author defines surveillance as a program to periodically assess the reactor vessel condition in terms of radiation embrittlement through test and analysis of the vessel's fracture potential through proxy specimens removed from capsules which were placed at or near the vessel wall so as to receive neutron exposures to closely and progressively simulate the current state of the reactor vessel inner wall. The basis for such programs was initiated by volunteer members of standards activities within the American Society for Testing and Materials (ASTM). These later were incorporated in federal regulations.

* Naval Research Laboratory, Washington, D.C. 20375, U.S.A.

RADIATION EFFECTS AND POTENTIAL FRACTURE OF VESSEL STEELS

A review of developments and factors leading to the current status of radiation damage surveillance in the USA is helpful to a citation of the current situation. First, the use of ferritic steels with their inherent ductile-to-brittle transition characteristics was established. An early, though still appropriate, listing of steels used (or approved for use) in USA light water reactors is shown in Table 1 (1). Added to this was the requirement for thick section to provide adequate structural strength for the high pressure water required for both boiling (BWR) and pressurized (PWR) water reactors. Besides the design and materials selection choices there was added the discovery of the fundamental problem of reduction of toughness or embrittlement which was shown to be potentially severe (2). Given these factors, it became clear to early nuclear materials specialists that knowledge, both general and specific, of the possibility for brittle fracture was an imperative within nuclear technology. Early studies at the U. S. Naval Research Laboratory sought to establish a reference nil ductility or brittleness limit point. This was done using the Pellini drop-weight test which provided an empirical reference point called the nil ductility transition temperature (NDTT) (See ASTM Standard E-208). However, size limitations forced use of the smaller Charpy V-notch specimen to define a ductile-brittle transition range and this became the primary reference for both materials radiation effects studies in test reactors and the early surveillance programs defined and implemented for power reactor surveillance.

TABLE 1 - Ferritic Steel Plate, Forging, and Weld Filler Compositions used in Primary System of U.S.-built Light-water Reactors.

Plate	Forging	Weld
SA 302 Grade B[a]	SA 105 Grade 2	Manual
SA 515 Grade 70	SA 181 Equivalent to A266 Cl 2	E-7015
SA 516 Grade 60	SA 182 Grade F1	E-7016
Grade 70	Grade F6	E-7018[a]
SA 517 Grade B	SA 508 Class 1	E-8015
Grade F	SA 508 Class 2[a]	E-8016
SA 533 Class 1	Class 2 New Grade	E-8018[a]
Grade A	Class 3	E-9016[a]
Grade B[a]	Class 4	E-9018
Grade B low Cu[a]		Submerged arc
Grade B ESR+[b]		High Mn, Mo, Ni[a]
SA 533 Class 2		MIL B-4 MOD
Grade A		Flux-Linde 80
SA 537 Grade B		Linde 0091
SA 542 (proposed)[c]		Linde 8091
SA 543 Class 1		
Grade B[c]		

[a] Most commonly used for reactor primary vessel construction.
[b] ESR = electroslag refined - Lukens Steel.
[c] These compositions are not now accepted by the ASME Code for Class 1 nuclear vessel construction but are under consideration.

A major debate arose concerning whether or not the very heavy sections (to 300 mm) required would exhibit the same type of transition as the small (10 mm) Charpy specimens. Accordingly, dynamic tear specimens to 300 mm thickness were tested and vividly sharp and elevated, transition curves were determined. Parallel K_{Ic} tests showed a similar pattern though displaced to lower temperatures. With this established, the next step was to attempt to define limits in terms of toughness which would also allow establishment of a limit on stress (operational limit) with an assumed flaw of significant size. Building upon these results and those of radiation effects results, came a series of codes, standards and regulatory rules:

a. Lower bound reference fracture toughness curve for heavy section steels (the K_{IR} curve) (3). (See Fig. 1).

b. Establishment of a reference point, called RT_{NDT}, which sets rules for use of NDT drop-weight test and related reference points from Charpy V-notch tests.

c. Acceptance of these concepts for use on individual vessels through the ASME, Code Section III, (5) and the closely related U. S. Nuclear Regulatory Colmmission (NRC) specific regulatory rules on fracture toughness requirements (6).

The bases for this series of actions and related ones dealing with surveillance are, of course, the real concern for assuring vessel integrity and the primary factor observed neutron radiation effects as are illustrated in Fig. 2 (7). The implications are evident from the large radiation induced changes.

SURVEILLANCE OF RADIATION EFFECTS

The primary intent of pressure vessel surveillance is to provide knowledge which will allow the reactor operator to learn enough about the response of his specific reactor vessel steel to neutron bombardment that he takes action to preclude failure. Radiation embrittlement of the particular vessel steel is a crucial element but, as noted, is only one of three key elements to failure by a fast-running brittle separation; the other two key elements are presence of a flaw of critical size and an applied stress (K) adequate to drive the crack beyond an initiation point to a "through wall" condition. In this paper only the role of surveillance of radiation embrittlement is considered which by inference assumes the other two conditions may exist.

Use of the list in Table 1 showing the steels, plate, forging, and weld requires further consideration since the validity of surveillance programs for the cited primary purpose depends upon the proper selection of materials for inclusion in the surveillance capsule. The key is to make the proper analyses of composition and microstructure in order to judge those steels most sensitive to neutron irradiation. The approach taken by the Combustion Engineering Company (C-E) and the inherent complexity is shown by Fig. 3 (7). A critical point is the level of copper in the component and the specimen made to represent it over the forty or more years as well as other factors including other residual elements in the weld which is the component usually identified as that most sensitive to radiation embrittlement and often that having the poorest fracture toughness before irradiation. How, then is surveillance designed and implemented.

The usual plan for surveillance of pressurized water reactors involves the construction of six or eight, and sometimes even more, capsules. Further, besides those specimens inserted in reactor capsule locations, a large number of unirradiated specimens are tested to aid in selecting the most appropriate component specimens. For example, C-E tests drop weight (DW), Charpy (C_V) impact and tension (T) specimens in two orientations, longitudinal ("strong") and transverse ("weak") of base metal (plate or forging), weld metal, heat affected zone, and a standard reference steel. The number of weld metal specimens, for example, include 12 DW, 30 C_V and 18 T, all considered transverse, tested in the unirradiated condition, as well as 72 C_V and 18 T tested after irradiation (six capsules). The capsules containing each 12 C_V and 3 T specimens are located as shown in Fig. 4 (7) and are removed on a schedule as outlined in Table 2 (7). (New C-E capsule replacements contain fracture mechanics specimens, 1/2 CT, as well.)

TABLE 2 - Typical Capsule Assembly Removal Schedule

Capsule No.	Azimuthal Location, deg	Removal Time Years	Target Fluence n/cm^2
1	97	7	$6.0x10^{18}$
2	104	19	$1.6x10^{19}$
3	284	30	$2.5x10^{19}$
4	263	standby	...
5	277	standby	...
6	83	standby	...

Many USA programs now incorporate fracture mechanics specimens. For example, of twenty-eight USA reactor vessel surveillance programs surveyed in a special review (7) only eleven reported no fracture mechanics specimens. However, most of the specimens cited were the wedge opening loading (WOL) type, a non-standard specimen but still a possible basis for elasto-plastic fracture mechanics analysis as the technology advances. Further, Charpy V-notch specimens precracked before testing can guide an analysis to some basis for non-elastic analysis which may be crucial to continued licensability of a nuclear plant if all other indications are positive.

Besides the fracture potential described by analysis of specimens representing the vessel, surveillance capsules must provide 1) evidence that the capsule temperature matched that of the vessel and 2) the neutron fluence to which the specimens were exposed. The former is usually assessed by the placement of fusible alloys in a configuration appropriate to assessing fusion or non-fusion. The vessel fusible alloys used are (7):

Alloy	Melting Point
90 Pb-5 Ag-5 Sn	292°C (558°F)
94.5 Pb-2.5 Ag-3 Sn	304°C (580°F)
97.5 Pb-2.5 Ag-3 Sn	309°C (590°F)
Cadmium	321°C (610°F)
Lead	327°C (621°F)

Neutron fluence monitors in the form of carefully manufactured threshold detectors, usually thin metal foils of well known purity, are used for this purpose. Long half-life and a readily detectable decay product are key features of these foils (detectors). A good grouping of these is shown in Table 3 (7).

TABLE 3 - Materials for Neutron Threshold Detectors

Materials	Reaction	Threshold Energy, MeV	Half-Life
Uranium	$^{238}U(n,f)^{90}Sr$	0.7	28 years
	$^{238}U(n,f)^{137}Cs$	0.7	30.2 years
Sulfur	$^{32}S(n,p)^{32}P$	2.9	14.3 days
Iron	$^{54}Fe(n,p)^{54}Mn$	4.0	314 days
Nickel	$^{58}Ni(n,p)^{58}Co$	5.0	71 days
Copper	$^{63}Cu(n,a)^{60}Co$	7.0	5.3 years
Titanium	$^{46}Ti(n,p)^{46}Sc$	8.0	84 days
Cobalt	$^{59}Co(n,\gamma)^{60}Co$	thermal	5.3 years

USING SURVEILLANCE FOR FRACTURE PREVENTION

In spite of advances in elastic-plastic fracture mechanics, its standardization through ASTM and it use by some reactor owners in assessing the current fracture toughness of operating reactor vessels, the key to date is still the Charpy-V data. For example, the most recent NRC guide to fracture toughness of reactor vessels (8) retains as the principal basis ΔT at 30 ft-lb or 41 J and a shelf toughness of 50 ft-lb (68 J). This is necessary in view of the scarcity of irradiated K_{Ic}, J-R and similar data for the irradiated state and the lack of good correlative bases for projecting such quantitative data from a larger base of qualitative C_v and NDT results. Nevertheless, the first steps have been taken by test reactor results on J_{Ic}, J-R, T-tearing instability numbers and by the testing of specimens by Westinghouse to obtain dynamic fracture toughness data using WOL specimens exposed with surveillance capsules V and R of the R. E. Ginna Reactor (Unit No. 1) and analysis of these using the "equivalent energy" method (not a standard test method). A quick view of these results is published in reference 7 (pp. 179-187). The data compare K_{Id} and K data for pressure vessel shell forgings and weld metal irradiated to a fluence of 7.6 X 10^{18} n/cm^2 (E >1 MeV). The most notable feature of the data which involved testing at 25 to 111°C, after irradiation at 288°C, was the wide variation of results. K_{Id} ranged from a low of 115 MPa$\sqrt{m}$ for one forging tested at 38°C to 250 MPa $\sqrt{m}$ for a weldment tested at 110°C. While it is possible to identify a "weak link" by this technique, the results can have little real meaning until a significant data base compared with C_v data has been amassed. Further, the base must be rational relative to test versus exposure temperatures.

SUMMARY OF SURVEILLANCE RESULTS

Results based on C_v data and evaluated in terms of the principal NRC limiting criteria have been made in reference 7 for twenty-eight USA reactors. A summary review of these results for critical observations may be helpful in assessing the value of surveillance in determining the status of or at least warnings of potential future areas requiring attention. It should be noted that the remaining forty-plus reactors generally were either of the type receiving very low vessel neutron exposures (most BWRs) or had operated so short a time at the survey date that no meaningful surveillance data were yet available. This summary is based on a massive review of surveillance data analyzed in the final chapter of reference 7 (pp. 227-272) by this author: (Data analyzed were those available in January 1980.)

Features of surveillance capsule content for twenty-eight reactors include:

1) All vessels were constructed of the ASTM type A302-B, A508-CL2 or A533-B steels.

2) Twenty-four contained weld metal specimens and twenty-three contained heat affected zone (HAZ) specimens.

3) Twenty-one contained a standard (well characterized) reference steel besides the vessel steel.

4) Sixteen contained fracture mechanics specimens most of the wedge opening loading (WOL) design.

Important features of surveillance results for the twenty eight reactors surveyed include:

1) In all cases the fluence received by the capsule exceeded that of the peak vessel wall position some by an order of magnitude.

2) In fifteen cases a projection as to the vessel condition was made; these included current condition, some for a future date and some at the one quarter thickness point within the vessel.

3) In twenty-three cases a C_V shelf level value was provided either based on the capsule or a projection of the vessels condition. Startlingly, twenty of these showed by capsule data or life projection a shelf level less than 96 joules (70 ft-lb) and seventeen a shelf level of less than 82 joules (60 ft-lb).

4) Nineteen of the twenty eight had identified the vessel weld as the limiting material; that is the component most likely to reach undesirable levels of toughness during the planned reactor life.

5) In nineteen shelf level toughness was identified as the likely limiting material during vessel lifetime. (7)

A limited selection of examples of principal surveillance results by reactor are shown in Table 4.

TABLE 4 - Surveillance Data from several USA Reactors (7)
(All data projected for end of life - For detailed data and references see Table 8.2b - ref. 7)

Reactor	Start date	Neutron Exposure (n/cm^2 >1MeV)	Toughness Data RT_{NDT} (°C)	USE (J)	Vessel limit
Connecticut Yankee	8/68	$3.6x10^{19}$	106	NP	Weld
Robert Ginna	3/70	$3.7x10^{19}$	132	NP	Weld
Palisades	12/71	$3.2x10^{19}$	152	73	Weld
Turkey Point 3	12/72	$6.6x10^{19}$	166(1/4T)	79	Weld
Zion 1	7/73	NP-capsule=$1.8x10^{19}$	93	76	Weld
Indian Point 2	8/73	$8.2x10^{18}$	138	68	Plate
Arkansas 1	9/74	NP-capsule $7.3x10^{17}$	NP	<68	Weld
Oconee	10/74	$1.7x10^{19}$	NP	~68	Weld
Donald Cook	4/75	$1.7x10^{19}$	66	66	NP

RT = Reference transition or nil ductility at end of life
USE = Charpy V-notch upper shelf energy at end of life
Vessel limit = Material component determining life limit or likely to be "weak link" requiring continuing careful surveillance
NP = Not projected (usually means insufficient data for numerical projection)

CONCLUSIONS

The most meaningful application of surveillance data to fracture prevention currently derives from projecting RT_{NDT} limits (see figure 1) based upon transposition of the K_{IR} curve to the right with continuing ractor operation and from inferred toughness degradation based upon the somewhat arbitrary point when the vessel wall reaches a C_v shelf level of 68J (50 ft-lb). Those bases have been highlighted by recent studies of the potential for overcooling with repressurization during a loss of coolant accident. Needed is a more quantitative basis for determining the critical point at which the uncertainties of crack initiation and fast propagation become too great for reasonable statistical assurance of non-occurence. Closer definition of the latter will depend upon current studies of large section irradiated specimen tests, full sized or model vessel tests and their correlation to the surveillance data and thence to projection of the limiting conditions for vessel failure.

All of these steps are being taken in research or experimental studies and their integration with results of surveillance test results, especially those based upon the irradiated fracture mechanics studies will have profound positive effects upon the degree of confidence surrounding decisions to operate nuclear power plants after years of nuclear exposure.

REFERENCES

1. Annual Book of ASTM Standards, Part 4, A 647, Special Requirements for Steel Plates for Nuclear and Other Special Applications, American Society for Testing and Materials, Philadelphia, Pa., 1979, pp. 609-621.

2. Steele, L. E., "Neutron Irradiation Embrittlement of Reactor Pressure Vessel Steels," IAEA Technical Report Series No. 163, International Atomic Energy Agency, Vienna, Austria, 1975.

3. "Recommendations on Toughness Requirements for Ferritic Materials," Welding Research Council Bulletin No. 175, New York, Aug. 1972.

4. ASME Boiler and Pressure Vessel Code Section III, Summer Addenda, 1972 Amer. Soc. Mech. Eng., New York, 30 June 1972

5. ASME Boiler and Pressure Vessel Code, Section III, Nuclear Power Plant Components, Sub-Section N, Appendix G, American Society for Mechanical Engineers, New York, 1 July 1974, p. 487.

6. "Fracture Toughness Program Requirements," Appendix G, Title 10, Code of Federal Regulations, Part 50 (10CFR50), U. S. Atomic Energy Commission, Federal Register, Volume 38, 136, 19012, 17 July 1973.

7. Steele, L. E., Editor, "Status of USA Nuclear Reactor Pressure Vessel Surveillance for Radiation Effects," ASTM Special Technical Publication 784, 1983.

8. Nuclear Regulatory Commission, Fracture Toughness Requirements for Light Water Nuclear Power Reactors, Federal Regulation 10CFR 50 Federal Register, Vol. 48, No. 104, May 27, 1983.

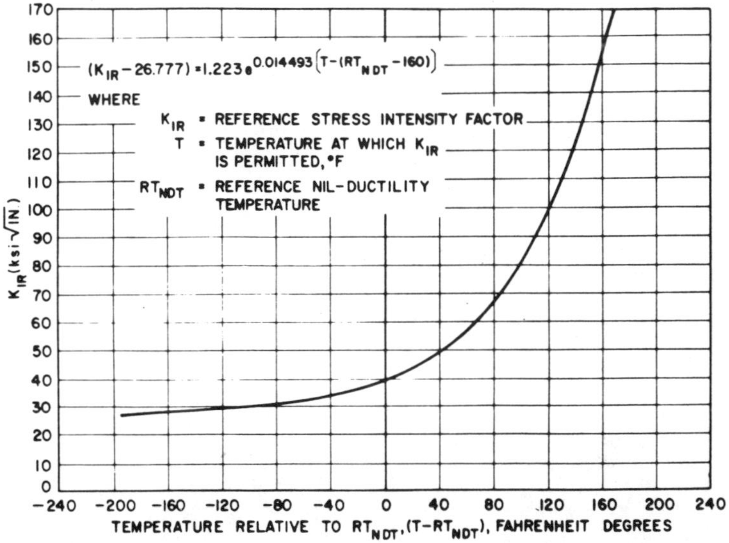

Fig. 1 The ASME K_{IR} Curve, a Reference Transition Curve to Guide Status of A Nuclear Reactor Pressure Vessel during Operation.

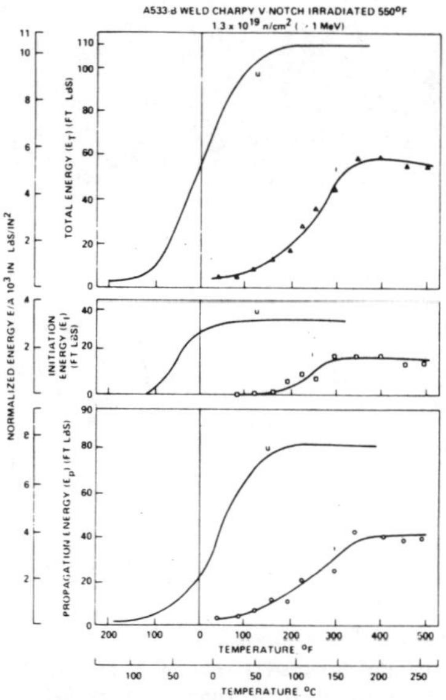

Fig. 2 Instrumented Test Results for Standard Charpy Specimens of Maine Yankee Weld Metal Irradiated to 1.3 X 10^{19} n/cm^2 (E > 1 MeV) at 288°C (550°F).

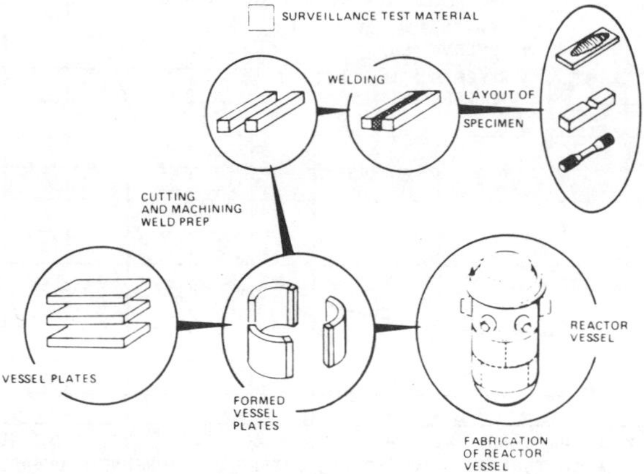

Fig. 3 Schematic of Operations included in Preparation of Surveillance Specimens and Fabrication of Reactor Vessel Shell Course. Note the location of Surveillance Material on the Formed Shell Plate.

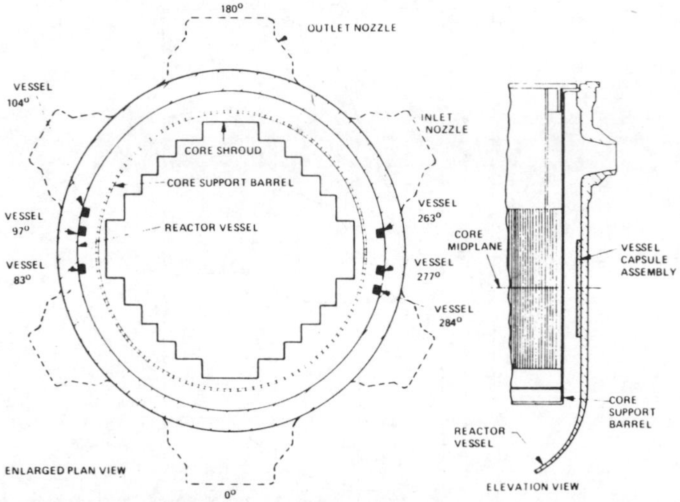

Fig. 4 Location of Capsule Holders with respect to the Peak Fluence of the Vessel, which occurs at the 90-deg locations. Physical Constraints prevent use of the 0-deg and 180-deg Positions for this prupose. The Elevation of the Capsule Assembly Disects the Geometric Centerline of the Core.

CRITICAL ASPECTS OF FRACTURE PREVENTION IN MATERIALS USED IN THE ENERGY AND TRANSPORTATION INDUSTRIES

J.F. Knott*

The paper treats four major modes of fracture in engineering alloys which have particular relevance to critical components used in energy and transportation applications. Transgranular cleavage is described, with reference to carbon-manganese weld-metals, used for pipelines or offshore structures. Intergranular fracture mechanisms are discussed in relation to stress-relief cracking in pressure-vessel steels. Attention is drawn to the role of second-phase particles in determining the fracture toughness of high strength-to-weight materials, in which the mode of fracture is "fast shear". The importance of defect distribution in determining fatigue life is emphasised, using examples of aluminium-bronze propellers and nickel-superalloy gas-turbine discs.

INTRODUCTION

Materials used in energy and transport systems are subjected to extreme conditions. The applied stresses may be extreme, approaching the yield stress in gas-turbine discs and other aircraft components. The service temperatures may be extreme, ranging from 1300K for a gas-turbine blade to 100K for tanks used to store liquefied hydrocarbons. The chemical environment may be extreme: oxidising, in some combustion systems; reducing, in pipelines transporting "sour" gas or in coal gasification plant; concentrated in chloride ions in offshore applications. Extreme service conditions result from the need to produce and utilise energy in the most cost-effective manner. An aero-engine, for example, is subjected to high temperatures and stresses, because it is more efficient at high temperatures and because high stresses allow load-bearing cross-sectional areas to be reduced. The power-to-weight ratio of the engine is therefore maximised and this is perceived by an airline as higher payload or better fuel economy for a given size of engine.

The skill of the engineer has traditionally been demonstrated by his ability to employ designs which exploit to the full the strengths and stiffnesses of his materials, whilst ensuring that they can, at the same time, withstand the most extreme anticipated conditions without premature failure. This skill has developed into a science as a result of the adoption of the principles of fracture mechanics, which provide quantitative techniques for the calculation of fracture stresses or lifetimes.

It is recognized that the successful application of fracture mechanics often depends crucially on the ability of non-destructive-

* Department of Metallurgy & Materials Science, University of Cambridge.

testing (NDT) methods to detect and size defects and here it must be appreciated that there are substantial differences between surface-breaking defects and buried defects. The former may be more severe as stress-intensifiers and are subjected to the service environment, but they are much easier to detect and size. Approximate detection limits, using ultrasonic inspection on a component such as a gas-turbine disc, are 0.2mm (surface), 2mm (buried). For a large, thick, component, such as a thick-walled PWR pressure vessel, the figures might be 2mm (surface), 20mm (buried).

The parameters which characterise fracture under monotonically increasing load are critical values of the stress intensity factor, K, for linear elastic conditions and the J-integral, J, or the crack-opening-displacement (COD), δ, for conditions of extensive or general yielding. In the "small-scale-yielding" (quasi-elastic) limit, the parameters are related through the expressions:

$$K^2 = E'J = ME'\sigma_Y \delta \qquad 1)$$

where E' is Young's modulus, E, in plane stress, or $E/(1-\nu^2)$ in plane strain, where ν is Poisson's ratio. The value of M is unity in plane stress but may range from 1 to 3 in plane strain. For ductile fractures, instability is not usually coincident with initiation and the crack growth "resistance" is then expressed by the slope of the J-based or C.O.D.-based "R-curve", $(J-J_i)/(a-a_o)$ or $(\delta - \delta_i)/(a-a_o)$ where a_o is the initial crack length.

The rate of subcritical crack growth under monotonic loading (stress-corrosion, creep) or cyclic loading (fatigue) may be expressed generally by relating the "periodic" increment in crack length, da/dx, where x is a "period" variable (time or number of cycles) to the product of polynomial functions of a "stress" variable, s (where s is monotonic stress, σ, or cyclic stress, $\Delta\sigma$) and crack length:

$$da/dx = \text{const}\ s^v a^w \qquad 2)$$

In many cases, v = 2w, and the combination of stress and crack length is expressed as a stress intensity. For fatigue-crack growth, use is often made of the Paris law:

$$da/dN = A\,\Delta K^m \qquad 3)$$

where N is number of cycles, ΔK is the alternating stress intensity, and m is a constant, having a value between 2 and 3 for ductile materials. Modifications to equation 3) have to be made to take account of the fatigue "threshold", ΔK_{th} and of accelerated growth as K_{max} approaches K_{IC}. It is arguable that fatigue crack growth would be more realistically based on values of the alternating crack-tip COD, $\Delta\delta$, which implies that:

$$da/dN \propto \{(1+R)/(1-R)\}\,\Delta K^2 \qquad 4)$$

where $R = K_{min}/K_{max}$. Association of the threshold with a constant minimum value of $\Delta\delta$ gives the relationship:

$$\Delta K_{th(R)} = \{(1-R)/(1+R)\}^{1/2}\ \Delta K_o \qquad 5)$$

The lifetime of a component may be calculated by separating the variables in equation 2) and integrating the left-hand-side, $a^{-w}da$, between limits a_o, the initial defect size, determined by processing control or by the NDT inspection limit, and a_{crit}, the critical crack length, derived from fracture toughness or plastic collapse criteria. If a_o and a_{crit} do not vary substantially with s, lifetimes under a combination of stress levels may be obtained by sequential integration of equation 2) to give Miner's Law for fatigue loading, the Life Fraction Rule for creep loading, or equivalent expressions for stress-corrosion exposure, see Knott (1). "Damage accumulation" can then often be attributed to crack growth. It should be noted that the stress-intensity formulation is not necessary to derive these relationships: indeed, the crack length variable, a^w, may be omitted entirely, in which case, da integrates simply to $(a_{crit}-a_o)$.

Materials may become degraded, not only by mechanical "damage" or interactions with an external environment, but by changes in microstructure (coarsening of grains or particles, overageing), segregation of trace impurity elements to grain boundaries or other interfaces, or matrix hardening associated with point defects produced by neutron irradiation. The extent to which such degradation is sufficient to produce failure under operating or overload conditions is usually assessed by means of "surveillance" specimens. In some cases, particularly that of neutron irradiation, these specimens must be small (to be accommodated in a reactor core) and it is important, not only to be able to measure appropriate fracture toughness parameters on small specimens, but also, in steels, to ensure that the state of triaxial stress is sufficiently well understood to predict effects on the ductile/brittle transition temperature.

In the remainder of this paper, attention is focussed on a number of specific issues, chosen both to illustrate basic micromechanisms of fracture in engineering alloys and to draw attention to some new and interesting aspects of the integrity of materials used in energy and transport systems.

Transgranular Cleavage Fracture in C-Mn Weld Metals

Offshore drilling platforms and oil- or gas-pipelines are fabricated by welding together carbon-manganese steel plates and tubes. Assuming good steelmaking practice, the parent material has a combination of high yield stress (up to 450 MPa) and high toughness, produced by controlled-rolling, in combination with additions of Nb or V to give grain-refinement, and close attention to the levels of P and S (0.02 max and 0.003 max in some recent compositions). If the weldment is not to prove the weak link in the structure or pipeline, the parent material properties must be matched in the weld metal and heat-affected-zone (HAZ). These regions do not benefit from the grain-refinement produced by controlled-rolling, but grains in the HAZ should not coarsen unduly during the welding process because the parent material contains particles such as niobium or vanadium carbo-nitrides, which restrict grain growth.

One method of improving the properties of as-deposited weld-metal is to add nickel, but this is expensive and it is of interest to know whether the strength and toughness values of a simple C-Mn weld deposit could be improved by controlling "process variables" such as cooling-rates or reheating procedures. A second point of interest is the wide variability in toughness values of as-deposited C-Mn weld metals observed when tests are carried out at sub-zero temperatures. For offshore applications, a temperature of 263K is often chosen as a standard, to represent severe service conditions, although, for pipelines subjected to arctic environments, lower temperatures (perhaps as low as 233K) could be contemplated.

In recent work, Tweed and Knott (2) have simulated the microstructural effects of process variables by the application of controlled heating and cooling sequences, using induction heating, to a single, large weld bead of constant composition, (0.06C 1.15Mn 0.3Si). To assess the toughness properties, C.O.D. specimens were prepared with their fatigue-crack tips lying in the as-deposited or heat-treated microstructure; see fig.1. Tensile specimens were extracted so that their gauge lengths crossed the weld bead. The as-deposited microstructure (fig.2) is composed of a mixture of coarse, "grain-boundary" ferrite and fine "acicular" or "basket-weave" ferrite, which has probably nucleated on non-metallic inclusions, produced by deoxidation reactions in the molten weld-pool. Note that carbides and other "non-ferritic products" or "micro-phase" are concentrated in the acicular ferrite. This microstructure has a yield strength of 580 MPa at 233K but the critical C.O.D. is only 30 μm, and the fracture mode is transgranular cleavage. The effect of a grain-refinement heat-treatment cycle, peaking for 1s at 1175K is to transform the microstructure to uniform, fine-grained, ferrite, with fine carbides, which has a yield strength at 233K of 450 MPa. The critical C.O.D. is increased to 0.38mm, which is a δ_c value, associated with ductile crack extension, followed by unstable fracture.

An observation of critical importance with respect to the development of tougher weld-metals was that cleavage microcrack nuclei in the as-deposited state appeared to be non-metallic inclusions, rather than carbides or microphase (see figs. 3 and 4). The distribution of inclusion sizes produced by deoxidation was found to terminate at a maximum size of approx. 2 μm, but occasional spurious, or "exogenous" inclusions of diameter up to 13 μm were found and these gave rise to particularly poor toughness, thereby increasing the scatter in properties. Elimination of large inclusions of this sort by careful attention to processing has now been shown to produce weld metals of consistently better toughnesses, see Judson and McKeown (3). Note that the sizes of defects involved are so small that NDT techniques are of no assistance in guaranteeing properties: even 10 μm is an order-of-magnitude smaller than the sensitivity limit for surface-breaking cracks. High and consistent toughness of the weld metal can be achieved only through metallurgical process control, combined with mechanical testing and metallography.

Welding process control, in terms of both the elimination of spurious, large inclusions and the employment of overlapping beads to produce grain-refinement, can therefore improve the toughness of simple C-Mn weldments. The use of "weaving" to slow down cooling-rates is not beneficial, because it encourages the formation of grain-boundary ferrite and the coarsening of carbides. It is plausible that a stage is reached at which carbides coarsen sufficiently to become the critical microcrack nuclei, as they are in wrought mild steel, and an increase in the carbon content of a weld metal might produce a similar effect. This is one possible reason for the relatively poor toughness exhibited by the "root-run" in a C-Mn weldment. The first run to be deposited generally suffers the highest "dilution" (uptake of elements, including carbon, from the wrought plate or tube) and may therefore develop thicker carbides than those produced in successive passes.

A second possibility is that the root-run is subjected to a number of severe strain-ageing cycles as successive passes are deposited and that this produces strain-age embrittlement, because the yield stress is increased. McRobie (4) is currently studying the different effects of carbon content and strain-ageing on the toughness of C-Mn weld deposits and has shown clearly that three successive applications of a strain-ageing cycle comprising a uniform 2% strain plus 30 min ageing at 525K is sufficient to change the fracture mode at 263K from fibrous to cleavage, with a consequently large reduction in critical C.O.D., even in grain-refined material.

There is, therefore, a reasonable understanding of the factors controlling the toughnesses of the different individual types of microstructure found in C-Mn weldments and expectation of the development of consistently good properties through process control. A remaining unknown, however, is the engineering significance with respect to fast fracture of a relatively small brittle "patch" of material, such as a single unrefined pass, in a weldment which otherwise possesses good toughness. Estimates of critical defect size or design stress based on the toughness of the brittle patch will be over-pessimistic if any brittle cracking is arrested by tougher surrounding material, but calculations are complicated by the fact that the conditions ahead of the growing crack tip are those of high strain-rate deformation.

Stress-Relief Cracking in Boiler-Tubes and Pressure-Vessels

Weldable, quenched-and-tempered steels are used in structural applications for two main reasons: either to achieve a combination of high yield stress and low-temperature toughness, as in the steel HY80 (0.15C 3Ni 1.3Cr 0.4Mo) used for the hulls of submersible vessels, at a yield strength of 500MPa, or to obtain good high-temperature strength. Examples of steels for these latter applications are $2\frac{1}{4}$CrMo (0.13C 2.25Cr 1Mo), used for boiler-tubes, operating at temperatures up to 840K, or thick-walled chemical "reactor" vessels, operating between 670K and 825K; and the steels A533B (plate) or A508 (forgings) of composition 0.15-0.23C, 1.4Mn 0.5-0.7Ni 0.5Mo; which are used for thick-walled PWR or BWR nuclear pressure vessels, operating at 560-570K. Hydrogen cracking in the HAZ is avoided by the use of high preheat temperatures, possibly as high as 575K.

Contraction of the weld metal and phase-changes in the HAZ lead to the production of residual stresses in the as-welded joint and, in the absence of more precise information, these must be assumed to be of yield stress magnitude. Since the yield stresses are high, the assumed levels of residual stress are also high, with consequent deleterious effects on calculations of critical defect size. Weldments are therefore subjected to a "stress-relief" or "reheat" treatment, in which the joint is heated at a rate of some 50-100 Kh^{-1} to temperatures in the range 900-1000K. The aim is to allow the residual stresses to relax by plastic flow, since the yield stress decreases with increase in temperature, and the residual stress level assumed in subsequent calculations is then reduced to the high-temperature value.

A problem which is sometimes encountered is that weldments which have been subjected to stress-relief heat-treatments are found to contain cracks in prior-austenite grain-boundaries in coarse-grained regions of the HAZ. The cracking is often worse if the steel contains a strong secondary-hardening element, because this makes it difficult to produce plastic flow at the stress-relief temperature. For this reason, there has been a trend to change from ½Cr½Mo¼V to 2¼CrMo compositions for boiler-tube applications.

Detailed studies of stress-relief-cracking phenomena, as observed by Hippsley et al. (5-8) in a recently-developed simulation test, have been made on the three steel types 2¼CrMo (superpure; doped with P; doped with Sn; commercial), A533B aand HY80. Certain common features are observed. High austenitising temperatures effect the dissolution of grain-boundary pinning particles (particularly molybdenum carbide), not only allowing grains to coarsen, but also increasing hardenability, because the amount of carbon in solution is increased. At the same time, sulphur and phosphorus are taken into solution and, if the cooling-rate is not sufficiently rapid, these elements can concentrate at, or close to, the prior austenite grain boundaries in the martensitic or bainitic HAZ. Sulphur concentrates predominantly as small, discrete MnS particles, whereas phosphorus is segregated in atomic form as a (fraction of a) monolayer.

Two kinds of stress-relief cracks are observed. At temperatures greater than approx. 870K (by which stage, the level of residual stress is low), cracks are produced by the fine-scale coalescence of micro-voids formed on the MnS particles which decorate the prior austenite boundaries. This fracture mode has been termed "intergranular microvoid coalescence" (IMVC), see fig. 5. At lower temperatures, (and higher residual stresses) the intergranular facets appear to be smooth, but at high magnifications, indications of grain-boundary carbides (typically less than 0.1 μm in diameter) can be discerned, see fig.6. This mode has been termed "low ductility intergranular fracture" (LDIGF) and the micro-mechanisms involved are closely related to those of "one-step temper embrittlement". In the as-cooled condition, the coarse-grained HAZ is either auto-tempered martensite or lower bainite, depending on section thickness and the preheat temperature. Usually, there will be some degree of phosphorus segregation at prior austenite grain-boundaries. As the material is heated, carbides (particularly those in the grain-boundary) coarsen, and the phosphorus concentration increases, either by "equilibrium" segregation or by "carbide rejection". The net result is that a critical combination of carbide size, phosphorus concentration and matrix hardness can a) confine deformation to the grain-boundary region and b) lower the grain-boundary cohesion to an extent such that LDIGF ensues. At high temperatures, the phosphorus desegregates and any cracking that occurs must proceed by IMVC mechanisms. The extent to which other trace impurity elements act in the same way as phosphorus is not fully established and there is evidence that in some steels, LDIGF can be produced by the dynamic segregation of sulphur from solution to the localised high stress region ahead of the advancing crack tip.

In practical terms, resistance to reheat cracking is improved by control of trace impurity elements, and a good example of this is that plans for a new PWR at Sizewell in Britain specify A508 with levels of S,P,Sb, and Sn held to 0.01 max; As held to 0.015 max and Cu held to 0.09 max. Additional benefit can be obtained by selection of matrix composition to avoid excessive secondary hardening compatible with necessary high-temperature strength and design of the welded joint and welding procedures to avoid the presence of long, continuous bands of coarse-grained HAZ.

Fibrous Fracture in High-Strength Alloys

Fibrous fracture is not usually considered as a problem in thick-section, low-strength alloy structures under normal service loads, because the displacements associated with the growth of a crack, by the "internal necking" mechanism of void coalescence, are so large that general yielding of the ligament must precede any fracture instability. In high-strength alloys, such as marageing steels, quenched-and-tempered (QT) low alloy steels, or quenched-and-aged aluminium alloys, however, the fibrous fracture mechanism is one of "fast shear" and fracture can occur under "quasi-elastic" conditions in a fracture-toughness testpiece of moderate size, see fig.7. For a given class of alloy, it appears that, as the yield strength is increased, the work-hardening-rate decreases, flow becomes more localised, the displacements associated with crack growth are reduced, and the fracture toughness is lowered. Similar effects may be produced by cold prestrain and, potentially, by neutron irradiation, see Knott (10).

A typical application of the high strength alloys is that of an aircraft undercarriage, where strength-to-weight is important, but stress-corrosion resistance is also required. Alternative materials might be a marageing steel, of yield strength 1.9GPa, K_{IC} = 72MPam$^{1/2}$, K_{ISCC} = 30MPam$^{1/2}$; 300M (the low-alloy steel 4340 with an addition of 2Si), of yield strength 1.5GPa, K_{IC} = 50MPam$^{1/2}$, K_{ISCC} = 11.5MPam$^{1/2}$; 7010 or 7050 Al-Zn-Mg-Cu alloys, of yield strength 450MPa, K_{IC} = 36MPam$^{1/2}$, K_{ISCC} in the range 15-30MPam$^{1/2}$ (depending on alloy, orientation and heat-treatment). Comparing the specific strengths on the basis of the density of iron (7.9Mgm^{-3}) and aluminium (2.7Mgm^{-3}) gives figures of 240 (marageing steel), 190 (300M), and 170 (Al alloy). Assuming a high design load, of $0.8\sigma_Y$, critical defect sizes can be calculated from the following expressions:

for a buried "penny-shaped" crack of radius a:

$$K_{crit} = 0.51\ \sigma_Y\ (\pi a)^{1/2} \qquad 6)$$

for a semi-circular "thumbnail" surface-breaking crack of height a and length 2c (2c/a = 1)

$$K_{crit} = 0.56\ \sigma_Y\ (\pi a)^{1/2} \qquad 7)$$

Values of critical defect size based on K_{IC} and K_{ISCC} are given in Table I.

With respect to NDT detection limits, the values of a_{crit} should be dooubled for buried cracks to give figures of 3.6mm for marageing steel, 2.8mm for 300M and 15.6mm for the aluminium alloys. These are all larger than the limit of 2mm suggested in the introduction, although substantially more care would have to be taken for the steels. Similarly, surface crack lengths derived from K_{IC} values should be readily detectable. The figures derived from K_{ISCC}, however, are of more concern and, in terms of inspection would have to be classed as: possible, with good techniques (marageing steel); very difficult (300M),

TABLE I Values of Critical Defect Size

Material		Derived from K_{IC} a_{crit}, mm	Derived from K_{ISCC} a_{crit} mm
marageing steel	buried	1.8	*
	surface	1.5	0.25
300M	buried	1.4	*
	surface	1.1	0.06
Al alloy	buried	7.8	*
	surface	6.5	1.1 - 4.5

* not calculated, because stress-corrosion irrelevant to buried crack

detectable (Al alloy). On all these grounds there is advantage in using the Al alloy, if the physical bulk of an Al alloy component (load-bearing cross-sections roughly three times as large as those for steel) and the lower specific strength can be accommodated in the design.

In microstructural terms, the "fast shear" process involves the tangling of dislocations around second-phase particles, as in dispersion-hardening, followed by the fracture or shearing of the particle, or by decohesion of the particle/matrix interface. As the matrix strain is increased, the number of dislocations in any tangle increases, raising the local stress on a particle or on the interface. In a precracked testpiece, the critical C.O.D., and hence the K_{IC} value, derives from the integration of the matrix strains in a "process zone" ahead of the crack tip, up to the point of particle or interfacial failure, see Knott (10). In the highest-strength alloys the local dislocation stress fields may be significantly enhanced by "macroscopic" tensile stresses in the crack-tip region.

Apart from strain localisation, the toughness of an alloy depends on the amount of strain that a given second-phase particle can withstand without failure. In high-quality QT steels, where S is kept to 0.005max so that carbides are small and widely dispersed, the important particles are carbides, which, in the fully-tempered condition, are approximately spheroidal. Here, the failure mechanism is one of interfacial decohesion and, for moderately low volume fraction of carbides, the initiation strains are of order unity. These strains can, however, be reduced, either if the carbides are non-spheroidal or if the interfacial cohesion is reduced. During the early stages of tempering, carbides are produced, not only as a fine intra-lath dispersion, but also as thin plates in lath- or packet-boundaries. The strain required to crack these plates could be small and the blunting of crack nuclei would then give a set of closely-spaced microvoids. This effect gives a plausible explanation for the differences in toughness between lightly-tempered and fully-tempered steels, see Slatcher (13).

The effect of reduction of interfacial cohesion has been demonstrated by King and Knott (14), who compared values of C.O.D. for fibrous fracture in an alloy steel given a normal tempering treatment with those for the steel given a "temper embrittling" segregation treatment after tempering.

The initiation C.O.D. was reduced from 70μm to 40μm by this treatment and it was inferred that impurity elements (in particular, phosphorus) had segregated, not only to grain-boundaries but also to carbide-matrix interfaces, reducing the cohesion, and decreasing the initiation strain. In similar experiments on 300M steel, Hippsley and Druce (15) observed a factor-of-two decrease in J_{IC} and were able to demonstrate the presence of phosphorus in micro-voids centred on carbide particles, using Auger spectroscopy.

The chemical composition of the second-phase particle is also likely to affect the initiation strain, although few experiments designed to study this effect have been reported. In QT steels, high tempering temperatures induce transformations from cementite to alloy carbides if the steel contains Cr, Mo, V or W and a comparison of the toughnesses of steels tempered to the same yield stress on either side of the secondary hardening peak would be instructive. In the high-strength, 7000 series, Al-Zn-Mg-Cu alloys, the second-phase particles of importance with respect to fibrous fracture are generally of two kinds: large iron silicides (perhaps a few microns in size) and a variety of intermetallic "dispersoids", whose sizes lie in the range 0.05-0.5μm. High-toughness 7000 series alloys have been developed by limiting the Fe and Si contents to 0.1 max and the role of the dispersoid particles then assumes greater importance. Chen and Knott (16) have studied the effects on toughness of chemical composition of the dispersoid in the alloy 7475, which has Cr added for grain-refinement and contains S-phase ($Al_{18}Cr_2Mg$) dispersoids, and in 7010, which is Zr-treated and contains $ZrAl_3$ dispersoids. The S-phase particles have a complicated crystallographic structure and are relatively coarse (0.1-0.5 μm), whereas $ZrAl_3$ is tetragonal, semi-coherent with the matrix and appears in rather smaller sizes (approx. 50nm). For comparable yield stresses, the Zr-treated alloy exhibits higher toughness, presumably because the strain required to crack, cavitate or shear $ZrAl_3$ particles, is higher than that for S-phase particles. It could further be speculated that the high toughnesses of marageing steels derive from the absence of carbides and their replacement by intermetallics, which not only produce high strength, but are also able to withstand high strains without failure. Unusually low toughnesses in marageing steels are attributable to brittle, titanium carbo-nitrides.

In summary, there appears to be some scope for the development of high strength, high toughness alloys by paying attention to the properties of the particles on which voids initiate, although such improvement may be expensive if control of trace impurities has to be exerted or if carbides need to be replaced by nickel-containing intermetallics. It is also important to recognise that the hardening mechanisms which raise the yield strength, tend to promote strain localisation, so that the scope for developing large increases in toughness in high strength alloys may be limited.

Fatigue-Crack Propagation in Aluminium Bronze and Nickel-Base Alloys

A critical component of any marine vessel is the propeller. Many ships, even supertankers, are often designed with only one screw, and, if this should fail, the vessel becomes completely powerless, able only to drift, perhaps to run aground and produce oil-spills. The propellers are usually made as "one-off" nickel-aluminium-bronze (nikalium) castings, which are often extremely large. Due to viscous drag effects, the rotating propeller is subjected to a bending moment, so that the regions at the blade roots, which are the most highly stressed, are subjected to fatigue cycling, at a frequency of order 1Hz.

Designing to prevent fatigue failure in such components is not easy, particularly because it is seldom possible to carry out "spin-rig" tests on full-size propellers, or even on large models, as can be done for gas-turbine discs. Conventional procedures are to use S-N data, to apply a stress-concentration factor, and then to apply a further factor to take account of the fact that the component is a casting, rather than a wrought product.

An alternative is to try to apply fracture mechanics, recognising that the material contains a distribution of casting defects, which may grow as fatigue cracks. Work of this sort has been recently carried out by Taylor and Knott (17) who showed that the fatigue-crack growth of "thumbnail" defects greater than 0.5mm in size conformed to the same da/dN : ΔK behaviour as that for long cracks. Nominally-smooth testpieces each contained a distribution of shrinkage cavities such that one or more had a length of 1-2mm, and appropriate integration of the da/dN : ΔK curve was carried out to predict the S-N curve for nominally-smooth specimens. Agreement with experimental results was found to be good and further integrations could then be carried out to calculate fatigue lives for service propellers, making allowances for effects of the sea-water environment. The results, based on a 1mm initial defect as representative of large castings, showed that some design specifications were comfortably conservative, but that others allowed stresses which were close to the predicted failure stress. Propellers designed to such codes would, of course, be satisfactory if the material quality was such that the defects were consistently smaller than 1mm, and could be <u>guaranteed</u> to be safe (with respect to the assumed service loadings and lifetimes) if NDT on the service component demonstrated the absence of defects of 1mm size or greater. Note, however, that these sizes approach the limits of ultrasonics detection and sizing capabilities in large components.

A further point is that Taylor and Knott (18) observed anomalously fast growth-rates at low ΔK for defects less than 0.5mm in size. Here, the applied stress $\Delta\sigma$, is high and it is plausible that the value of the C.O.D. per cycle is increased by a contribution from "testpiece plasticity" in addition to K-controlled crack-tip plasticity. Even if the component contains no defect greater than 0.5mm in size, it is therefore advisable, for a conservative design in this material, always to integrate from a_o = 0.5mm.

The value of 0.5mm applies strictly to Taylor's nikalium alloy and is likely to vary with alloy system and strength level, which, for nikalium was approx. 250MPa (0.1% proof stress). Brown and Hicks (19) have shown that, in Astroloy (yield strength 950MPa) a small corner crack of 0.25mm in size still behaves as a "long crack" and it is perhaps general that, the higher a material's yield strength, the smaller the minimum defect size that exhibits "long crack" behaviour.

The use of fracture mechanics, as employed by Taylor for propellers, can be extended to a variety of applications. One of particular interest is that of a gas-turbine disc, made in a nickel-base superalloy. Here, design is based almost entirely on fatigue properties and the alternating stress during the main take-off cycle can approach the yield stress. In recent years, studies have been made of the possibility of making discs by powder-forming methods: hot-isostatic-pressing (HIP) and forging. A problem is that small pieces of refractory oxide can be scoured from the ladle in which the alloy is melted prior to atomisation in an argon gas stream, and may pass through the sieves used to grade the powder. Typically, a "150 mesh" may permit a particle of 0.15mm diameter to pass through. Calculations by Wildgoose et al. (20) show that, if a service life of 10^4 (take-off) cycles is required, a compromise between stress level and defect size must be achieved. For René 95 (yield stress 1200MPa) the defects must be restricted to 0.04mm in size, whereas, for Astroloy AP1 (yield stress 950MPa) sizes of 0.1mm can be tolerated. This has implications with respect to process control, see Knott (1).

The great advantage of the fracture mechanics approach in this application is that the ability of a particular process route to produce a distribution of sufficiently small defects can be assessed from metallography and crack propagation tests rather than by having to carry out exhaustive "smooth" bar and spin-rig testing. This approach will not always provide the answer, however, because local "tessellated" residual stresses around inclusions or chemical reactions of inclusions with the matrix may give rise to extended "initiation" periods. This is a general problem, if the initial defects are not cracks or cavities, but particles.

CONCLUSIONS

The paper has described some examples of different fracture modes involved in applications relevant to energy and transportation industries. For each example, the resistance of the material to fracture depends on the interrelation between applied stress, defect size and fracture toughness or crack growth-rate. The fracture toughness is controlled by careful attention to heat-treatment and levels of impurity elements, which demands care in material processing. To improve properties generally, defect sizes must be reduced and eventually their sizes will fall below those which can be detected by ultrasonics. Once this stage is reached, integrity can be guaranteed only by consistency of processing, control of which is one of the functions of the metallurgist. A major feature of the science of fracture mechanics is that not only does it provide quantitative techniques to assist the design engineer to exhibit his skills, but it also gives the metallurgist quantitative guidance as to what is required from his skills in the processing of materials and control of their microstructures.

Acknowledgements

The author wishes to thank Prof. R.W.K. Honeycombe FRS for provision of research facilities. Useful discussions have been held with Mr D.E. McRobie, Dr J.H. Tweed and Miss C.P. You, who have also given permission for the use of previously unpublished results.

REFERENCES

1. Knott, J.F., Proc. Intl. Conf. on "Fracture Mechanics Technology Applied to Material Evaluation and Structure Design" Melbourne Aug. 1982 ed. G. Sih, to be published.

2. Tweed, J.H. and Knott J.F., Metal Science 1983, 17, p45.

3. Judson, P. and McKeown, D., Prof. Intl. Conf. on "Offshore Welded Structures" London Nov. 1982, The Welding Institute paper 3.

4. McRobie, D.E., private communication.

5. Hippsley, C.A., Knott J.F. and Edwards, B.C., Acta Met. 1982, 30, p641.

6. Hippsley, C.A., King, J.E. and Knott, J.F., Proc. Conf. "Advances in the Physical Metallurgy and Applications of Steels" Liverpool, Sept. 1981, The Metals Society p.147.

7. Veron, P., Hippsley, C.A. and Knott, J.F., 1983 Intl. Jnl. of Pressure Vessels and Piping, to be published.

8. You, C.P., Hippsley, C.A. and Knott, J.F., 1983 submitted to Metals Science.

9. Edmondson, B., C.E.G.B. Proof of Evidence (P12) to the Sizewell Enquiry, 1983.

10. Knott, J.F., Metals Science 1980, 14, p327.

11. Wiltshire, B. and Knott, J.F., Intl. Jnl. Fracture, 1980, 16, pR19.

12. King, J.E. and Knott, J.F., Jnl. Mech. Phys. Solids, 1980, 28, p191.

13. Slatcher, S. and Knott, J.F., Proc. 5th Intl. Cong. on Fracture, Cannes 1981, ed. D. Francois (Pergamon) p201.

14. King, J.E. and Knott, J.F., Metal Science 1981, 15, p1.

15. Hippsley, C.A. and Druce, S.G., Acta Met., 1983, 31, p1861.

16. Chen, C.Q. and Knott, J.F., Metal Science 1981, 15, p357.

17. Taylor, D. and Knott, J.F., Metals Technology 1982, 9, p221.

18. Taylor, D. and Knott, J.F., Fatigue of Engineering Materials and Structures, 1981, 4, p147.

19. Brown C.W. and Hicks, M.A., Intl. Jnl. Fatigue, April 1982, p75.

20. Wildgoose, P., Turner, N.G., Davies, H.F., Helliwell B.J., Ubank, R. and Harrison, H., Powder Metallurgy 1981, No.2 p75.

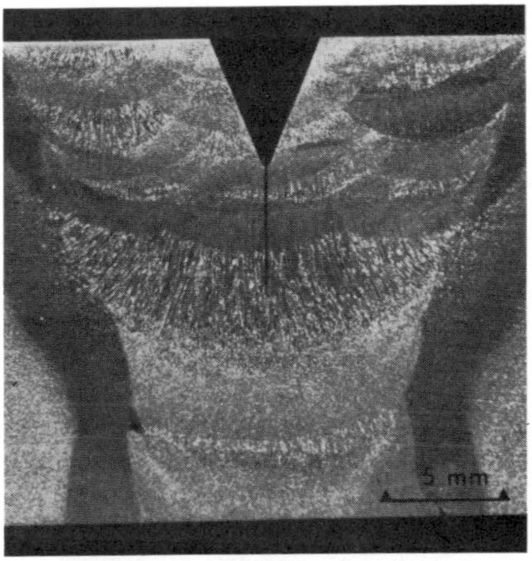

Figure 1 Welded testpiece, showing location of crack tip (courtesy J.H. Tweed)

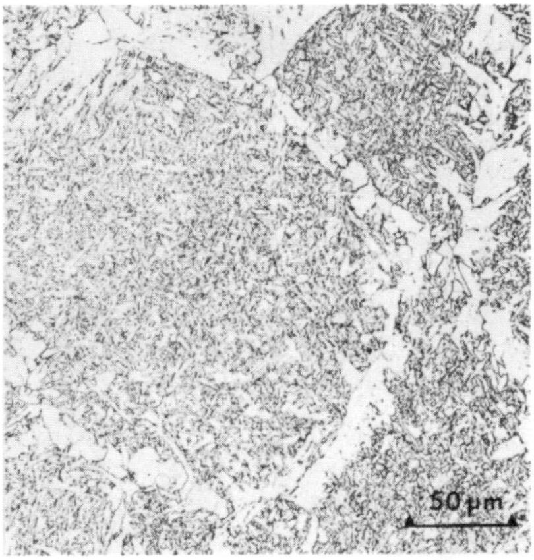

Figure 2 Unrefined microstructure (courtesy J.H. Tweed)

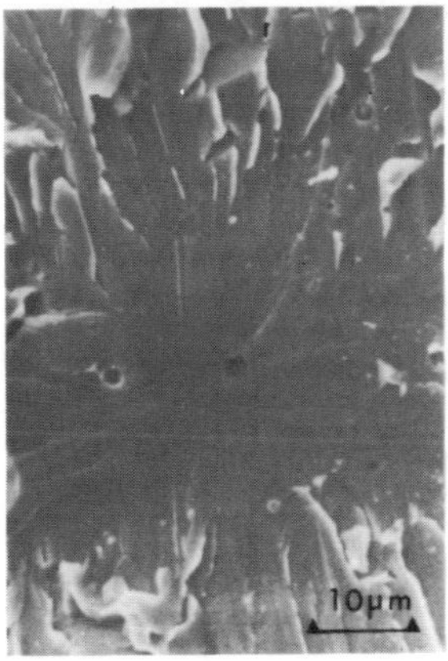

Figure 3 Cleavage facet nucleated by cracked inclusion (courtesy J.H. Tweed)

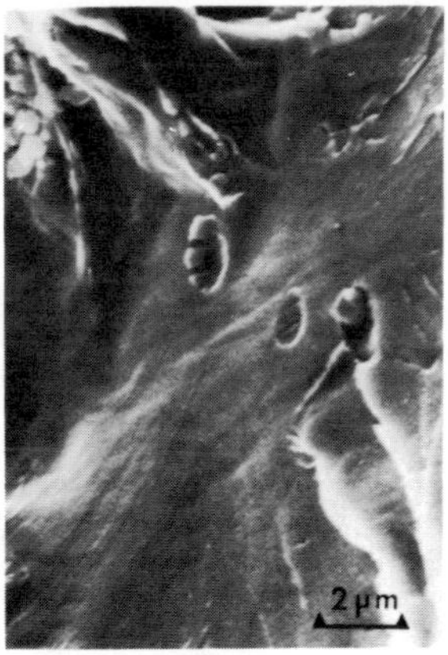

Figure 4 Cracked inclusion (blunted just above transition temperature) (courtesy J.H. Tweed)

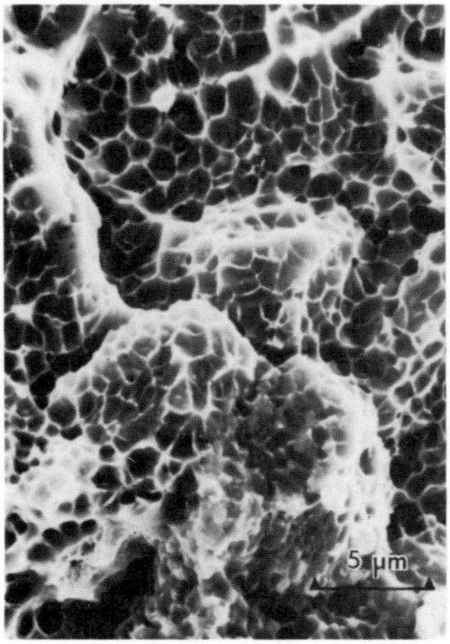

Figure 5 Stress-relief cracking IMVC mode (courtesy C.P. You)

Figure 6 Stress-relief cracking LDIGF mode (courtesy C.P. You)

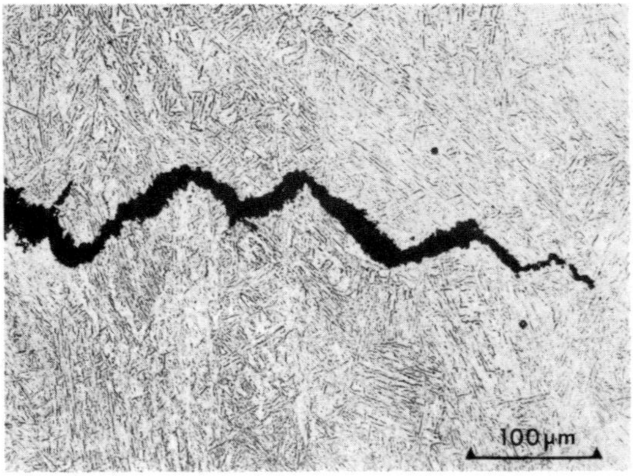

Figure 7 Fast shear fracture in high-strength weld metal (courtesy G.G. Saunders)

OFFSHORE OIL EXPLORATION AND PRODUCTION

SIGNIFICANCE OF FRACTURE MECHANICS ON DESIGN OF OFFSHORE STRUCTURES

J. Lereim*

This work describes the demand and significance of fracture mechanics on the design of offshore structures. The necessary strength assessments are reviewed, and the corresponding safety parameters are evaluated where the present results are highly representative for structural elements like plates, solid members, box girders and tubular members.

INTRODUCTION

Present experience of the condition of marine and offshore structures during service tells that cracks may be present as initial production cracks and/or as growing fatigue cracks. These are most likely to have significant influence on the strength, which is not reflected in today's common design practice and strength criteria used (1,2,3,4), unless the static strength criteria include analyses of the risk of brittle fracture (5,6) and a fracture mechanics based fatigue analysis is requested. Thus the conventional strength assessments such as plastic overloading in tension, buckling, punch and collapse of tubular joints may not predict the real strength properly if cracks are governing the strength. Consequently, fracture mechanics should be included as a supplementary strength criterion at the design stage, since fracture mechanics is the only tool available for a quantitative assessment.

In addition, the conventional strength criteria may also be influenced by the development of cracks, since the boundary conditions may be altered. Thus, the crack containing strength may become time dependent due to growing fatigue cracks, and certain safety levels should be guaranteed through the entire design life or service period.

In an optimization study of the design of welded structures, the strength criteria used including fracture mechanics

Det norske Veritas, Oslo, Norway.

criteria should achieve ideally approximately the same level of safety against failure at the end of the service period of the structure. If e.g. the fracture mechanics criteria predict the highest failure risks of the different criteria applied, modifications in the local design may be proposed rather than request for tougher materials or more refined inspection methods.

STRENGTH CRITERIA

Ultimate limit state

Conventional Approach. In most conventional ultimate strength assessments, the following criteria are included:

- Plastic tensile overloading
- Buckling of members.

For tubular connections, the following is also requested:

- Punch of brace through chord
- Collapse of brace/chord connection.

In addition, for accidental loading the following should be properly considered (7):

- Energy absorption capacity of structural members and the risk of progressive collapse.

Modified Conventional Approach. If cracks change the boundary conditions, the significance of cracks should be reflected even in the conventional strength criteria. Thus, also the conventional strength criteria when modified because of appearance of cracks, may become time dependent.

The simplest conventional criterion where cracks may be introduced is the plastic overloading criterion, where net section yielding may occur. Failure may then be characterized as:

$$\sigma \geq \sigma_{f.net} = \sigma_f \; (1 - a(N,a_o....)/t)^n \qquad (1)$$

Specific solutions of equation (1) exist for a variety of crack and element geometries and stress fields (8).

Concerning buckling of members, the real elastic plastic strength is highly dependent on the boundary conditions present. If the size of a crack influences the boundary conditions and/or the effective buckling length, the actual ultimate buckling capacity may decrease with time or growth of a crack. For such conditions the net cross section ahead of the crack leads to reduced local stiffness and may partly act like a hinge or torsional spring. If a crack is introduced e.g. in the mid cross section of a solid member, the actual assymptotic value of the elastic solution may vary with the crack size according to the following expression:

$$P_{EULER}(a) = \frac{\pi^2 EI}{L} \; (1 - \frac{a}{2t})^2 \qquad (2)$$

The corresponding possible actual elastic strength may be

characterized as

$$P_{crit.el.}(a) = \left[1 - e^{-b(\delta - \delta_o)}\right] P_{EULER}(a) \tag{3}$$

The maximum allowable initial lateral deflection δ_o is given according to structural codes to be 0.015 · L.(10)

Further, the corresponding critical axial compressive stress leading to yielding may be crack dependent according to the following (9):

$$\sigma_{AXIAL} = \frac{\sigma_y \cdot t}{4\,\delta} (1 - a/t)^2 \tag{3}$$

Thus the elastic solution given in equation (2) as well as the plastic solution in equation (3) are dependent on crack size, and thereby the real elastic plastic buckling strength varies with the crack size. This is schematically shown in figure 1 when a crack is present in the plastic hinge in the mid section of the member.

Similar reductions in buckling strength due to presence of cracks may occur for other locations (9) and types of members which should be taken into consideration in future recommended practice for assessments of compressive collapse strength.

For the case of accidental loading, the energy absorption capacity is of utmost importance during impacts and collisions.

Similar to the possible influence of cracks on the preceeding strength criteria described, one may expect reduced absorbed energy capability due to reduced plastic work at the locations of cracks.

Such reduced absorption capacity may also be expected for tubular members with fixed ends where cracks may appear in the plastic hinges at the ends. The energy absorption capability may be given by

$$E_{ab.TOT.} = E_{ab.Dent} + E_{ab.Ends} \tag{4}$$

where the latter term, $E_{ab.Ends}$, may be dependent on the crack size. This may be described as

$$E_{ab.Ends} = E^o_{ab.Ends} \left\{1 - \frac{q}{2}\left(\frac{2c}{\pi r}\right)^{n_1}\left(\frac{a}{t}\right)^{n_2}\right\} \tag{5}$$

for semi-elliptic surface cracks where n_1 is expected to be in the range 0.5 - 1.0, n_2 is close to 0.15 and q has the number 1 or 2 for a crack present at one or at both ends respectively.

For a given amount of kinetic energy avaiable, a rather moderate reduction in strength and energy absorption characteristics may lead to totally different damage histories (11,12). With no cracks present, the major part of the energy dissipation may happen in the supply vessel and minor or insignificant damage may occur on the offshore structure. This is favourable for fixed installations. See figure 2. Contrary, if strength characteristics of the structure becomes poorer than for the corresponding vessel, the major damage will occur in the structure which is highly unfavourable because of possible necessary repair at the location. Thus, small but critical reductions in strength may easily happen for small cracks i.e. early in the total service life. This effect may be particularly relevant for tubular structures where the fatigue crack growth through the thickness of tubular joints may be close to linear behaviour (13). Consequently, the reduced energy absorption capacity due to presence of cracks should be considered seriously, where sufficient impact strength and energy absorption capacity should remain at the end of the in service life or service period.

Fracture Mechanics Criteria. A variety of well known fracture mechanics criteria may be included, and most frequently used criteria within Veritas are briefly summarized as follows:

- Linear elastic conditions, failure when (14)

$$K \geq K_c \qquad (6)$$

- Elastic-plastic conditions (15,16,17)

$$J \geq J_c \qquad (7)$$

$$J \geq J_R, \frac{dJ}{da} = \frac{dJ_R}{da} \qquad (8)$$

$$CTOD \geq CTOD_c \qquad (9)$$

For the elastic plastic analyses, the equivalent elastic K-approach may be used successfully for the comparison and evaluations of various crack shapes under various boundary conditions. (18).

In addition, the Tearing modulus concept has been used in connection with the J-type elastic plastic fracture strength assessment (19,29).

Combined Strength Criteria. In real structures, the tensile strength behaviour when cracks are present is most frequently somewhere in between the brittle fracture condition and the net section yield condition for welded offshore structures. This is excellently combined in the R6 - Failure Assessment Diagram (21, 22,23) where the failure locus is described through the following expression:

$$K_r = S_r\left\{\frac{8}{\pi^2} \ln \sec\left(\frac{\pi}{2} S_r\right)\right\}^{-\frac{1}{2}} \qquad (10)$$

where K_r may be characterized as the ratio K/K_c for linear elastic conditions or by the ratio $(J/J_R)^{\frac{1}{2}}$ for elastic plastic conditions. The corresponding load factor or safety parameter is given by:

$$F(a) = \frac{2}{\pi S_r}\cos^{-1}\left[\exp\left(-\frac{\pi^2}{8}\frac{S_r^{\,2}}{K_r^{\,2}}\right)\right] \tag{11}$$

Although the above criterion is mainly developed for pressure vessel steels and components, it is a rather general approach that may be highly suitable for structural elements.

SAFETY ASSESSMENTS

Deterministic Approach.

A first introductory crude estimate of the safety level present may be characterized through the ratio of the mean value of "strength" and "maximum load", SF_O, where "strength" and "load" may represent any of the various strength criteria given in the preceeding sections.

A more exact quasi statistical but still deterministic approach is obtained through the usage factors (19) when the usage factor (Safety factor), γ, represents the ratio of the characteristic strength and characteristic load.

Statistical approach.

The most realistic description of the safety against failure is obtained by calculations of the probability of failure (collapse) for a given set of input data when each basic parameter is treated as a stochastic variable. In probabilistic fracture mechanics terms, it means that each basic parameter in e.g. the stress intensity factor(crack size, nom. stress, geometry) is characterised statistically. With several basic variables, the problem becomes rather complex which however, may be solved sucessfully for most engineering purposes by use of the approximate level 2 reliability method (24). The latter statement is supported by comparison of results obtained by level 2 calculations and by use of accurate level 3 techniques for various fracture mechanics problems (25), and the actual calculation procedure is given in more detail in refs. (25) and (9).

PARTICULAR EFFECTS TO APPEAR THROUGH THE FRACTURE MECHANICS BASED STRENGTH CRITERIA

In addition to the sole presence of initial cracks that require fracture mechanics analyses, the following particular effects appear through the fracture mechanics analyses of strength only that are never reflected in the conventional strength criteria:
- The possible detrimental effect of thickness on the fracture toughness and applied stress intensity factor for surface cracks as well as through thickness cracks. (14,26).
- The effect of local geometry that appears in magnification factors or g-factors included in the stress intensity factor. (27).
- Time effect due to possible growth of fatigue cracks, including negative thickness effect on the fatigue life. (28).

- Effect of residual stresses.
- The possible large scatter in major input variables as initial crack size and fracture toughness.

For the modified conventional strength criteria only the time effect from possible fatigue crack growth is of importance. Since cracks will appear in welded offshore structures,the above items are of concern and the crack containing failure criteria (fracture mechanics strength and modified conventional criteria) are recommended for realistic strength assessments.

COMPARISON OF SAFETY LEVELS

In order to illustrate the demand for fracture mechanics criteria as supplementary ultimate limit state criteria for design, the various safety factors are derived for the different strength criteria with the common basic input data given in table 1. The present exercise is performed for plate components of various thicknesses containing a K-profile weld with a stress concentration and magnification factor according to ref. (27) at the weld toe. For a given crack depth, the stress profile through the thickness at the toe will thus lead to increasing applied stress intensity factor,K, with increasing plate thickness. Consequently, the safety will decrease with increasing plate thickness although the fracture toughness (strength) K_c is assumed to be constant.

TABLE 1 - BASIC INPUT DATA.

Variable	Maximum applied stress (MPa)	Yield stress (MPa)	Depth of surface crack (mm)	Fracture Toughness (MPa $\sqrt{m}$)
Type of dist.func.	Norm.	Norm.	Norm.	Norm.
Mean	180	360	3	60
1 std	18	15	0.5	6
Variable	**Plate thickness (mm)**	**Bean length (mm)**	**Initial deflection δ_o (mm)**	**Young's modulus (MPa)**
Type of dist.func.	Norm.	Norm.	Norm.	Norm.
Mean	10-100	1000	1.5	$2.05 \cdot 10^5$
1 std	2%	5	0.15	$0.05 \cdot 10^5$

The derived deterministic safety factors of lowest level, SF_o, are shown in Figure 3 for the various failure criteria where SF_o for the R-6 Failure Assessment Diagram is given by the load factor specified in equation (11). As shown in Figure 3, the safety factors for the conventional tensile yield criterion and the fracture mechanics criterion are of the same order, but the SF_o for the latter criterion decreases markedly with increasing plate thickness. The derived SF_o values are directly the ratio of mean values for the strength and load parameter.

The yield stress level used in the present evaluations is in accordance with the strength of the most widely used grades of steels for offshore purposes, and the applied fracture toughness level may be highly representative for HAZ of modern steels. The corresponding crack size used is within the range of the minimum limit of detectability during inservice inspection.

The corresponding failure probabilities calculated by the Level-2 procedure are shown in figure 4. As expected, the P_f values obtained for the fracture mechanics criterion increases with increasing plate thickness.

Similary, the R-6 Failure Assessment Diagram leads to increasing failure probability with increasing plate thickness in the K-dominated region, while decreasing failure probability with increasing plate thickness appears in the plastic overloading dominated region.

In contrast to the lowest level safety assessment as shown in fig. 3, a huge difference in safety level is present between the strength criteria incorporated when the statistical approach is applied, although very moderate scatter in fracture toughness is applied. Frequently, the scatter in the actual fracture toughness of welded connections is considerably larger than the values used in this parameter study (29), and an even larger difference in safety level between the various strength criteria may exist. Also the fracture mechanics criteria verifies the advantage of reducing the plate thickness if the nominal stress level may be unchanged. Thus, the results fully demonstrate the need for including fracture mechanics strength criteria in the overall strength assessments.

The basic results shown in figures 3 and 4 may be highly representative for the following types of structural elements:

- Simple solid member of width equal to plate thickness.
- Box girder.
- Tubular members.

For the simple solid member with input data from table 1, the optimum plate thickness is approximately 50 mm unless a tougher material and/or stiffeners are requested. In the 40-55 mm thickness range the failure probabilities for the buckling, fracture mechanics based and combined criteria show the same probability level which is equal to or below a frequently recommended maximum element failure probability level of 10^{-4} for welded structures. But how can the thickness be reduced from 100 to 50 mm without decreasing the actual tensile load bearing capacity?

A single simple solid member of 100 mm plate thickness may be replaced by two members of 50 mm thickness. Then the tensile load-bearing capacity is remained together with unchanged stiffness in tension. Thus the failure probability is reduced from approximately $(1\text{-}2)\times10^{-3}$ to $(0.3\text{-}1)\times10^{-4}$ for the given combination of input variables. Additional advantageous effects are the increased redundancy, possible reductions in residual stress level, avoid possible request for stress relieving, and better conditions for welding and repair.

Correspondingly, the conventional load bearing capacity of a boxgirder may be maintained with reduced plate thickness if the shape of the cross section is changed in order to maintain the required bending stiffness for pure bending loading while the cross sectional area must remain constant for tensile loading.

For tubular members the plate thickness may be reduced if the tube diameter is increased accordingly to maintain the cross sectional area for tension/compression loading. By such a solution the moment of inertia increases significantly and the buckling strength is enhanced. Alternatively only slight increase in tube diameter is required to maintain the moment of inertia which is requested for a maintained load bearing capacity under pure bending loading.

WHEN AND WHERE SHOULD FRACTURE MECHANICS BASED ANALYSES BE APPLIED?

Although the preceeding sections fully demonstrate the need for inclusion of fracture mechanics in the strength assessments, and seems very attractive, the analyses may become more complex and require extended engineering knowledge for the designers. In order to make the design and strength analyses as efficient as possible, the possible demand for an extended strength assessment route including fracture mechanics should be dependent on the type of structure to be considered. The overall structural safety level, which is of primary importance, may be achieved although moderate safety levels may be present for single elements in a high redundant structure. Thus, a high redundant structure of well known design and materials may require limited amount of fracture mechanics assessments and crack modified conventional strength criteria. On the contrary, a low redundant structure and new design and/or material may require further consideration in terms of fracture mechanics analyses and a possible need for fracture toughness testing. During such procedures the corresponding estimated required fracture toughness level may vary from one structure to another where the actual stress level, location of cracks and the consequence of local collapse should be taken into consideration. This philosophy is recently partly incorporated in present design codes and recommendations through the notifications primary and secondary structure (5,6,7,30).

Finally, a recommended practice on the design of offshore structure including fracture mechanics type strength assessments should give credit for successful accumulated experience for identical structures of concern. The comments above are briefly summarized in table 2 which may act as some guidance on the extent of use of fracture mechanics and the crack modified conventional strength criteria and energy absorption characteristics.

TABLE 2 - Proposed recommended practice for requirements of applications of fracture mechanics and crack modified strength criteria.

Combination	
Group I	
Well known and long term experienced design, materials used, and welding procedure.	Moderate extent of materials testing. Documentation of basic production quality control tests. Very limited extent of fracture mechanics testing, however, dep. on actual loading cond.
Group II	
New design solution, but well known materials and welding procedures used.	Basic mechanical prop. documented through testing. Fracture mechanics analysis may be requested at design stage for design optimization, but necessary fracture mechanics parameters may be verified from existing literature data. The possible request for fracture mechanics testing and analyses dependent on redundancy, consequence of local failure and risk of progr. collapse, environment, loading conditions, min. design temperature, plate thickness and the use of PWHT.
Group III	
Well known and long term experienced design, but new materials and or new welding procedures.	Basic mechanical prop. documented through testing. Possible request for fracture mechanics testing and the extent of testing dependent on redundancy, plate thickness PWHT, consequences of local failure and risk of progressive collapse. Extent of testing also dependent on real life experience with present design.
Group IV	
New design New class of materials and welding procedures.	Basic mechanical properties and impact toughness requested through testing. Request for fracture mechanics analyses and testing as for Group II but fracture mechanics properties should be verified through testing.

CONCLUDING REMARKS

Based on the present work, the following main items should be paid great attention:

- Fracture mechanics criteria are necessary as supplementary tools in the design assessment of strength and risk of failure.
- Unsafe predictions of strength may be made when based on conventional criteria only for welded structures containing and developing cracks during the service life.
- Analysis of strength through proper reliability calculations with stochastic basic variables may reflect detrimental effect more pronounced than corresponding deterministic criteria.

- Cracks may have significant influence on the boundary conditions incorporated in the conventional strength criteria and thereby the derived strength.
- Dependent on the type of structure, future design codes for welded structures may require extended strength assessments by inclusion of fracture mechanics criteria and modified crack containing conventional criteria.

ACKNOWLEDGEMENT

The work is financed by Det norske Veritas and NTNF (The Royal Norwegian Council for Scientific and Industrial Research).

SYMBOLS USED

σ	:	Stress (MPa)
σ_f	:	Flow stress (MPa)
$\sigma_{f\ net}$	:	Nominal stress corresp. to plastic flow in net section. (MPa)
C	:	Crack length. (mm)
a	:	Crack depth. (mm)
a_o	:	Initial crack depth. (mm)
N	:	No of cycles.
P_{EULER}	:	Theoretical instability Euler load.
E	:	Young's modulus. (MPa)
I	:	Moment of inertia.
t	:	Plate thickness (mm)
L	:	Length of element. (mm)
δ	:	Lateral deflection (imperfection) (mm)
δ_o	:	Initial lateral deflection. (mm)
b	:	deflection parameter (mm^{-1})
σ_y	:	Yield stress (MPa)
$E_{ab\ TOT}$	:	Total energy absorption in member. (MNm)
$E_{ab\ Dent}$	:	Energy absorption at indentation. (MNm)
$E^o_{ab\ Ends}$	:	Energy absorption at ends of member un-cracked condition. (MNm)
$E_{ab\ Ends}$	:	Energy absorption at ends containing cracks. (MNn)
K	:	Stress intensity factor. (MPa $\sqrt{m}$)
K_c	:	Critical Stress intensity factor. (MPa $\sqrt{m}$)
J	:	J-integral. (N/mm)
J_c	:	Critical J-integral. (N/mm)
CTOD	:	Crack tip opening Displacement. (mm)
K_r	:	Normalised stress intensity factor.

S_r : Normalised load parameter.
F(a) : Load Factor.
SF_o : Lowest level safety factor.
P_f : Failure Probability.

REFERENCES

(1) Det norske Veritas, 1977. Rules for the Design, Construction and Inspection of Offshore Structures, Høvik, Norway.
(2) Det norske Veritas, 1980. Rules for Classification. Steel Ships, Høvik, Norway.
(3) Lloyd's Register of Shipping, 1978. Rules for Steel Ship Design.
(4) American Bureau of Shipping, 1980. Classification of Ships.
(5) Technical Note TN-A404. DnV, 1982. Guidance for Assessing the Safety Against Brittle Fracture in Offshore Installations by Fracture Mechanics.
(6) Statoil Design Specifications for Offshore Installations. Structural, May 1981.
(7) Norwegian Petroleum Directorate, 1983. Rule Proposal. NPD Regulations Appendix 3 For Structural Design of Steel Structures.
(8) G.G. Chell. 1979 England. "Development in Fracture Mechanics -1". Editor G.G. Chell, Applied Science Publ. Ltd. London.
(9) J. Lereim, 1983. Proceedings "Application of Fracture Mechanics to Materials and Structures", Freiburg, Germany.
(10) European Convention for Constructional Steelwork; 1976/77. "Introductory Report" Second International Colloquium on Stability.
(11) G. Edvardsen, G. Foss, 1982. OTC 4217, Offshore Technology Conference, Houston, USA.
(12) G. Edvardsen, J. Lereim, O.P. Torset, 1983. Paper Brazil Offshore Conference 83, Rio de Janeiro, Brazil.
(13) M.B. Gibstein, 1981, Paper 8.5. Proceedings "Steel In Marine Structures", Paris, France.
(14) J.M. Barsom, S.T. Rolfe, 1977. "Fracture and Fatigue Control in Structures", Prentice Hall.
(15) C.E. Turner, 1979 Proceedings, A J-Based Design Curve, 2nd Adv. Seminar on Fracture Mechanics, Ispra, Italy.
(16) C.E. Turner. C.E. Turner. The application of J_r Curves to Slow Stable Crack Growth and Unstable Tearing in the Plastic Regime, Ibid.
(17) F.M. Burdekin, M.G. Dawes. 1971. Proc. "Conf. Prac. App. Fr. Mech. to Pressure Vessel Technology.
(18) J. Lereim, 1982. Proceedings, "Second Int. Conf. on Offshore Welded Structures". London.
(19) P.C. Paris, H. Tada, A. Zahoor, A. Ernst, 1977. ASTM STP 668 " Elastic Plastic Fracture".
(20) A. Zahoor, M.F. Kanninen, 1981, Trans ASME Journ. Press. Vessel Tech., 103, 352.
(21) I. Milne, K. Loosemore and R.P. Harrison, 1978. Paper C106/78. Conf. on Tolerance of Flaws in Pressureized Components. I. Mech. E, London.

REFS. CONT.:

(22) R.P. Harrsion, K. Loosemore, I. Milne and A.R. Dowling. CEGB Report R/H/R6 - Rev.2, 1980. Assessment of the Integrity of Structures Containing Defects.
(23) I. Milne, 1979. Mats. Sci. and Eng. 39. Pp 65-79.
(24) Rationalization of Safety and Serviceability in Structural Codes. CIRIA Report 63, London, July 1977.
(25) A. Harbitz, 1983. ICASP 4, Firenze, Italy.
(26) J. Lereim. 1983. Engng Fracture Mech. 18, No. 3, 703.
(27) T.R. Gurney, 1979. Stress Intensity Factors for Cracks at the Toes of Transverse Butt Welds. W.I. Research Report No. 88/1979. The Welding Institute, England.
(28) S. Berge and K. Engsvik, 1981. Paper 2.5, Proceedings Int. Conf. Steel in Marine Structures, Paris, France.
(29) S. Slatcher, T.B. Larsson, J. Lereim, 1983. Proceedings Fracture Prevention in Energy and Transport Systems, Rio de Janeiro, Brazil.
(30) Department of Energy, 1977, Offshore installations: Guidance on design and construction. Her Majesty's Stationery Office, London, England.

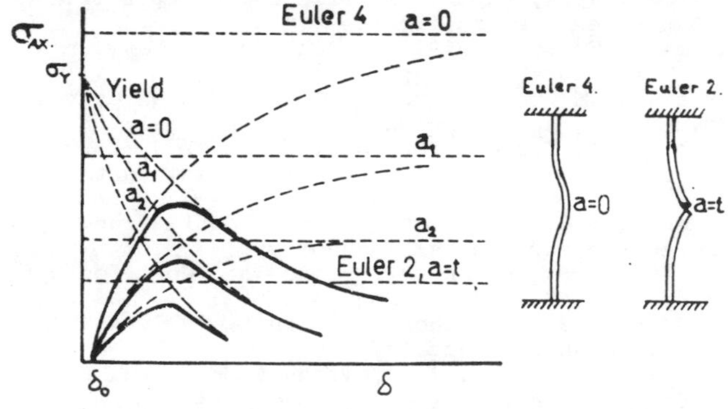

Fig. 1 Schematic illustration of real buckling strength curves which are dependent on crack size.

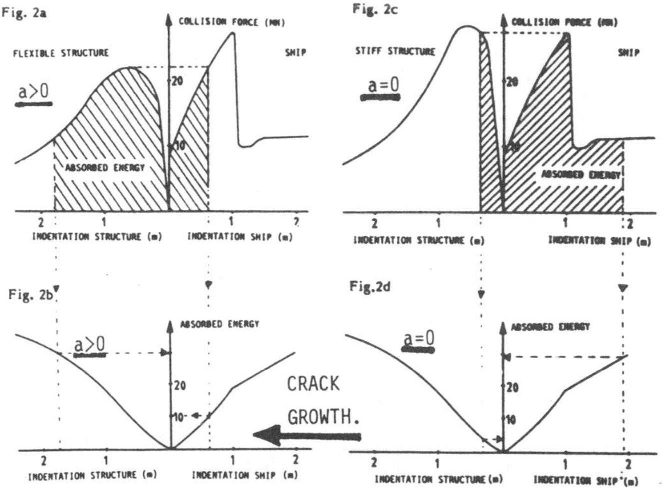

Fig. 2 Collision Impact Strength and Energy absorption characteristics.

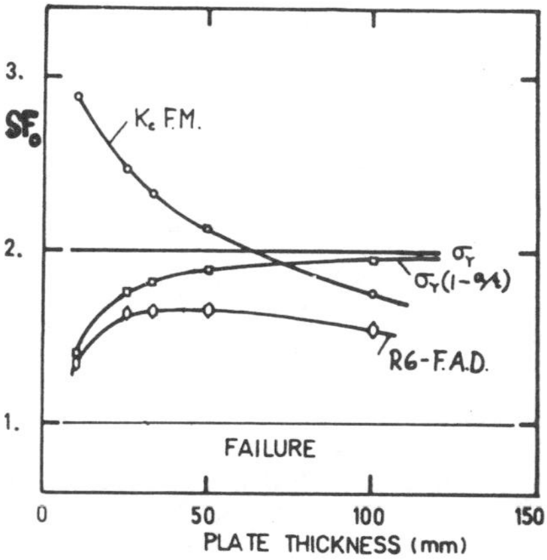

Fig. 3 SF_O of different strength criteria.

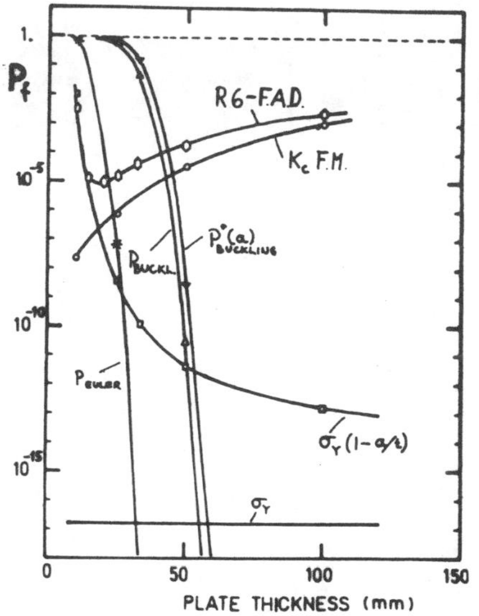

Fig. 4 Failure prob. of different strength criteria.

FATIGUE CRACK PROPAGATION IN THE PARENT MATERIAL AND THE WELDMENT OF A STRUCTURAL STEEL

S.P. Moghadam, J.C. Balthazar and J.C. Radon

This paper discusses the fatigue crack propagation in the base material and the weldment of structural steel BS4360-50D used in offshore structures. The base material and the weldments were tested at R-values of 0.08 and 0.7 at two different frequencies of 0.25 and 30 Hz. All the specimens were tested in the 'as-received' condition, and tests were performed in laboratory air at 20°C. The stress ratio and frequency of loading were found to have a significant effect on the fatigue crack propagation behaviour of the base metal. Fatigue crack growth rates in the weldments were similar to or slower than in the base material, probably due to favourable residual stresses. The fractography of the weldments was performed using a standard SEM. The influence of defects in the weld beads was investigated. The deleterious effect of secondary cracking, damage and porosity on the crack growth rate was also noted.

INTRODUCTION

Failure of engineering structures subjected to repeated load is usually caused by the initiation of subcritical cracks and their subsequent growth to a critical size at which fast fracture occurs. Depending on the structure and its design, the initiation and propagation phases may occupy a smaller or larger part of the useful service life. In large installations, such as offshore platforms, and particularly in welded structures, small crack-like defects are invariably present from the time of their commissioning.

Although a large amount of work has been completed on characterising the fatigue crack growth properties of structural materials such as the steel used in the present investigation, there are conflicting reports as to how certain mechanical and metallurgical factors affect the fatigue crack growth rate. Also, relatively little work has been done on characterising the fatigue crack growth properties of weldments developed specially for these oil platforms. Fatigue crack propagation in BS4360 was investigated by Musuva [1] using the LEFM approach. However, for fatigue cracks in a weldment, the applicability of fracture mechanics is not so straightforward because of the internal defects often observed in an otherwise sound weld. Fatigue cracks may initiate from these internal defects or from regions of high stress concentration, due to the sharp microscopic slag intrusions that are found to be an inherent feature of welds, particularly when produced by manual arc welding methods [2]. In order to apply fracture mechanics to weldments, the applicability of some cyclic crack propagation law has to be investigated. The factors which control the stress state at the crack tip may substantially affect the crack growth rate. These include the fracture mode, plastic zone size, microstructure and environment. The objective of the present work was to compare

Department of Mechanical Engineering, Imperial College of Science & Technology, Exhibition Road, London SW7 2BX, England.

the fatigue crack growth properties of the base metal and the weldment in identical mechanical and environmental conditions.

MATERIALS AND EXPERIMENTAL BEHAVIOUR

The material investigated was structural steel BS4360-50D, supplied in the form of a rolled plate 25 mm thick, used in offshore structures. The chemical composition and mechanical properties are given in Table 1.

The butt welded specimens were prepared by manual arc welding of two plates of about 50 mm wide, 95 mm long and 25 mm thick using a C-Mn electrode [3], which is frequently specified for welding of offshore platforms. The joint preparation was a double V. All the welds were ground flat before testing. The chemical and mechanical properties of the weld metal are given in Table 2.

Standard compact type specimens 79.5 mm wide, 95.4 mm deep and 25 mm thick were used in the present study. The notches were oriented perpendicular to the rolling direction and, in the case of butt welded specimens, parallel to the weldment.

The tests were performed in laboratory air and at room temperature (20°C and 50% RH) using three different fatigue machines: a Dowty 60 kN, a Mayes 100 kN, and a Dartec 200 kN.

To investigate the effect of stress ratio and frequency, tests were performed at R-values equal to 0.08 and 0.7, while loading frequencies were 30 Hz and 0.25 Hz. All the specimens were tested under identical maximum tensile load (i.e. K_{max}). The minimum load was appropriately adjusted in order to obtain the required stress ratios. A travelling microscope was used to measure the crack length. The experimental readings of crack length, a, and corresponding number of cycles, N, were recorded periodically after suitable crack increments. To calculate the crack growth rate, da/dN, from the experimental data, the secant method was used. The stress intensity factor, K, was calculated using the standard formula recommended for compact-type geometry:

$$K = \frac{P}{B\,W^{\frac{1}{2}}}\, f\left(\frac{a}{W}\right) \qquad (1)$$

where $0.3 < a/W < 0.7$. The crack length, a, is the average of the two successive readings used to calculate the corresponding da/dN.

RESULTS

The results of crack growth rate, da/dN, versus ΔK values for the parent metal and the weldment are shown in Figures 1 to 4 for a range of R-values and loading frequencies. The data correspond with the Paris expression:

$$\frac{da}{dN} = C\,(\Delta K)^m \qquad (2)$$

Figure 1 represents the results obtained in the parent metal tests at 0.25 Hz for R-values of 0.08 and 0.7, indicating the effect of stress ratio. Similar, but less pronounced, differences were recorded at 30 Hz.

In order to evaluate the effect of frequency on crack growth rate at both

R-values, the best fit lines are shown in Figure 2. Similarly, Figure 3 shows the results for the weldments for the identical frequency of 0.25 Hz and the same R-values. Again, a very similar, but stronger, effect of stress ratio and frequency to that of the parent metal may be observed (Figure 4).

Figures 5 to 8 represent a comparison of the results obtained for the parent metal and the weldment under identical testing conditions. From these results, we can conclude that for low values of ΔK (about 12 $MN/m^{3/2}$), the crack growth rate in the weldment is similar to or up to five times slower than in the parent material. At higher frequencies and lower R-values, the crack growth rate in the weldment may be even slower than recorded here.

FRACTOGRAPHY

The weldment fracture surfaces of fatigue cracked specimens (at $R = 0.7$ and 30 Hz) were sectioned and mounted for study in the scanning electron microscope (SEM).

All the variations in the fracture surfaces were examined; it was noted in particular that the dendritic formations might be responsible for the differences in the crack lengths as measured on the sides of the specimen. This was attributed to the difference in the cooling rate of the weld beads. Figure 9 shows a typical surface close to the specimen side.

The cracks showed a tendency to branching (Figure 10). It can be seen that these branches were random in direction, but there is no evidence that the main crack path was a result of a series of random paths. Also, a high proportion of secondary cracks was often found in a more brittle fracture observed at low ΔK values.

The failure surfaces showed a number of welding defects which may have some bearing on the results obtained. The most common were 'worm' holes originating from the root of the weldments. The size of these defects varied from a pinhole to a gross defect size (Figure 11). Some defects originated from unmelted electrode (Figure 12). It was concluded that these defects caused a noticeable increase of crack growth rate.

The fracture mechanisms observed in the Paris regime were microvoid coalescence and striations. A microvoid coalescence area is shown in Figure 13 and a typical striated area at $\Delta K = 20$ $MN/m^{3/2}$, $R = 0.7$ and at 30 Hz is presented in Figure 14. Cleavage fracture was observed at very low values of ΔK (7 to 10 $MN/m^{3/2}$) close to the near threshold region, as shown in Figure 15.

As evidenced by the data (Figure 4) and fractographs (Figure 15), the loading frequency plays an important part in fatigue crack growth. For low frequencies and low ΔK values, cleavage fracture was evident, and this may be connected with the hydrogen embrittlement mechanism. The hydrogen generated may be able to diffuse a certain distance ahead of the crack tip, which results in the crack front advancing at a greater distance per cycle. However, for each frequency, there will be a point at which the diffusion of hydrogen within the lattice cannot keep up with the advancing crack and the fracture mode will change from brittle to a ductile fatigue mechanism. This explains the observed significant increase in the crack growth rates over certain ranges of stress intensity for each frequency associated with the change in fracture mode observed.

DISCUSSION

Base Metal

Figures 1 and 2 represent the experimentally-determined fatigue crack growth rates, da/dN, as a function of stress intensity factor, ΔK, for a range of stress ratios and frequencies. It can be seen that all data fall approximately on a straight line, confirming that the Paris law for fatigue crack growth is applicable, at least for the investigated region 10^{-6} to 10^{-3} mm/cycle.

Structural materials usually exhibit increasing fatigue crack growth rates with increasing R-values. This is attributed to local static fracture modes at high stress intensity factors [4]. In the present investigation, K_{Ic} reached the value 30 MN/m$^{3/2}$ for $R = 0.08$ and 50 MN/m$^{3/2}$ for $R = 0.7$ (Figure 2).

Figures 1 and 2 also show that, for the material tested, there was no significant difference in fatigue crack growth rates for the different R-values. In other words, for the load range investigated, the material has sufficient inherent toughness to avoid local static fracture.

Crack closure has often been used to explain the observed effect of stress ratio on fatigue crack growth rates. According to this concept, closure of the crack surfaces may occur at tensile loads during the loading cycle as a result of plastic deformation left in the wake of a growing crack at high stress intensities. This phenomenon reduces the effective stress intensity factor causing crack growth. However, at high stress ratios, the crack remains open for a larger part of the load cycle and thus closure effect becomes less pronounced [1].

It is also possible to explain the effect of stress ratio in terms of environmental effects. Hydrogen in moist air can cause embrittlement at the crack tip, thus leading to increased growth rates. This conclusion is supported by the effect of frequency (Figure 1). At high stress ratios, the crack remains fully open for a larger part of the cycle and, consequently, the environmental effects are also maximised. This process was confirmed by the results obtained for the steels tested in vacuum [5] where the influence of stress ratio was minimised.

The Weldment

Figures 3 and 4 present the experimentally-determined fatigue crack growth rates, da/dN, as a function of the stress intensity factor, ΔK, in the weldments. Again, these data for welded specimens with the crack growing in the plane of the weld fall approximately on a straight line as observed for the base material.

However, at low ΔK (7 to 15 MN/m$^{3/2}$), the crack growth rate in the weld metal was lower than the growth rate in the base material (Figures 5 to 8), possibly due to favourable residual stresses.

Residual stresses in butt welded test sections have been investigated in [6]. The most significant residual stress component in the weld is the longitudinal σ_x which can reach the magnitude of yield strength. The transverse stress component, σ_y, is usually substantially smaller. In the present work, no measurement of the residual stress was made, however, a qualitative discussion of the influence of the residual stress follows.

The decreased fatigue crack growth rate in weldments has been frequently attributed to the favourable residual stresses normal to the crack plane [7]. However, the influence of these residual stresses ought to be equivalent to a change in the mean stress and thus it appears not to influence greatly the fatigue crack growth for tough materials as they are not sensitive to changes in the mean stress (R-ratio).

In some specimens, especially at low ΔK (7 to 15 $MN/m^{3/2}$), the crack grew faster on one side of the specimen where the first bead was deposited. On that side, the transverse residual stresses ought to be lower than on the side where the second bead was deposited. Also, when grinding the specimen, most of the transverse residual stresses may be released and therefore the crack growth rate ought to be lower.

Although stresses parallel to the crack plane and in the transverse direction to the plate of the specimen may not influence the stress intensity factor, they have been shown to influence the plastic flow around the crack [4]. A tensile stress component parallel to the crack plane will decrease the plastic flow and a compressive stress component will increase the plastic flow around the crack tip upon loading. Therefore, the net effect over one cycle is not easily predicted. The distribution of longitudinal residual stresses in the direction perpendicular to the crack may induce a closing moment which would resist the opening of the crack and therefore tend to decrease the crack growth rate.

The influence of R-values is shown in Figures 2 and 4. It can be seen that at low values of ΔK, an increase in R-values from 0.08 to 0.7 has a significant effect on the rate of fatigue crack propagation which can be explained in terms of crack closure.

CONCLUSIONS

1. Stress ratio and frequency of loading significantly affect crack growth rates in both parent material and weldment.

2. A comparison of maximum rates of fatigue crack growth in the weldment and the parent plate suggest that fatigue crack propagation will be faster in the parent material due to favourable residual stresses in the weldment.

REFERENCES

1. Musuva, J.K., and Radon, J.C., 1979, Fatigue of Eng. Mats. and Structures 1, 457.

2. Signes, E.G., 1967, British Welding Journal 14, 108.

3. BOC Murex International, August and September 1980.

4. Musuva, J.K., and Radon, J.C., 1981, "Threshold of Fatigue Crack Growth in Low Alloy Steels", 5th International Conference on Fracture Proceedings "Advances in Fracture Research", Pergamon Press, London, England.

5. Cooke, R.J., Loving, P.E., Booth, G.S., and Beevers, C.J., 1975, Eng. Fract. Mech. 7, 69.

6. Nordmark, G.E., Mueller, L.N., and Kelsey, R.A., 1982, "Effect of Residual Stresses on Fatigue Crack Growth Rates in Weldments of Aluminium Alloy 5456 Plate", ASTM STP 776, 44.

7. Kapadia, B.M., 1977, "The Rôle of Residual Stresses in Fatigue Crack Propagation in Weldments", ASTM STP 648, 244.

TABLE 1

STEEL BS4360-50D

Chemical Composition (Weight)

Element	C	Si	Mn	P	S	Cr	Mo	Ni	Al	Cu	Nb
%	0.180	0.36	1.40	0.018	0.003	0.11	0.020	0.095	0.035	0.16	0.039

Mechanical Properties

	Direction		
	Longitudinal	Transverse	Through thickness
Yield strength (MN/m^2)	386	382	388
Ultimate tensile strength (MN/m^2)	560	551	563
% elongation (GL equal 3")	30	29	18
% reduction in area	74	68	61

TABLE 2.

Welding Electrode BS 639 : E 4311 R21 (3)

Chemical Composition (Weight)

Element	C	Mn	Si	S	P
%	0.06	0.58	0.43	0.02max	0.03max

Mechanical Properties

Yield strength N/mm^2	448
UTS N/mm^2	510
% Elongation	22
% Reduction of area	50

Charpy V-notch at RT (20°C) 80 joules

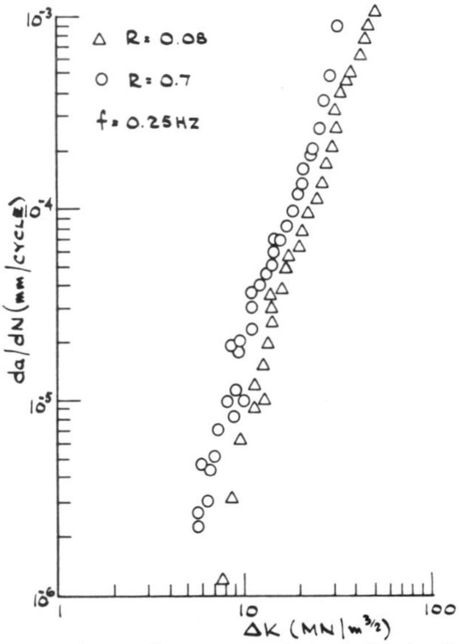

Figure 1 Parent plate-effect of stress ratio.

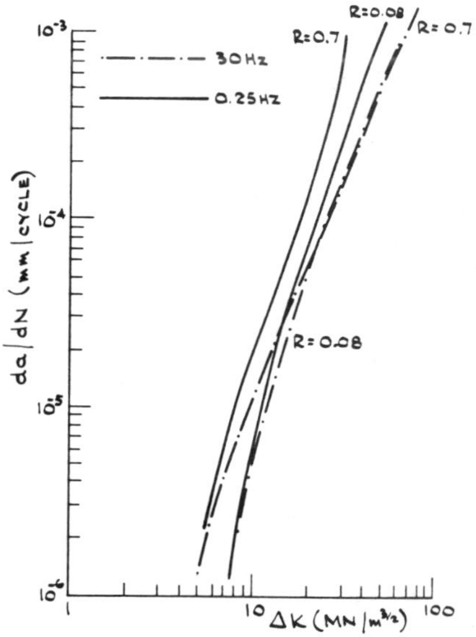

Figure 2 Parent plate-effect of frequency.

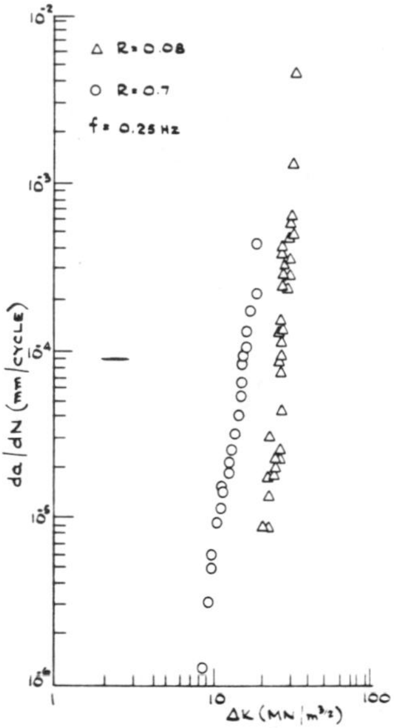

Figure 3 Weldment-effect of stress ratio.

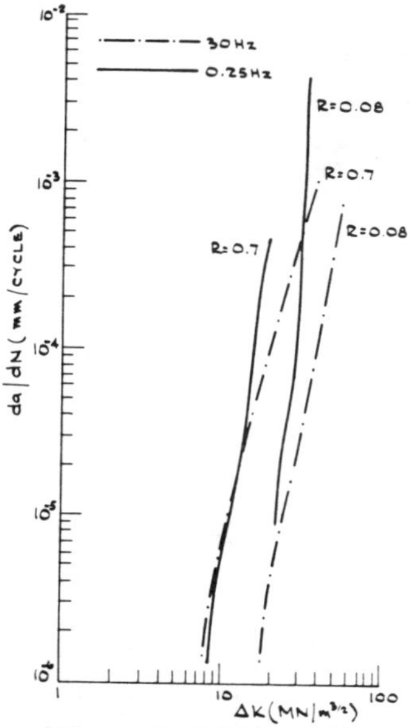

Figure 4 Weldment-effect of frequency.

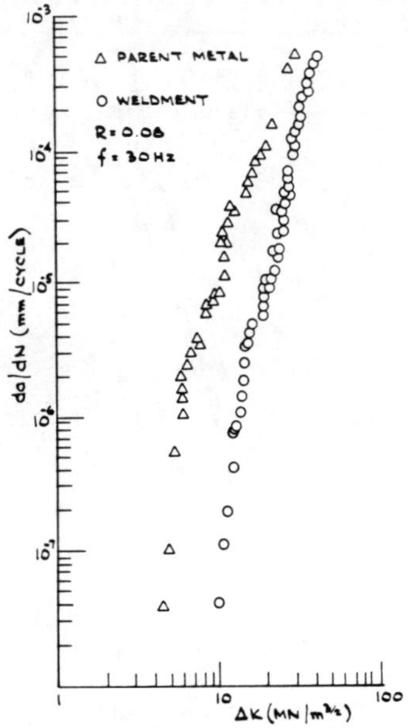

Figure 5 Parent metal and the weldment - R = 0.08, 30 Hz.

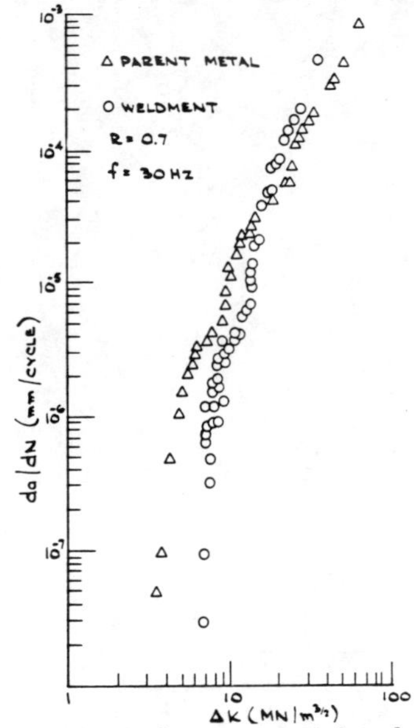

Figure 6 Parent metal and the weldment - R = 0.7, 30 Hz.

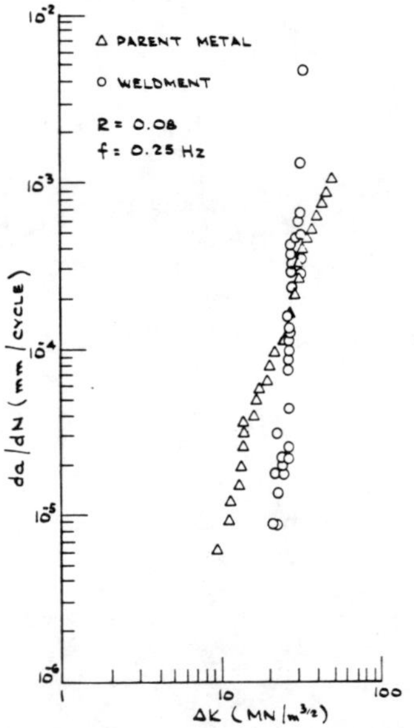

Figure 7 Parent metal and the weldment - R = 0.08, 0.25 Hz.

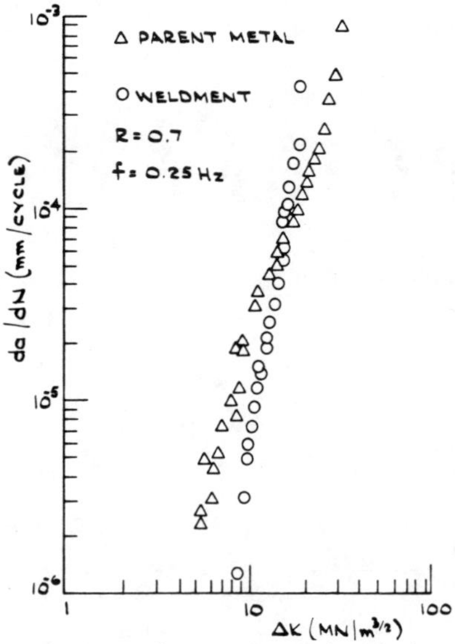

Figure 8 Parent metal and the weldment - R = 0.7, 0.25 Hz.

Figure 9 Dendritic formations with columnar grains

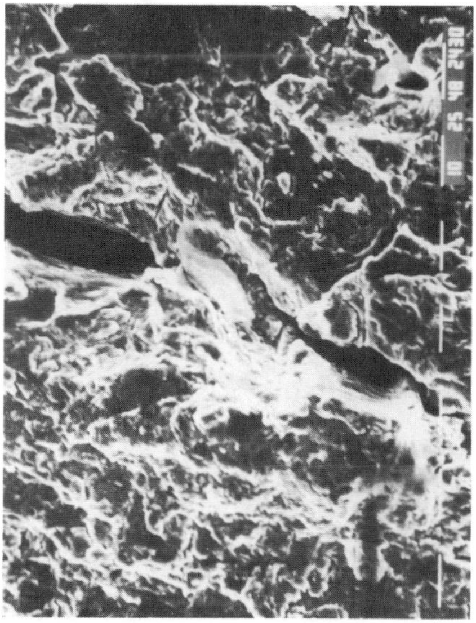

Figure 10 Secondary fatigue cracks

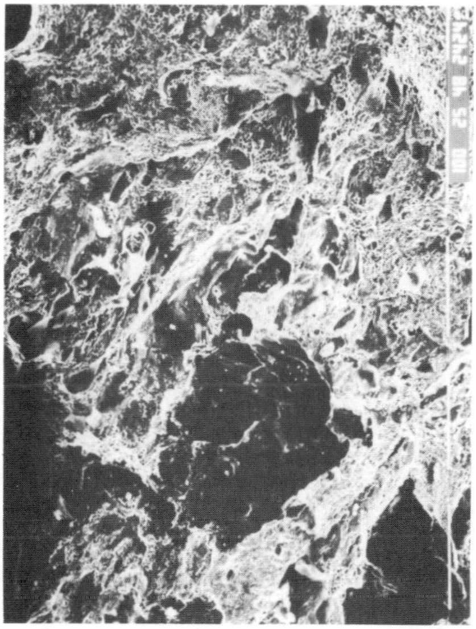

Figure 11 Defects

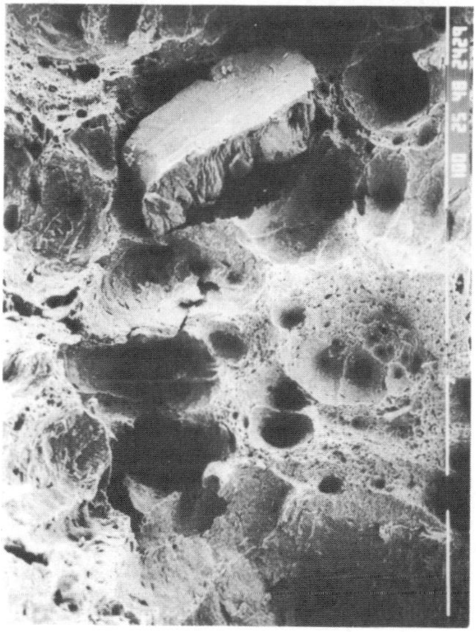

Figure 12 Unmelted electrode

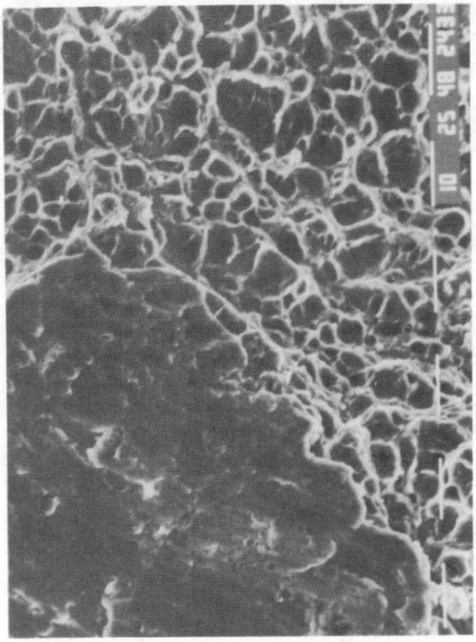

Figure 13 Microvoid coalescence

Figure 14 Fatigue striations

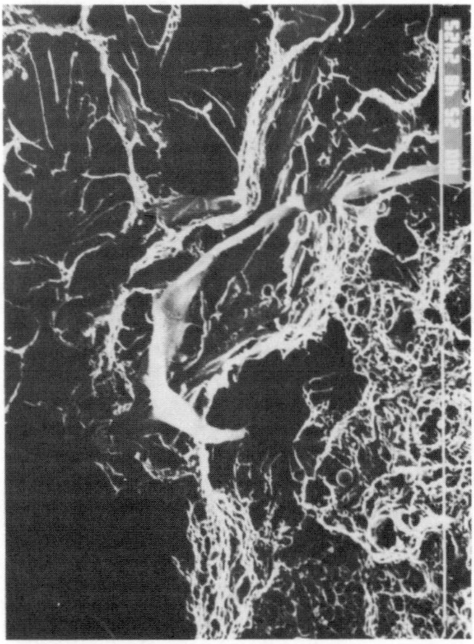

Figure 15 Cleavage

INFLUENCE OF PLASTIC ZONE SIZE ON FATIGUE THRESHOLD IN STEELS

L.Guerra Rosa* and C.M.Branco**

Threshold and low fatigue crack growth rate data were obtained as a function of R in air and 3.5% NaCl in a medium strength plain carbon steel. The true ΔK_{th}-value was obtained and used to establish a relationship between fatigue threshold of cracked specimens and fatigue strength $S_{N=10^7}$ of plain specimens.
It was found that in this material the size of the cyclic plastic zone and the material grain size are the controlling parameters in ultralow crack growth rate tests and define the transition between Region I and Region II of crack propagation.

INTRODUCTION

It is known that the fatigue threshold, ΔK_{th}, may depend on stress ratio R, specimen thickness and environment (temperature included). For fatigue design it is very important to use safe ΔK_{th}-values and hence it is worthwhile to develop suitable methods to obtain reliable values of ΔK_{th}.

Over the past 25 years a vast amount of effort has been done in the field of fatigue crack growth. However, it was only during the last decade that data on the region of ultralow fatigue crack rate has been obtained in a wide range of materials. In fact, the value of stress intensity range ΔK, below which cracks remain dormant or grow at insignificant rates, has been shown to be essential in the design of structures or components subjected to high frequency loading for long periods of time. Presently, a significant number of papers present data and theories for the observed fatigue-crack propagation thresholds. In 1981 an important conference on "Fatigue Thresholds" was held in Stockholm: many and excellent contributions to this scientific field were given and the main conclusion was that crack-closure phenomenon is the key factor that "disturbs" the study of fatigue crack growth. However, environmental interactions and different crack-closure concepts do not contribute to a clear understanding of presently accepted conclusions such as:

- the plain fatigue limit, S_f, (or the plain fatigue strength S_N for $N \rightarrow 10^7$ cycles) and the "true" ΔK_{th}-value (herein called ΔK^t_{th}) may be related;
- a thermodynamic and physically meaningful lower limit (which is ΔK^t_{th}) for fatigue-crack growth must exist;
- the ΔK^t_{th}-value may be found by testing at a very high stress ratio.

*CEMUL-Instituto Superior Técnico, 1096 Lisboa Codex, Portugal
**Universidade do Minho, Braga, Portugal

It is the purpose of this paper to help to define a more clear scene of "fatigue thresholds" and to provide a simplified view of this subject to the designers so that they can trust on ΔK_{th}-values, at least as they do on fatigue limits (S_f) or fatigue strengths ($S_{N\rightarrow 10^7}$). A medium strength steel (BM45) was chosen for this investigation since it is quite extensively used in pipelines and other components in the energy and chemical industries where fatigue and corrosion fatigue failures are quite frequent.

EXPERIMENTAL

The material studied was the BM45 steel (CK 45 according to DIN 17200) in the as-rolled condition having a normalized ferritic-pearlitic microstructure. The chemical composition is C-0.45% Mn-0.74% Si-0.20% Ni-0.06% S-0.027% P-0.027% Cr<0.03%. The relevant mechanical properties are: σ_y(0.2% yield stress)=335 MPa; σ_{UTS}(ultimate tensile strength) = 640 MPa; ε_{max}(engineering strain at σ_{UTS}) = 16.5% and $E = 2.07 \times 10^5$ MPa.

Two types of tests were carried out: a) fatigue tests in rotating bending plain specimens, and b) fatigue crack propagation tests in CT specimens. These two types of tests were done in air and in a 3.5% NaCl solution in distilled water. The same frequency (25 Hz) was used in all tests.

Plain Specimen Fatigue Tests

Plain fatigue lives (S-N data) were obtained in rotating bending ($R = -1$) using smooth highly polished specimens according to DIN 50113. The specimen diameter was $d_o = 6.70 \pm .05$ mm. A good surface finish was achieved by careful polishing: after specimen machining, metallographic grinding papers were used followed by polishing alumina with a particle size of 5 µm and visual inspection at a stereo-microscope (40 x).

Results in salt water solution were obtained by continuous renewal of the solution (approx. 40ml of fresh solution per hour) through an imbibed wick in contact with the specimen surface.

The S-N data in air and in 3.5% NaCl solution are presented in Fig.1. Other tests were also performed in air after specimen pre-exposure for 8 hours in the salt water solution. These tests did not show any difference to the results obtained in air without pre-exposure.

Fatigue Crack Propagation Tests

Compact type (CT) 6mm thick specimens with the crack growing normal to the rolling direction were used to obtain fatigue crack growth data for three values of stress ratio (R=0.1, 0.5 and 0.8). All tests were carried out in a load controlled closed loop hydraulic fatigue machine, applying a sinusoidal load wave with 25 Hz cyclic frequency. ΔK-values were calculated using the formula recommended by the ASTM Method E 647-81.

Near-threshold crack growth rates were attained using both the load--shedding (decreasing ΔK at constant R) technique or the increasing R (constant K_{max}) technique. With these methods it was possible to measure crack growth rates in Region I of the $da/_{dN}$ vs. ΔK curve and obtain the threshold values for the different values of R. Crack propagation was monitored in the tests in air with a travelling microscope with an accuracy of 0.02mm. For the tests in NaCl solution a elastic-compliance method was applied using a calibration curve. This technique could detect crack increments of the order of 0.05mm. An environmental cell enclosing only the cracked zone of the specimen was used enabling the strain gauges to be attached. The fatigue crack front was always immersed in the salt water solution that was renewed at a rate of approximately 40ml/hour. The fatigue crack growth results in air and those in salt water solution are presented respectively in Fig.2 and Fig.3.

Table 1 summarizes the ΔK_{th}-values obtained at different stress ratios in air and in 3.5% NaCl solution. The threshold values decrease with increasing values of R and also in the salt water solution as compared with air. Some part of Region II in air is not affected by the R-values, whereas there are some differences in the results obtained in salt water solution probably due to the occurrence of a superimposed stress corrosion phenomenon in Region II of the R=0.8 curve (Fig.3).

DISCUSSION

The Role of Microstructure

The results of previous investigations carried out by the authors and reported in the literature (1,2) evidenced that in steady state fatigue (or continuum mode of crack growth: Region II of the da/dN vs.ΔK curve) the cyclic plastic zone is generated under plane strain ($P\varepsilon$) conditions. Observations made in air in this intermediate region of the crack propagation curve where Paris equation is valid showed that fatigue failure generally occurs by a transgranular plastic striation mechanism inside the soft phase (in steels, generally ferrite or austenite) (3) the striations being due to alternating shear in the planes of maximum resolved shear stress (slip planes). These studies and others recently reported in the literature (4-6) have emphasized the importance of the plastic zone size to the understanding of different aspects of fatigue crack growth namely threshold behaviour, transitions in the da/dN vs.ΔK curve, overloads and loading history effects.

Recently it has been proposed (4,5) that when the size of the cyclic plastic zone at the crack tip approaches the size of a microstructural feature (for instance, the grain size) a transition is observed in the da/dN vs.ΔK curve. This transition point of coordinates: $(da/dN)_T$, ΔK_T can be defined as the point where the relationship described by Paris law starts being applicable (beginning of Region II of the fatigue crack propagation curve) and is schematically represented in Fig.4 for different values of R. Most of the experimental data available in the literature indicate that crack growth rates corresponding to ΔK-values below ΔK_T (and also the threshold value ΔK_{th}) are particularly sensitive to microstructure (specially grain size), stress ratio R, monotonic and cyclic yield stress and environment. In this region (Region I) a structure sensitive and non-continuum mechanism of crack growth occurs and is often characterized by transgranular and intergranular facets (3,6-8). The measured crack propagation rates can be less than an interatomic spacing per cycle, indicating that crack growth is not occurring always after each load cycle and therefore is a non-continuum process. For crack growth rates corresponding to ΔK-values above ΔK_T crack propagation can be treated as a continuum process and hence not dependent directly on parameters of the microstructural constituents.

TABLE 1 - Near-threshold results in air and 3.5% Na Cl

Environment	R	ΔK_{th} ($MN\ m^{-3/2}$)	ΔK_T ($MN\ m^{-3/2}$)	r_c at transition (μm)
Air	0.1	6.7	9.8	13
Air	0.5	4.9	6.0	15
Air	0.8	3.5	4.0	43
Na Cl	0.1	4.8	-	-
Na Cl	0.8	2.6	-	-

SEM observations were carried out on several fracture surfaces of the BM45 steel. These are shown in Fig.5. Thus, Fig.5A reveals the microstructure on the plane of the crack, typically a ferrite-pearlite structure. Fig.5B was obtained with a ΔK-value near the threshold value. It is seen that the fracture is of mixed type, transgranular and intergranular, while in Fig.5C obtained at a ΔK-value in Region II the fracture is predominantly transgranular with secondary cracks. Finally, Fig.5D is an example of a fracture obtained in Region III at a very high crack-growth rate when K_{max} approached K_c. The rupture mechanism is that of microvoid coalescence, the final voids with a size close to the grain size of the material.

The Transition Between Regions I and II

The ΔK_T-values were obtained in the da/dN vs. ΔK curves in air and are given in Table 1. The average radius of the cyclic plastic zone, r_c, may be estimated by the following equation (1,2):

$$r_c = 0.012\left(\frac{K_{max}}{\sigma_y}\right)^2 \qquad \text{Eq. 1}$$

The r_c-values at the transition points for R=0.1,0.5 and 0.8 are also presented in Table 1. Table 2 gives the microstructural parameters obtained on the BM45 steel. Observations made by Kao and Byrne (6) on a normalised AISI 1060 steel at R=0.1 are also considered for comparison. The r_c-values at the transition points for R=0.1 and R=0.5 are very close. For R=0.8 the r_c-value at the transition is larger, however it is worthwhile to observe in Fig.2 that the crack growth rate at the transition is remarkably close to one lattice spacing per cycle. It seems reasonable to conclude that Region II (or continuum mechanism of crack growth) only may occur in this type of microstructure if cyclic plastic zone sizes are larger than a microstructural feature whose dimension is close to 1-2 grain diameters and if crack growth rates are higher than one lattice spacing per cycle. Figure 6 shows schematically the fatigue crack growth in Regions I and II also confirmed by the fracture types revealed in Fig.5B and 5C.

The Effect of Stress Ratio

The influence of stress ratio R on near-threshold growth rates measured in steels is well documented in the literature. This influence depends on specimen thickness and environment but the general trend can be described as follows: ΔK_{th} decreases with increasing R to a minimum value (herein called the "true" threshold ΔK^t_{th}) and then, remains constant. However some data obtained in inert environments (5,9)(e.g.in argon or in vacuum) or in very thick specimens (10) show lack of, or markedly reduced, stress ratio effect on ΔK_{th}. The available data for R<0 also show that when the compressive part of ΔK is deducted from the total range the resulting ΔK_{th}-values are found to be very close to ΔK_{th} for R=0 (5,10).

Based on the above-mentioned facts the influence of R on thresholds of cracked specimens has been explained in terms of crack closure and/or environment-assisted cracking. Sufficient number of observations prove that crack closure during cyclic loading is due to many "asperities" that are generated locally within the crack (11,12). If, at the minimum value of K (K_{min}) the crack is not sufficiently open (low $CTOD_{min}$) then during part of the loading cycle the crack is propped open by the asperities. These asperities can be due to corrosion or oxidation deposits (environment-induced closure)(8,12, 13) or fracture surface roughness (roughness-induced closure)(12).

In Fig.7 K_{op} represents the minimum K-value necessary to open the crack or to avoid the asperities to sustain the crack surfaces. It is not obvious that K_{op} must be constant for all R-values however, for simplicity, K_{op} is

TABLE 2 - Microstructural parameters

Steel	Crystallographic Unit Size	Interlamellar Spacing in Pearlite	Hardness Ferrite	Hardness Pearlite	r_c at transition R=0.1
BM 45 this work	9.2[a)]μm	0.20 μm	H_V 20g 211	H_V 20g 245	13 μm
AISI 1060 reference (6)	90 μm	0.29 μm	H_V 15g 176	H_V 200g 227	81 μm

a) average grain diameter in the rolling plane

represented as a constant in the figure and R_c is the minimum value of R above which the measured ΔK_{th} remains constant and equal to ΔK^t_{th}. The existence of a constant ΔK^t_{th} can be explained considering that, theoretically, if crack closure and environmental effects were avoided, the stress ratio R should not have any influence in Region I and Region II fatigue crack growth behaviour. In fact, the stress and strain distributions within the cyclic plastic zone depend only on the cyclic yield stress (or strain) of the material (2,16). Therefore for a given material the hysteresis loop of the CTOD-affected zone (process zone)(2,16) is independent of R.

The fatigue crack growth process can be explained in energetical terms: each hysteresis loop corresponds to a certain amount of strain energy dissipated in the process zone. This strain energy U can be approximately given by:

$$U = \Delta\varepsilon_p \times \sigma^c_y \qquad \text{Eq. 2}$$

where $\Delta\varepsilon_p$ is the plastic strain range at the process zone and σ^c_y is the local cyclic yield stress. If a strain energy concept is used, e.g.,"failure will occur when the strain energy reaches a critical value U_c", it is possible to understand that crack growth may occur after each cycle ($\Delta\varepsilon_p\, \sigma^c_y = U_c$; continuum process or Region II - fatigue crack growth) or after a certain number N of cycles ($N\,\Delta\varepsilon_p\, \sigma^c_y = U_c$; non-continuum process in near-threshold fatigue crack growth).

The strain $\Delta\varepsilon_p$ at the process zone (CTOD-affected zone) depends only on ΔCTOD. ΔCTOD is the variation of CTOD between K_{min} and K_{max} and is proportional to ΔK^2 (2,9,16,17):

$$\Delta CTOD = CTOD_{max} - CTOD_{min} = 0.25\,\frac{\Delta K^2}{E\sigma_y} \qquad \text{Eq. 3}$$

$CTOD_{max}$ is given by:

$$CTOD_{max} = 0.5\,\frac{K^2_{max}}{E\sigma_y} = \frac{0.5}{E\sigma_y}\frac{\Delta K^2}{(1-R)^2} \qquad \text{Eq. 4}$$

Combining Eqs. 3 and 4 comes

$$CTOD_{min} = \frac{0.5}{E\sigma_y}\left[\frac{\Delta K^2}{(1-R)^2} - \frac{\Delta K^2}{2}\right] \qquad \text{Eq. 5}$$

Considering ΔK constant, equations 4 and 5 show that the effect of an increase in the value of R is to have the crack front more open during the entire load cycle. Then, if K_{min} is greater than K_{op} (see Fig. 7) a constant ΔCTOD (independent of R) can be obtained. In this case, $\Delta\varepsilon_p$ at the process zone should be independent of R and consequently the crack growth rate will depend only on the applied ΔK-value.

The Relation Between K_{th}^{t} and $S_{N=10^7}$

To obtain fatigue crack growth it is required to have cyclic plasticity (dislocation motion) at the crack-tip which consists in some amount of blunting and resharpening after each cycle or after some number of cycles. However, cyclic plasticity may occur within the cyclic plastic zone of the crack and then may be stopped or arrested for a large number of cycles without the growth of the boundaries of that cyclic plastic zone. In ferritic-pearlitic steels grain boundaries can act as barriers to the transmission of slip to the next grains. Substantial data show that a decrease in the ferrite grain size and/or, to a lesser extent, in the interlamellar spacing in pearlite, leads also to a decrease in the threshold values (14,18,19).

Long time ago (1951), T. Yokobori observed that slip bands in carbon steel appear well below the fatigue limit of plain specimens. Some critical shear stress τ_f is required for these slip bands to form (15). Also micro-cracks can be formed well below the fatigue limit. These micro-cracks have a length far smaller than the grain size. However some stress greater than τ_f is required for the growth (propagation) of the micro-cracks. This critical stress will be the fatigue limit of smooth (plain) specimens. A similar mechanism was observed in cracked specimens: when stress cycling was below the threshold value the slip bands were restricted within a grain (5,20).

To check the validity of this theory to the present experimental results the fatigue strengths S_N for $N = 10^7$ cycles in the BM 45 steel were taken from Fig.1 and those were: S_N(in air) = 273 M Pa and S_N(in Na Cl) = 170 M Pa. The "true" ΔK_{th}-values may be estimated as being the threshold values for R=0.8 (Fig.8): ΔK_{th}^{t}(in air)=3.5 MN $m^{-3/2}$ and ΔK_{th}^{t}(in Na Cl) = 2.6 MN $m^{-3/2}$. Taking into account that, for the nucleation of a crack in a grain of a plain (smooth) specimen, the compressive part of the stress range also contributes, the effective stress range will be $\sigma_{max}-\sigma_{min}=2S_N$ and the following relationship between ΔK_{th}^{t} and fatigue strength S_N may be established:

$$\Delta K_{th}^{t} = 1.12(2\,S_N)\sqrt{\pi a_o} \qquad \text{Eq. 6}$$

where a_o is the size of the nucleated crack and 1.12 is the geometrical factor Y for a rotating bending test piece with a crack far smaller than the specimen diameter. Substituting in Eq.6 the proper ΔK_{th}^{t} and S_N-values in air and in salt water solution the following a_o values were found: a_o(in air)=10.4 μm and a_o(in Na Cl) = 14.8 μm which are very close to the grain size of the BM 45 steel (see Table 2).

CONCLUSIONS

I. Threshold and low fatigue crack growth rate data obtained in the medium strength steel BM 45 in air and in 3.5% Na Cl showed that in this material the size of the cyclic plastic zone and the grain size define the transition between Regions I and II of the fatigue crack propagation curve.

II. Considering crack closure a very close linear relationship between ΔK_{th} and R was established for values of R less than 0.8 to which corresponds a minimum value of ΔK_{th} (estimatedas being the "true"threshold ΔK_{th}^{t}). The "true" threshold should be used in fatigue design and must be determined by testing (in the proper environment) at the highest possible R-value since in this case there is no closure and the effective ΔK becomes equal to the applied ΔK.

III. The threshold values obtained by full immersion of BM 45 steel in 3.5% NaCl solution are lower than those measured in air environment.

IV. A relationship between the "true" fatigue threshold of cracked specimens and fatigue strength of plain specimens was established. Using this relationship it was found that the calculated minimum values of crack length for crack propagation on plain specimens are very close to the grain size of the material.

ACKNOWLEDGEMENTS

The experimental facilities provided by Departamento de Metalurgia e Metalomecânica of L.N.E.T.I. (Lisbon-Portugal) are gratefully acknowledged. Thanks are due to Dr.J.C.Radon for helpful and stimulating discussions.

REFERENCES

1. Guerra Rosa.L., Branco,C.M. and Radon,J.C.,"Effects of Plasticity and Strain Rate on Fatigue Crack Growth", Proceedings of the 4th European Conference on Fracture held in Leoben, Austria, E.M.A.S.,Vol.2, September 1982, pp. 449-456.
2. Guerra Rosa,L., Branco,C.M. and Radon,J.C.,"Monotonic and Cyclic Crack-Tip Plasticity", to be published in International Journal of Fatigue, 1983.
3. Ritchie,R.O.,"Near-Threshold Fatigue Crack Propagation in Steels", Intern. Met.Rev., Vol.24(1979), pp.205-230.
4. Yoder,G.R., Cooley,L.A. and Crooker,T.W.,"On Microstructural Control of Near-Threshold Fatigue Crack Growth in 7000-Series Aluminium Alloys",NRL Memorandum Report 4787 (1982).
5. Usami,S.,"Applications of Threshold Cyclic-Plastic-Zone-Size Criterion to some Fatigue Limit Problems", Fatigue Thresholds, Proceedings of an Intern. Conf. held in Stockholm, E.M.A.S., Vol.1, June 1981, pp.205-238.
6. Kao,P. and Byrne,J.G.,"Microstructural Influences on Fatigue Crack Propagation in Pearlitic Steels", ibid., pp.313-327.
7. Cadman,A.J., Nicholson,C.E. and Brook,R.,"Microstructural Effects at and near the Fatigue Threshold", ibid., pp.293-311.
8. Minakawa,K. and McEvily,A.J.,"On Near-Threshold Fatigue Crack Growth in Steels and Aluminium Alloys", ibid., pp.373-390.
9. Beevers,C.J.,"Some Aspects of the Influence of Microstructure and Environment on ΔK Thresholds", ibid., pp.257-275.
10. Radon,J.C.,"Fatigue Crack Growth in the Threshold Region",ibid.,pp.113-132.
11. Paris,P.C. and Hermann,L., "Some Observations of Crack Closure", ibid., pp.11-32.
12. Ritchie,R.O.,"Environment Effects on Near-Threshold Fatigue Crack Propagation in Steels: A Re-Assessment", ibid., pp.503-526.
13. Suresh,S., Parks,D.M. and Ritchie,R.O.,"Crack Tip Oxide Formation and its Influence on Fatigue Threshold", ibid., pp.391-408.
14. Gray,G.T. et al.,"Influence of Microstructure on Fatigue Crack Growth Behaviour in Fully Pearlitic Steels", ibid., pp.345-361.
15. Yokobori Jr.,A.T. and Yokobori,T.,"On Micro- and Macro-Mechanics of Fatigue Thresholds", ibid., pp.171-189.
16. Hahn,G.T., Hoagland,R.G. and Rosenfield,A.R.,"Local Yielding Attending Fatigue Crack Growth", Met.Trans.3 (1972), pp.1189-1202.
17. Guerra Rosa,L., Branco,C.M. and Radon,J.C."Influence of the Strain Rate on Fatigue Crack Tip Plasticity", to be published.
18. Masounave,J. and Bailon,J.P.,"Effect of Grain Size on the Threshold Stress Intensity Factor in Fatigue of a Ferritic Steel", Scripta Metallurgica, Vol.10 (1976), pp.165-170.
19. Benson,J.P.,"Influence of Grain Size and Yield Strength on Threshold Fatigue Behaviour of Low-Alloy Steel", Metal Science, Vol.13 (1979), pp.535-539.
20. Ohuchida,H., Nishioka,A. and Usami,S.,"Elastic-Plastic Approach to Fatigue Crack Propagation and Fatigue Limit of Material with Crack", Proc. 3rd Int.Conf.on Fracture,München,V-442/A, (1973), pp.1-8.

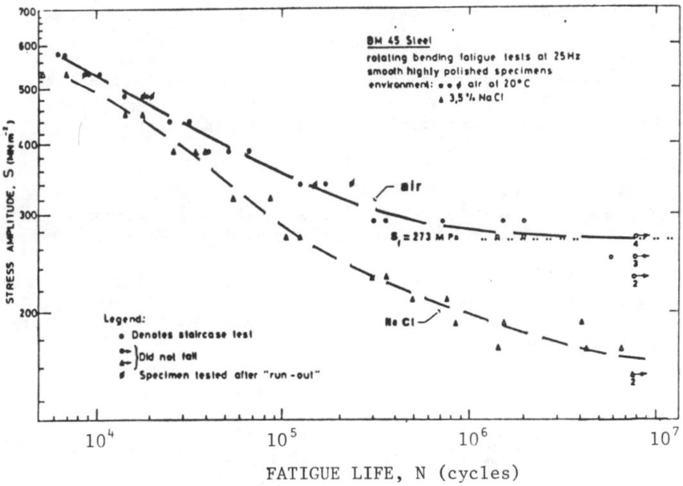

Figure 1. S-N data in air and in 3.5% NaCl solution

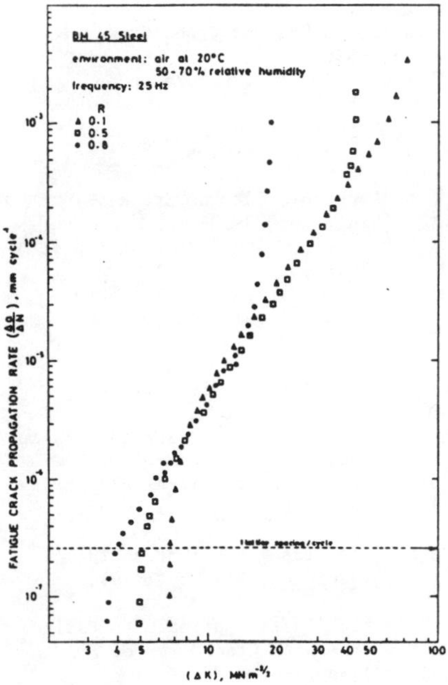

Fig.2 Fatigue crack growth in air

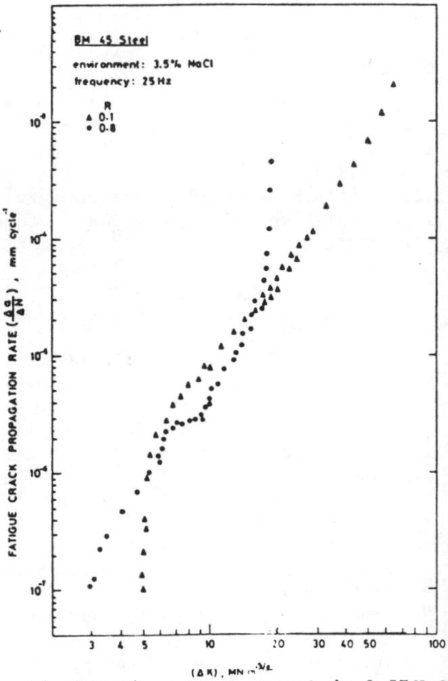

Fig.3 Fatigue crack growth in 3.5% NaCl

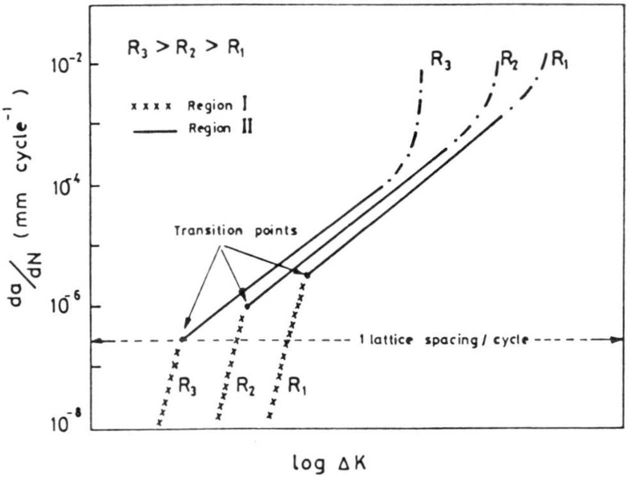

Figure 4. Schematic fatigue crack growth rate curves showing the usual effect of stress ratio R

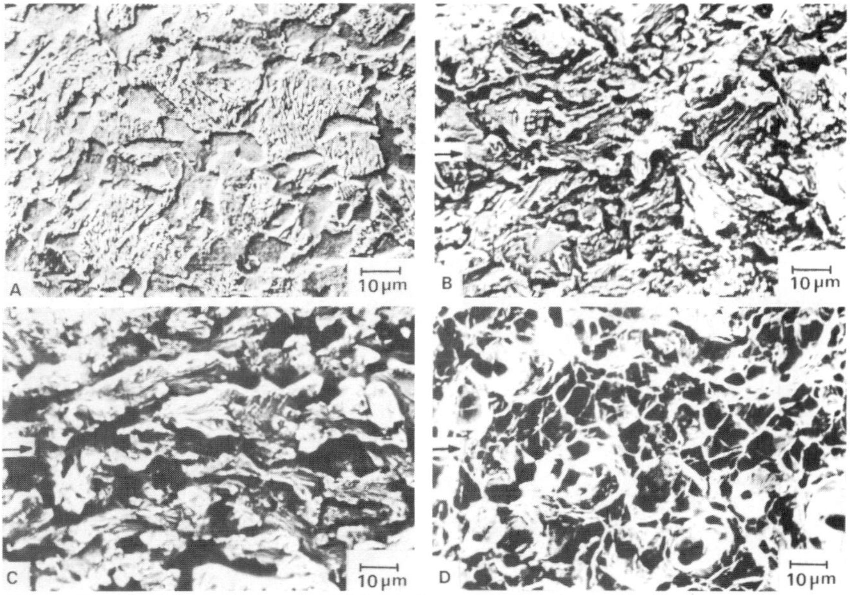

Figure 5. SEM observations on BM 45 steel tested in air: A. microstructure on the fracture plane, prior to the test, revealed by etching with Nital, B. fractography at $\Delta K=3.7\ MN\ m^{-3/2}$ $R=0.8$ (Region I), C. fractography at $\Delta K=20\ MN\ m^{-3/2}$ $R=0.1$ (Region II), D. fractography of Region III

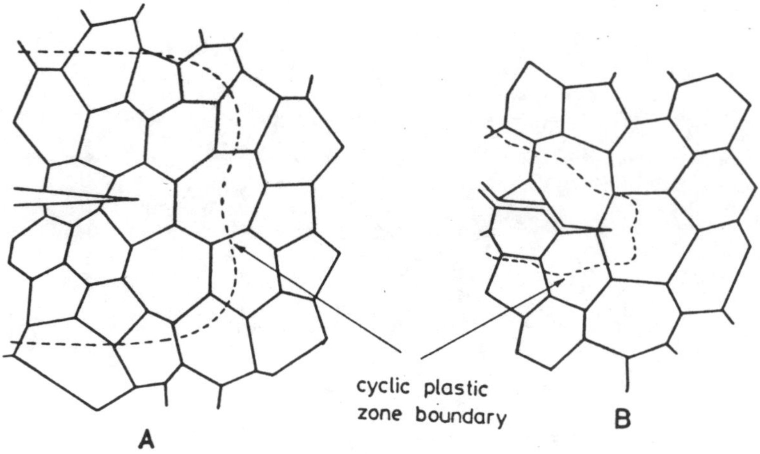

Figure 6. Fatigue crack growth mechanisms: A.in Region II: B.in Region I approaching the threshold value by decreasing ΔK

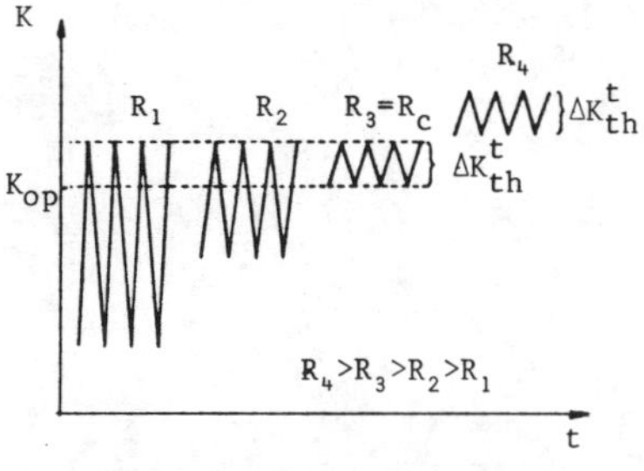

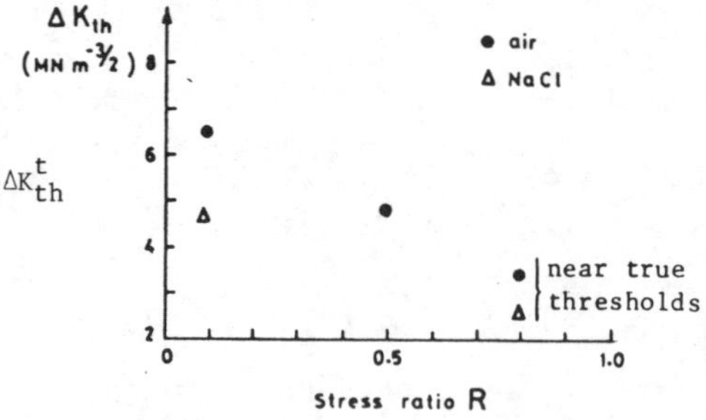

Fig.7 Effect of R on the measured ΔK_{th} Fig.8 ΔK_{th} versus R for the BM 45 steel

THE INFLUENCE OF WELDING POSITION, TECHNIQUE AND HEAT INPUT ON THE FRACTURE TOUGHNESS OF BASIC ELECTRODE WELDS

P.C.R. CUNHA* AND A.M.POPE*

The influence of welding position and technique as well as the heat input on the as welded fracture toughness of basic electrode welds were studied using CTOD and Charpy tests. The parent material was BS 4360 gr 50D steel and the electrodes were of AWS E 7016 and 7018 types. Charpy tests were not so sensitive as were the CTOD tests in detecting the influence of heat input, welding position and technique. It was shown that for the selection of consumables and or welding procedures to prevent brittle fracture on offshore structures, the choice of welding in the vertical up position may not be the most conservative one at least when the restricted weave bead technique is allowed in the construction.

INTRODUCTION

Welds in offshore structures are a point of particular concern in the prevention of brittle fracture. In general the welds of the nodes are the most critical ones.

Generally the materials for offshore platforms are selected obeying the rules of the various certifying authorities. The design codes and standards have stringent requirements with respect to weld metal toughness to prevent unstable fractures.

When the fabrication of the structures include positional manual metal arc (MMA) welding, the vertical up position should be the one used for welding the test assemblies (1). For MMA welds the lowest toughness is normally associated with welds made in the vertical up position (2).

The use of low heat input and stringer bead techniques (1) are some of the ways by which improvements in the as welded metal toughness are achieved. The extent of weaving during the welding seems to have a dual effect on the as welded weld metal toughness. As increasing the weaving leads to higher welding heat input it would be expected that fully weaved welds would have lower toughness than restricted weaved ones. However, in a fully weaved weld, the proportion of reheated weld metal tends to be increased and in fact it was observed that the full weave technique improves the subsurface toughness of welds (3). Therefore it is difficult to generalize about the effects of weaving on weld metal toughness. It is the usual practice to allow the use of weave bead technique in constructions if it is restricted to 3 times the elec-

* EQUIPMENT ENGINEERS, MSc - Petrobrás - CENPES - Brasil.

trode diameter. This technique when used in this work, is called restricted weave bead.

The objective of this study was to verify the influences of welding position, techniques of welding (stringer or restricted weave bead) and heat input on the as welded fracture toughness of basic electrode welds, measured by CTOD and Charpy tests. The results should be considered for the selection of consumables and welding procedures.

MATERIALS AND WELDING PROCEDURES

The steel plates used were BS 4360 grade 50D in the normalized condition. The consumables selected were of the basic, low hydrogen type AWS E 7016 and 7018. General details of the welding procedures followed are summarized in table 1. The test plates were 500 mm wide and 1200mm long. The range of heat inputs used in the welding test plates was the same used in the fabrication of the platforms (15-35 kJ/cm). All the joints were symmetrical double V with an included angle of 60°. The root was backgouged together with some grinding. Heavy restraining bars,welded across the pannels at top and bottom, prevented "butterflying". All the welding consumables were dried as specified by the manufacturers and stored at 120° C until used.

SPECIMEN PREPARATION AND TEST METHODS

Square section (T vs. T, where T is the plate thickness) specimens of the subsidiary geometry were used to measure weld metal toughness by the CTOD tests. The specimens were notched to a depth of 0.3T, through the thickness of the weld and parallel to the welding direction (figure 1). The fatigue pre-cracking of the welds was done using the minimum to maximum load ratio of 0.5 (4) to obtain a straight crack front.

The CTOD tests were conducted in three point bending in accordance with British Standard 5762/1979 (5). The test temperature was 10° C, minimum design temperature for offshore structures in Brazil. The specimens were tested in the as welded condition.

The CTOD was obtained from clip gauge displacement records using the theoretical formula from ref. (5) and calculated at the initiation of instability, when it occurred, or at the start of the maximum load plateau, when considerable ductility occurred. For the AWS E 7016 welds (nº 21 to 28) Charpy specimens were taken at subsurface and root positions, while for the AWS E 7018 welds (nº 66 to 71), these specimens were taken at quarter thickness.

A Charpy V notch impact energy transition curve with temperature was obtained in the range of - 80 to + 20° C. Standard 10 vs. 10mm Charpy specimens were used with the notch oriented in the same direction as the CTOD specimens.

The percentage of microstructural constituents in the columnar region of each weldment was measured in a Swift point count er. The nomenclature of the constituents was that recommended by the IIW Doc II-A-389-76 (6). At least 500 points were counted in each sample. The ferritic grain size in the fine grained regions of the weld metals was measured by the lineal intercept procedure.

The relative proportions of the columnar and fine grained regions were determined by measuring, under optical microscope, the widths of each region near the fatigue pre-crack as illustrated in ref. (7). For these measurements, the specimen of the lowest CTOD value of each weld metal tested was used.

The acicular ferrite content of the welds was taken as the product of the acicular ferrite content in the columnar region and the columnar region percent in the weldments.

Vickers hardness measurements (10 kg) were made in both columnar (CR) and fine grained (FGR) regions of transverse sections of weldments. These measurements were taken on the weld center line at approximately 1/4 thickness.

The mean Vickers hardness of the welds was taken as

$$\overline{HV} = \frac{(HV(CR) \times \% \, CR) + (HV(FGR) \times \% \, FGR)}{100} \qquad (1)$$

RESULTS

The weld metal compositions are shown in table 2, with their tensile properties given in table 3, each value being the average of two specimens. The CTOD data in the as welded condition are also given in table 3, while CTOD versus welding heat inputs are plotted for the MMA welds of AWS E 7016 and E 7018 electrodes in figures 2 and 3 respectively.

The Charpy V notch data are given in table 4, and the transition temperature curves for the MMA welds of the AWS E 7016 and E 7018 electrodes are plotted in figures 4 and 5 respectively. The 40 J Charpy transition temperature data obtained from these figures are given in table 4.

The microstructure and hardness data are given in table 5.

DISCUSSION

The experiments with the AWS E 7016 electrode showed that for all welds, except the vertical weld manufactured with the restricted weave bead technique, there is a tendency for the mean CTOD to decrease with increase of heat input for a given welding technique (figure 2). This effect of heat input on toughness has been attributed to the influence of heat input on microstructures (8). High heat inputs tend to produce coarse microstructures,decrease the acicular ferrite content in the region of columnar grains in favour of proeutectoid ferrite, and increase the ferritic grain size in the region of equiaxed grains. These changes are detrimental to toughness.

In this work, the welds manufactured using the same technique presented a tendency to decrease the acicular ferrite content with increasing heat input.

One of the consequences of weaving is to increase heat input. Therefore, using this technique, it would be expected that a loss of toughness should be associated with a corresponding increase of heat input. The mean CTOD seems to follow this trend (figures 2 and 3). However, with respect to minimum CTOD values, it is observed that the welds manufactured using the restricted weave bead technique presented toughness lower than those welded with higher heat inputs but manufactured using the stringer bead technique. In particular (figure 2) the vertical welds (high heat input) presented minimum CTOD values higher than welds performed in other positions with lower heat inputs but where the restricted weave bead technique were used.

Other workers (9) found for E 7016 weld metals that horizontal welds had lower toughness than certain flat and vertical up welds produced at higher levels of heat input. No comments were given about welding technique.

It can also be seen from figure 2 that the difference between minimum and mean CTOD values for stringer bead welds is greater for flat than for other positional welds.

For the vertical up welds, Robinson (3) found that variations in arc energy may contribute to toughness differences within a weld. Although no observations regarding heat input variations were made in this work, it seems reasonable to suppose that welds performed in a difficult position would be less subjected to heat input variations because more control of the weld pool is required from the welder. Also in figure 2, comparing the minimum and mean CTOD values for the same welding position, it is seen that the use of restricted weave technique led to considerable differences between such values. This may be atributed to the loss of control of heat input (3) and/or bead width (10) associated with the restricted weave bead technique. Both factors were found to be responsible for major differences in properties (3,10).

The results with the AWS E 7016 weld metals show that the vertical up position or high heat input welds are not necessarily associated with low fracture toughness. Indeed, the toughness depends on the welding technique used. Another worker (11) has also found that vertical welds are not necessarily less tough, but no comments were made about heat input or welding techniques used.

So, for the selection of consumables and/or welding procedures, the choice of welding in the vertical up position may not be the most conservative one, at least, when the restricted weave bead technique is allowed in the construction.

Comparing the influence of heat input on fracture toughness of the welds manufactured using the AWS E 7016 (figure 2) and AWS E 7018 (figure 3) electrodes, it can be seen that the latter showed better results in the range of heat inputs studied. These observations could be explained by the more favourable microstructure of the AWS E 7018 electrode (table 5 and figure 6) or any other effect related to the welding position. (The AWS E 7018 weldments were performed only in the vertical up position).

It can be observed from figures 4 and 5 that the Charpy transition temperature curves did not show the same tendencies of toughness variation with welding technique and position as did the CTOD at 10°C. For the same welding position, the variations in Charpy transition temperature curves with welding technique were not noticeable. In particular, the Charpy tests were not so effective in detecting the influence of welding technique on the toughness of the welds performed in the horizontal position (figure 4 (a)). It is important to remember that the welds performed in this position were those that showed the greatest loss on toughness measured by CTOD tests when the restricted weave bead was used instead of stringer bead technique.

Berkhout et al (12) argue that the CTOD test is more responsive to strain aging embrittlement than the Charpy V test. The latter responds to changes in composition and microstructure. These workers (12) consider strain aging embrittlement to be the major factor causing low CTOD values.

Despite these comments, it can be observed from table 4 and figure 7, that for all the welding positions, except the vertical up one, the restricted weave technique led to some increase in the Charpy V transition temperature of root specimens.

The CTOD tests were performed on through thickness specimens. As the central part of the specimens is that which has greatest influence on the CTOD results, and because the weldments had a double V preparation, any comparison between CTOD and Charpy results in this study was possible only for the Charpy root specimens of the AWS E 7016 weld metal. (The Charpy specimens from the AWS E 7018 weld metal were taken at quarter thickness). Figure 7 shows that the mean CTOD values were higher than 0.60 mm and the 40 J Charpy transition temperature was below -30 °C (for the AWS E 7016 weld metals).

However, it was observed that the welds performed with the restricted weave bead technique, except the vertical up one, showed minimum CTOD values very low in spite of the 40 J Charpy transition temperature being below - 30°C.

A minimum Charpy energy of 40 J at - 30°C specified for the root region, ensures high mean CTOD values (greater than 0.6 mm), but does not guarantee satisfactory values of minimum CTOD. In this case, in order to achieve satisfactory values of minimum

CTOD at 10°C the weld metals would have to achieve 40 J at -45°C.

CONCLUSIONS

1. AWS E 7016 weld metal deposited in the flat, horizontal and overhead positions presented an accentuated loss of fracture toughness at 10°C when the restricted weave bead technique was used instead of stringer bead technique. The use of restricted weave technique in the vertical position (high heat input welds), on the contrary, led an improvement of the fracture toughness.

2. For both electrodes the weld metal fracture toughness decreases with heat input increase for weldments made with the stringer bead technique.

3. In the range of heat input studied, AWS E 7018 weld metal presented fracture toughness higher than AWS E 7016 weld metal. The former electrode deposits were not so sensitive to heat input variation and welding technique as the latter was.

4. The 40J Charpy Transition temperature of AWS E 7016 root specimens increased when the restricted weave bead technique was used instead of stringer bead technique for all positions except the vertical up one. However the Charpy tests were not so sensitive as were CTOD tests in showing the influence of heat input, welding position and technique.

5. The deleterious effects of the restricted weave technique on fracture toughness may impair the beneficial ones brought about by low heat input welding.

6. The selection of electrodes for offshore construction based on Charpy energy requirements of 40J at - 30°C for root specimens seems to ensure adequate mean CTOD values.

7. For selection of consumables and/or welding procedures, the choice of welding in the vertical up position may not be the most conservative one, at least when the restricted weave bead technique is allowed in the construction.

ACKNOWLEDGEMENTS

The authors are grateful to Eletrodos Torsima S.A. and Armco do Brasil S.A. that contributed to this research programme and to Mr. Godfrey H.W. Deane for the revision of the manuscript.

REFERENCES

1 - Pisarski, H.G., and Dawes, M.G., 1979 "Measurement of crack opening displacement in weldments with particular reference to offshore structures" Doc. for discussion at the ECSC/WG2 meeting, Genova, Italy.

2 - Dawes, M.G., 1972, *Welding and Metal Fabrication,* 95.

3 - Robinson, J.L., 1973, *Weld. Res. Int., 8,* 425

4 - Doucet, J.P., et Rebouillat, C., 1977 "Mesure de la ténacité dans les joints soudés". 2e partie Rapport IS/CECA nº 6479.

5 - British Standard BS 5762/79 "Methods for crack opening (COD) testing", BSI, The British Standards Institution.

6 - Davey, T.G., and Widgery, D.J.,1976, "A technique for the characterization of weld metal microstructure". IIW Doc.II-A-389-76.

7 - Cunha, P.C.R., Pope, A.M., and Nóbrega, A.F., 1982, "Fracture toughness of weld metals for Brazilian offshore platforms". 2nd Int. Conf. on offshore structures, London, England.

8 - Evans, G.M., 1982, *Weld. Journal 61,* 125s.

9 - Nickolson, S., and Rogers, P.F., 1974, "Controlling weld metal toughness in manual metal - arc welds". Proc. Int. Conf. on Welding in offshore, Newcastle-on-Tyne.

10 - Dawson, G.W., and Judson, P., 1982., "Procedural guidelines for the achievement of tough welded joints in structural steels for offshore applications" 2nd Int. Conf. on offshore structures, London, England.

11 - Wildschut, H., 1981, "COD measurements and wide plate tests on welded material with thicknesses of 30 and 50mm" Int. Conference "Steel in Marine structures", Paris, France.

12 - Berkhout, C.F., Van den Brink, S.H., and Vaessen, G.H.G. , 1978, "Controlling Weld metal toughness of manual metal-arc and submerged-arc welds in carbon-manganese steel". Proc . European offshore steels Research Seminar, The Welding Institute, Cambridge, England.

TABLE 1 - Summary of Welding Procedures

Weld Code Nº	Plate Thickness (mm)	Number of runs	Electrode AWS class.	Welding Position	Welding Technique	Heat Input (KJ/cm)
21	40	30	7016	Horizontal	W	17.4
22	40	34	7016	Horizontal	S	15.1
23	40	18	7016	Overhead	W	26.6
24	40	28	7016	Oberhead	S	18.5
25	40	18	7016	Flat	W	24.6
26	40	27	7016	Flat	S	16.5
27	40	15	7016	Vertical	W	32.1
28	40	18	7016	Vertical	S	28.1
66	32	22	7018	Vertical	S	17.2
67	32	18	7018	Vertical	W	21.7
68	32	19	7018	Vertical	S	22.4
69	32	16	7018	Vertical	W	24.7
70	32	18	7018	Vertical	S	25.5
71	32	14	7018	Vertical	W	31.3

W = Weave bead

S = Stringer bead

Obs.:

- Preheat temperature: 150 °C., maximum interpass temperature: 150 °C.

TABLE 2 - Chemical Composition of Weld Metal Deposits

Weld Code Nº	Composition, wt %												
	C	Mn	Si	Cu	Mo	V	Nb	Ti	P	S	Sb	Sn	Al (ppm)
21	0.08	1.05	0.55	0.020	-	0.02	0.008	0.032	0.025	0.014	0.0064	-	56
22	0.08	0.94	0.52	0.072	0.028	0.02	0.014	0.020	0.026	0.010	0.0064	0.010	71
23	0.09	1.15	0.54	-	-	0.02	-	0.020	0.026	0.014	-	-	69
24	0.09	1.10	0.59	-	-	0.06	-	0.038	0.026	0.009	0.01	-	77
25	0.06	1.06	0.48	0.040	0.025	0.008	0.0034	0.023	0.021	0.020	0.0026	-	121
26	0.08	1.05	0.57	0.064	0.024	0.01	0.02	0.022	0.021	0.014	0.0042	0.010	69
27	0.08	1.00	0.52	0.040	-	0.01	0.015	0.024	0.021	0.010	0.008	-	78
28	0.09	0.85	0.50	0.040	-	0.01	0.015	0.020	0.022	0.013	0.008	-	58
66	0.09	1.10	0.47	-	-	-	-	-	0.016	0.010	-	-	100
67	0.08	1.12	0.44	0.160	0.060	0.01	0.038	0.0054	0.011	0.012	0.026	0.032	100
68	0.10	1.09	0.37	0.025	0.040	0.008	-	0.0062	0.010	0.012	0.02	-	100
69	0.10	1.04	0.37	0.047	0.030	0.01	0.0025	0.0072	0.006	0.013	0.012	0.014	100
70	0.09	1.00	0.37	-	-	-	-	-	0.011	0.014	-	-	100
71	0.10	0.95	0.36	-	-	0.01	-	0.004	0.009	0.013	-	-	100

TABLE 3 - Tensile Properties and CTOD Values of Weld Metals at 10 °C

Weld Code Nº	Yield Stress (N/mm2)	Tensile Strength (N/mm2)	Elongation on 25 mm (%)	Reduction of area (%)	CTOD, (mm)*			
								mean
21	527.2	592.9	30.0	74.5	1.50	0.96	0.11	0.86
22	523.3	585.1	29.0	75.5	1.36	1.36	1.23	1.32
23	471.4	583.1	33.0	76.0	0.10	1.44	0.28	0.61
24	507.6	595.8	27.5	73.5	0.74	1.01	0.61	0.79
25	479.2	554.7	30.9	77.6	0.47	0.10	1.52	0.70
26	491.0	568.4	32.0	77.5	0.60	1.41	0.75	0.92
27	490.0	592.9	27.0	73.5	0.63	1.50	0.96	1.03
28	479.2	575.3	29.0	75.0	0.51	0.48	0.84	0.61
66	502.7	561.5	33.0	76.0	1.52	1.45	1.54	1.50
67	482.2	542.9	33.0	77.0	1.49	1.54	1.58	1.54
68	490.0	558.6	27.0	73.0	1.25	1.26	1.29	1.27
69	489.0	562.5	30.0	72.0	1.25	1.31	0.64	1.07
70	479.2	552.7	27.0	74.0	1.41	1.13	0.74	1.09
71	470.4	551.7	33.0	72.0	1.12	0.79	1.09	1.00

* The lowest CTOD value for each weld code Nº is underlined.

TABLE 4 - Charpy Energy of Weld Metals vs Temperature of Tests and 40 Joule Charpy Transition temperature (40J, TT)
Charpy, Joules*

Weld Code Nº	Notch location	Temperature (°C)									
		20	10	0	-10	-20	-30	-40	-60	-80	40J, TT
21	R**	146	173	136	60	71	96	23	11	6	-31
	S***	218	215	207	199	200	164	118	53	14	-64
22	R	180	160	147	96	68	55	23	16	9	-34.5
	S	235	245	164	200	201	164	134	49	16	-63
23	R	168	192	125	71	122	60	20	10	12	-30
	S	266	169	204	189	188	172	146	84	22	-73
24	R	168	166	148	142	77	72	59	26	12	-49.5
	S	211	190	213	195	157	97	109	40	13	-60
25	R	157	144	142	105	77	74	53	18	8	-44
	S	287	274	289	207	184	111	45	19	-	-48
26	R	172	133	141	108	85	102	85	32	9	-54
	S	250	208	219	174	178	141	124	50	11	-59.5
27	R	155	145	126	101	86	93	28	13	9	-38.5
	S	183	160	157	128	137	76	84	25	14	-49.5
28	R	147	136	102	72	98	59	37	16	9	-36.5
	S	200	180	172	135	139	138	72	39	-	-59
66	1/4****	-	-	177	-	113	-	48	17	-	-44
67	1/4	-	-	177	-	79	-	43	15	-	-37.5
68	1/4	-	-	143	-	103	-	31	13	-	-37
69	1/4	-	-	152	-	83	-	74	17	-	-46
70	1/4	-	-	155	-	126	-	78	13	-	-49
71	1/4	-	-	134	-	101	-	44	12	-	-41

* mean of 3 values **R-root ***S-2mm Subsurface ****1/4 - quarter Thickness of Plate

TABLE 5 - Microstructure and Vickers Hardness of the Weld Metals

Weld Code Nº	Relative proportions of regions in the fatigue precrack %		Region: CR, %			Region: FGR, µm	Acicular ferrite in weld, %	Hardness, HV (10)		
	CR	FGR	AF	PF	LC	FGS		Region CR	Region FGR	$\overline{HV}$
21	45	55	69	21	10	8.3	3.1	201	190	195
22	54	46	70	22	8	10.5	37.8	219	185	203
23	40	60	66	26	8	12.0	26.4	209	180	192
24	51	49	64	27	9	8.5	32.6	216	184	200
25	39	61	60	22	18	9.3	23.4	184	180	182
26	44	56	63	25	12	8.2	27.7	216	199	206
27	56	44	69	23	8	9.0	38.6	205	185	196
28	49	51	67	25	8	10.0	32.8	212	177	194
66	60	40	79	17	4	8.5	47.4	206	192	200
67	52	48	75	22	3	9.0	39.0	211	203	207
68	52	48	74	24	2	8.3	38.5	176	194	185
69	53	47	72	23	5	9.4	38.2	195	182	189
70	52	48	74	22	4	7.5	38.5	197	186	192
71	54	46	72	25	3	10.0	38.9	229	210	220

CR - columnar region; FGR - fine-grained region; $\overline{HV}$ - mean hardness; AF - acicular ferrite;
PF - proeutectoid ferrite; LC - lamellar component; FGS - ferrite grain size; HV (10) Vickers hardness.

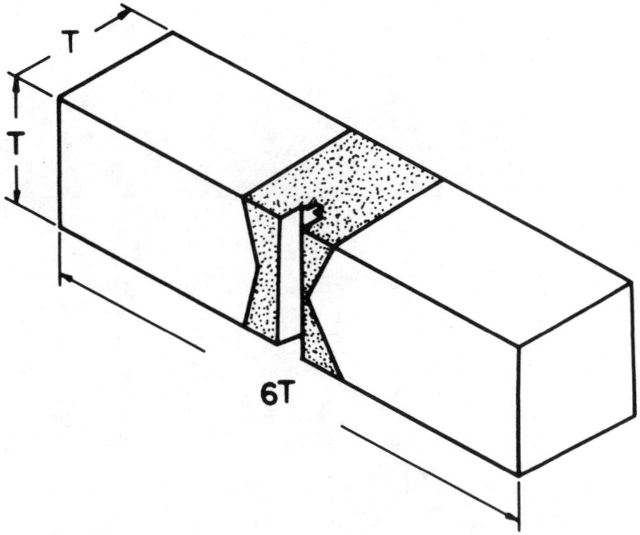

Figure 1 - Subsidiary CTOD specimen, through thickness notched.

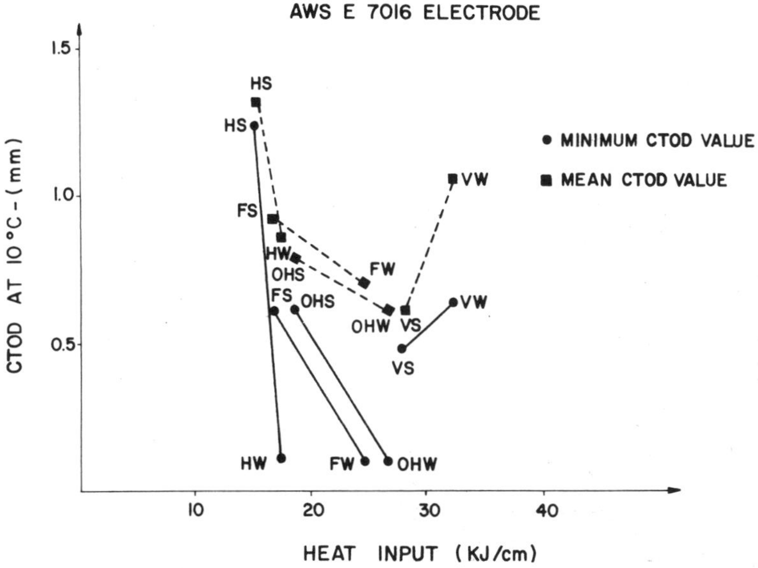

Figure 2 - Influence of heat input, welding position and technique on CTOD of AWS E 7016 weld metals.

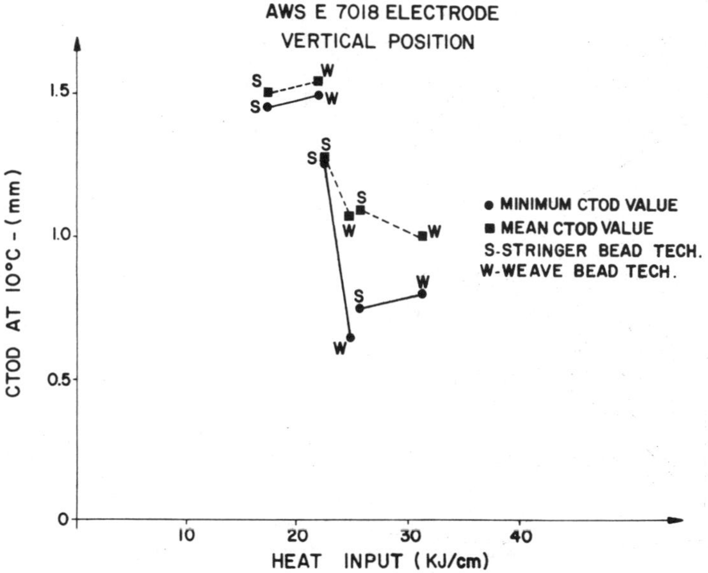

Figure 3 - Influence of heat input and welding technique on CTOD of AWS E 7018 weld metals performed in the vert. position.

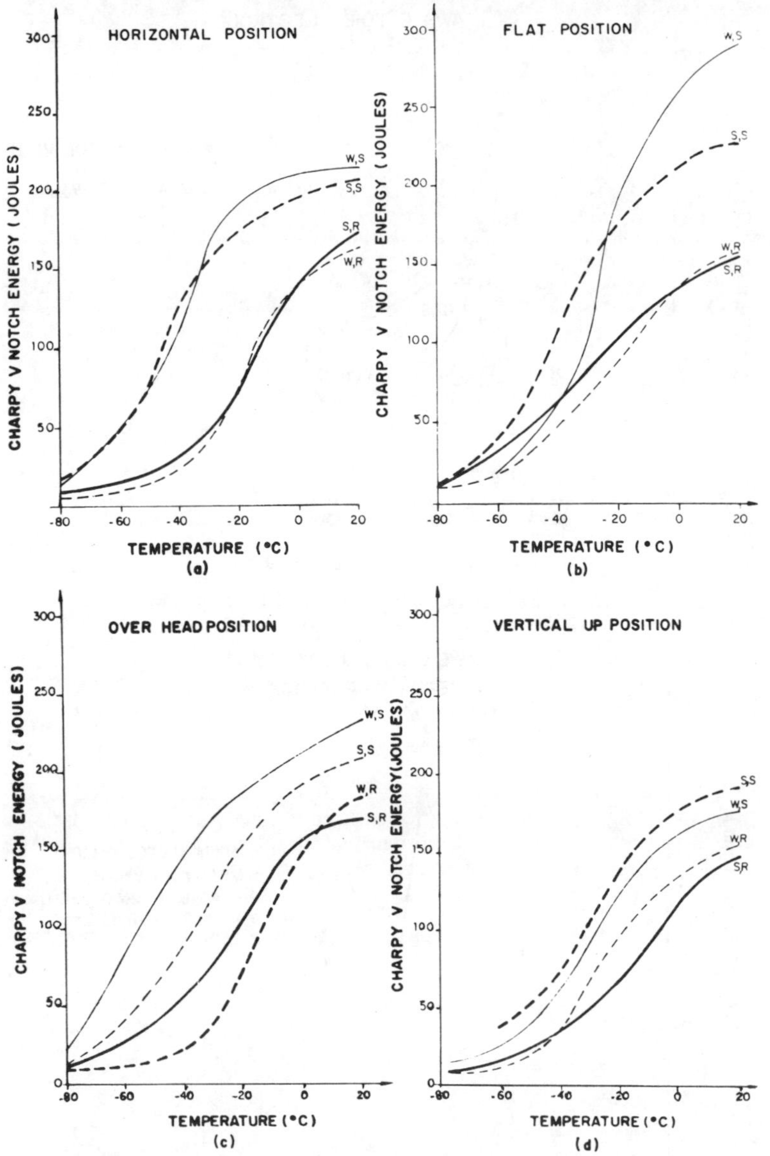

Figure 4 - Influence of welding position and technique on the Charpy trans. temp. curves of the 7016 welds. (a) horiz. (b) flat (c) over head (d) vertical up position. In each curve the first letter denotes the welding technique and the second the notch location.

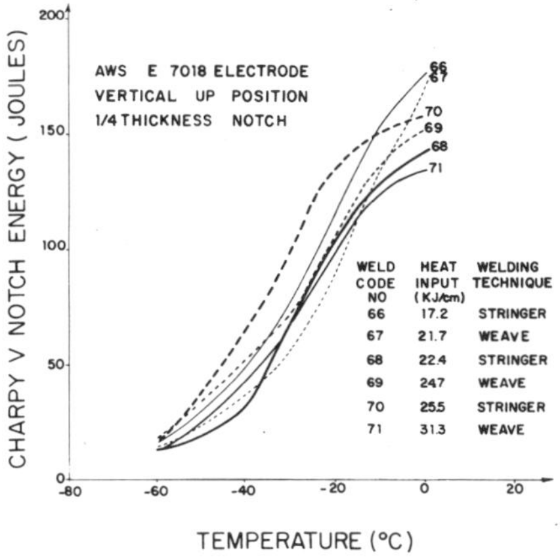

Figure 5 - Influence of heat input and welding technique on the Charpy transition temperature curves of AWS E 7018 weld metals performed in the vertical position.

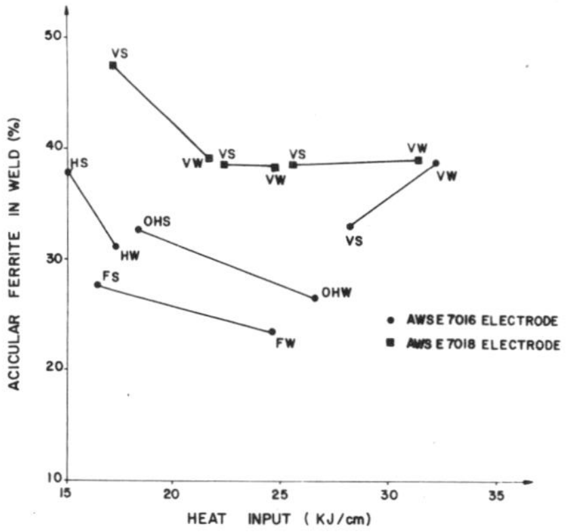

Figure 6 - Acicular ferrite content in the weld joint versus welding heat input for the AWS E 7016 and 7018 weld metals.

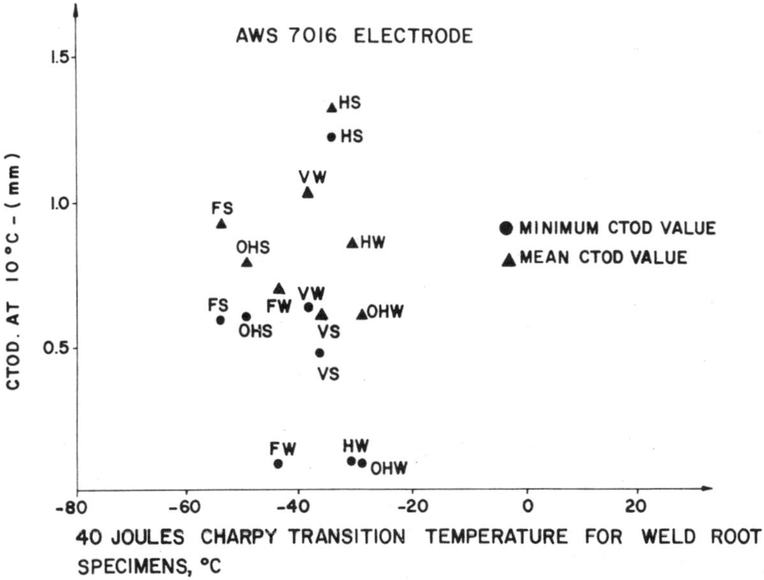

Figure 7-CTOD at 10 °C versus 40 Joules Charpy transition temperature of root specimens from the AWS E 7016 weld metals.

FRACTURE PREVENTION IN OFFSHORE PLATFORMS

A. S. P. FRAGOMENI*

The user's view of the "fitness for purpose" approach in the evaluation of the severity of weld defects is presented. Also analysed is its relation to the design, construction, in-service inspection and underwater repair of offshore platforms. It concludes that Fracture Mechanics should not be used to justify poor workmanship in the fabrication of offshore structures.

INTRODUCTION

The increase in the consumption of oil and natural gas during the last decade, together with the end of a long period of stable oil prices, has caused a great deal of exploratory work to be performed, particularly by the oil importing nations.

The increase in the exploration activities has led to significant new discoveries, notably along the continental shelf. It has been estimated that within this decade 30% of the "black gold" will be produced from offshore fields.

In the early seventies the first big steel jacket structure for offshore production was commissioned in the North Sea. Many other qualified as "giant", "massive", etc., have been installed afterwards. In the Gulf of Mexico, a monster like the Cognac Platform, standing 300 m high, is now on stream. In Brazil, after Campos Basin discovery, such enormous structures also appeared. The Garoupa jacket, installed in 1981, was at its time the biggest steel structure ever built in Latin America. In 1982 came Enchova, which is twice as big as Garoupa.

Water depths in Campos vary around the 120 meter mark and production capacities of the platforms are between 10.000 and 30.000 m^3/day of stabilized crude oil. Up to 1985 there will be 8 platforms installed, with about 120 modules in place and 8 drilling packages, representing a total fabrication and equipment weight of over 230.000 tonnes.

The figures contribute to justify the strict requirements for safety and

* Petrobrás, Brazil

realiability that are demanded from offshore installations. Needless to say that the loss of income caused by a shutdown in offshore installations is extremely high. The importance of the safety requirements for the people involved in the operation of platforms must be emphasized, since each one may accommodate 100 to 150 men.

Reasons of both safety and economy have led the Oil Companies to order the highest possible level of quality for the offshore structures. The consequences of failures are so harsh as to justify the search for perfection in the fabrication of those structures.

THE CONVENTIONAL QUALITY

The traditional quality concept for welded structures is based on acceptance criteria derived from "good workmanship", i.e., a quality level which can be readily achieved, provided good standard of workmanship is maintained throughout the manufacturing process.

Based on such concept, the acceptable defect level is established on arbitrary basis and cannot be rationally related to the defect level that could be allowed as a function of the purpose to which the structure is designed.

Many present design codes are based on the assumption that the structure is defect free. Such codes base their acceptance criteria in the radiographic technique which is more adequate to detect volumetric defects. Such defects are not important as far as fatigue and brittle fracture are concerned. The dangerous planar defect may often go undetected in the radiography, although the codes require their elimination irrespective of their dimensions, position and stress levels.

Very often, in trying to repair an inocuous volumetric defect we may introduce a much grave defect that will not be detected by the radiographic technique.

Fortunately, for the prevailing service conditions of those structures, the corresponding stress levels in their members and the type of material that have been used in their fabrication have very seldom conducted to critical situations, despite the use of the arbitrary criteria for defects acceptance.

It takes us to the conclusion that those sort of structures were more than adequate for the purpose for which they were designed, and then, more expensive than they should be. The application of the traditional quality concept may add something like 10% or more to direct construction costs without any significant increase to safety.

THE DEEP WATER OFFSHORE PLATFORMS

The general requirements for an offshore platform are similar to any other industrial structure. It must be (1) capable of fulfilling its intended purpose, (2) structurally adequate for both operational and environmental loading, (3) practical to construct and (4) cost-effective, providing a satisfactory return on the investment.

The design of platforms for deep water brought more severe problems as compared to shallow water platforms, mainly due to increased loading. The deep water platform is more slender and, therefore, more susceptible to stress amplification due to wave dynamics and fatigue.

In order to produce cost-effective structures, it is usually necessary to use steel with improved yield strength.

In the design of such platforms it is not possible to avoid the relatively high stress concentrations since they are inherent to the intersections (nodes) of tubular member fabricated by welding.

In such conditions the presence of planar defects assumes an increased importance. It is then necessary to use NDT techniques capable to detect with confidence the presence of this type of discontinuity.

The difficult geometry of a node makes it impossible to use the radiographic technique to inspect the joint. The extreme severity of a planar defect also makes it unreliable to use such a technique that will only detect volumetric defects.

The ultrasonic technique has proved to be the most appropriate in this case and with the widespread use of ultrasonic inspection, the old concept of defect free structure could not be further applied. It became reasonable, therefore, to design with a limiting defect size in mind.

THE FITNESS FOR PURPOSE CRITERIA

As every welded structure contains defects, it became important to evaluate their severity. In opposition to the arbitrary criteria for the acceptance of defects based on "good workmanship", a more rational approach has been developed based on "fitness for purpose" i.e., the defect is evaluated as a function of its influence over the performance of the structure in service.

Any qualified engineer understands the difference, for example, between the severity of a defect present on an atmospheric pipe for water drainage and the severity of a similar defect standing on a "hot spot" of a node in an offshore platform.

There is no question that a rational criteria based on fitness for purpose will bring the benefit of more reliable and safe structures and, in many cases, less expensive ones.

STRESS, TOUGHNESS AND DEFECT SIZE

The recent development of Fracture Mechanics has shown that three factors (Material Toughness, Defect Size, Stress Level) can be interrelated to predict the susceptibility of a welded structure to brittle fracture. By knowing the critical value of notch toughness (K_{Ic}), for a given steel of a particular thickness and at a specific temperature and loading rate, the designer can determine defect sizes that can be tolerated in structural members for a given design stress level.

Fracture Mechanics brought the understanding of the variables that influence the two most important "limit states" that ought to be considered in the design of an offshore platform: Brittle Fracture and Fatigue.

In order to avoid the possibility of Brittle Fracture in Offshore Platforms, the Oil Companies have adopted conservative measures, acting with emphasis, at the same time, over the three mentioned variables.

a) Notch Toughness

Select high toughness steel with impact energy charpy around 6,2 kgm, at -10°C and other improvements aiming at better resistance to Brittle Fracture. The quality of the welding consumables has also been improved.

b) Stress Level

Improve the quality of the structural design, using computer and finite element methods aiming at controlling the stress level applied to each member. Stress relief has also been specified in some cases for the reduction of the residual stresses.

c) Defect Size

Try to avoid the presence of defects by means of inspecting the steel plates, by qualifying the welding procedures and weldors and, finally, by applying adequate techniques to inspect the welded joints.

THE NECESSARY QUALITY

From the purely economic point of view, one could argue that it was not necessary to act over the three above mentioned conditions since if we could entirely control one of them, the importance of the others would decrease.

But, as previously mentioned, the most safe and reliable structure is necessary, and the Oil Companies have decided to put emphasis on all three points simultaneously.

It may be said that it is a waste of money. To use less expensive base material or consumables has been proposed, and some less expensive heat treatment. Possibly the design could be less conservative, with economy in material and fabrication costs. Finally, reducing stringency in the fabrication quality, would allow a lower standard for the acceptance of the defects.

But, in the case of Offshore Platforms none of these propositions have been adopted. The prevailing trend is just the opposite. The tendency is to select better materials, to improve the design and to increase the quality in the fabrication.

This behaviour stems from the fact that we usually face a "Probabilistic Phenomenon". The occurrence of Brittle Fracture in a platform is a function of the probability of the existence of a defect (not found during the inspection or grown afterwards) laying in a low toughness region which is subject to high stresses. The conservative position adopted is also bolstered by the possibility of fatigue or corrosion-fatigue. In particular, a great deal of attention is given to fatigue when sea conditions are similar to those occurring in Campos Basis or North Sea where sea states are virtually continuously stormy, with calm sea states being a rarity. In such conditions, every defect that has been left in a structure must be carefully monitored during the whole life of the structure.

The underwater inspection of deep water platforms is carried out by saturation diving which is a very expensive technique. Usually it is much safer and cheaper to perform repair during fabrication, than to leave a defect that may grow by fatigue and demand either underwater repair or constant and costly inspection. The fatigue tests of full size tubular joints carried out by J.G. Bouwkamp (1) have shown that weld defects significantly reduced the fatigue life of the joints. A reduction of 50% was observed. He also showed that completely repaired joints exhibited similar fatigue resistance as correctly fabricated joints. These very simple and straightforward conclusions justify the rigor with the quality during fabrication.

Another difficulty in the use of fracture mechanics approach is the uncertainty in the precise determination of the stresses acting over the tubular joints with complex geometries, and very often with added complications caused by the presence of ring stiffners.

Considering the above mentioned aspects we can understand the requirement for additional precautions taken by the Oil Companies before adopting fracture mechanics arguments. This approach should not be used in any case to justify acceptance of poor workmanship, since it may bring future situations that can override the benefits achieved by its application.

CONCLUSIONS

The application of Fracture Mechanics concepts to Offshore Installations has already been justified in many cases where defects have been detected. It has proved to be very useful to evaluate "engineering judgement", although it should be used with caution as it is very sensitive to input data.

The operators viewpoint is that Fracture Mechanics should be developed further to be able to be considered as a design tool. Meanwhile, all effort should be made to improve the quality of the structures for offshore platforms. As the target is achieving the lowest probability of failure, it is considered that a high degree of redundancy is a very effective safety item.

The operators strongly feel that they must participate in every decision before applying the fitness for purpose approach. It is not accepted from this application bias toward the economy in fabrication costs, leaving to the Operator the increased necessity for underwater inspection and less reliable structures. In cases when such approach is justified, a clear procedure must be previously established in order to identify precisely the responsibilities involved and to produce adequate documentation to be used as reference for future in-service inspections.

As a final conclusion I would like to quote the points raised by API-RP-2X (1980), item 3.3, which summarizes the above discussion:

"There may be cases where accepting some loss in performance is justified by the economics of expensive repair versus marginal improvement, or the risk that an attempted repair (made under less favorable conditions than the original weld), will lead to undetected flaws greater than the original. Thus, there is nothing inconsistent with an Operator purchasing a platform to the more restrictive workmanship quidelines, than subsequently choosing to analyze post-acceptance or in-service flaws on a fitness for purpose basis. However, it is not intended that this approach be used to relieve the fabricator from delivering the contracted level of quality, or to excuse poor performance after the fact."

REFERENCES

1. Bouwkamp, J. G., 1978, J. Pet. Tech., 649.

2. Fragomeni, A. S. P., 1977, B. Téc. PETROBRÁS, 249.

FATIGUE AND CORROSION-FATIGUE ON STEEL WIRES FOR PRESTRESSING CONCRETE.

V.Sánchez-Gálvez*, A. Valiente* and M.Elices*

Fatigue crack growth in steel wires for prestressing concrete has been measured. Experiments have been carried out on precracked wires of 7 mm. diameter with crack depths ranging from 1.5 to 3.5 mm. Fatigue tests have been performed both in air and in sea water with different frequencies and waveforms. Within the stress intensity range considered, the crack propagation results seem to show a negligible influence of frequency, but a detectable effect of wave form.

INTRODUCTION

Prestressed concrete is progressively more utilised for building structures subjected to more severe conditions, as higher loads and aggresive environments. That is the case for example of the off-shore concrete structures, in which a cyclic loading combined with a sea water environment may be acting on the material.

For such applications, the knowledge of the fatigue and corrosion fatigue behaviour of the different constitutive materials is of prime importance for a safe design of the structure. Despite the absence of serious problems in the past, a considerable research effort has been carried out on the fatigue behaviour of steel and concrete.

But the existing data are mainly concerned with reinforcing bars and plain concrete, and very little information is available about the fatigue behaviour of prestressing steels in an aggressive environment.

Published data on this subject are limited due to the general assumption that the stress ranges in the tendons usually fall below the values regarded as significant for fatigue according to present rules (see for instance Taylor and Sharp (1) and Price et al (2)) provided that the structure is designed to be uncracked for its service load.

If, for instance, a few cycles of load in extreme storm cause cracking of concrete, the cracks are assumed to be closed

*Departamento de Física y Física de Materiales.E.T.S. Ing. Caminos.Madrid.Spain

afterwards by the prestressing force. In many cases this may not be true and the cracks opened in the concrete could magnify locally the stress oscilations in the tendons and allow the aggresive environment to attain the tendons.

On the other hand, axial fatigue data of prestressing steels are based on the classical S-N curves without adequately distinguishing between crack initiation and crack propagation. Recent requirements, in particular the Model-Code (3) issued by CEB(Comité Euro-International du Béton), still specifies for this material an endurance limit from classical S-N tests. A recent paper by the authors presented the first published results of fatigue crack propagation in steel prestressing wires. (Sánchez-Gálvez et al.(4)) based on the Fracture Mechanics approach.

The purpose of this paper is to complement the referred one taking into account the influence of the environment on the fatigue crack growth on prestressing steel wires. The Fracture Mechanics approach will be used to determine crack growth rate for different stress ranges and crack sizes and also compare results for different frequencies, waveforms and environments.

EXPERIMENT

Experimental Method

The determination of fatigue crack growth rate in prestressing steel wires requires to solve previously two important difficulties. The first one is the need of possessing a K_I formula for a cylindrical bar in tension with an elliptical crack in the surface. That is the geometry found experimentally for fatigue cracks in prestressing steel wires, as can be seen in figure 1. This problem has been solved previously by Valiente (5) who, from a finite element calculation, obtained the following expression for the K_I as a mean value along the crack tip:

$$K_I = \sigma\sqrt{\pi a}\{0.473-3.286(\frac{a}{D})+14.797(\frac{a}{D})^2\}^{1/2}\{(\frac{a}{D})-(\frac{a}{D})^2\}^{-1/4} \quad (1)$$

$$\text{or } K_I = \sigma\sqrt{\pi a}\; M(\frac{a}{D}) \quad (2)$$

where a is the crack depth, D the diameter of the wire and σ the remote applied stress.

The stress intensity factor defined by equation (1) has been shown to be a suitable fracture parameter for cold drawn prestressing steel wires. The critical value of that parameter was found to be independent on flaw size, unless for a/D higher than 0.1. This critical value may thus be considered as a fracture toughness parameter characterizing 7 mm. diameter steel wires and so will be quoted as K_c hereafter.

The second difficulty arises from the continuous monitoring of the crack depth because of the geometry under consideration and the aqueous solution where the wire is immersed. In this case it is not possible to obtain the crack depth from a visual inspection of the specimen surface. On the other hand the potential drop method is not appropriate, since the electrochemical conditions of the environment may be affected by the electrical current applied. Finally, this difficulty has been solved by using the compliance method as described below.

First of all the compliance of the specimen has been determined as a function of crack depth by testing in tension several precracked samples with different crack depths. A 12.5mm. gauge length extensometer provides enough accuracy to achieve a stiffness vs. crack depth calibration curve, as shown in figure 2.

In fatigue and corrosion-fatigue tests, a 12.5 mm. gauge length dynamic extensometer attached to the precracked sample provides a continuous record of the compliance of the samples. The immersion of the extensometer in the solution, in corrosion-fatigue tests has been avoided by using a 12 mm. diameter flexible tube which keeps the crack immersed in the solution by circulating it with a peristaltic pump. The arrangement is described in figure 3. This experimental method only enables testing at the free corrosion potential of the steel, which on the other hand is the more frequently used in the corrosion fatigue data existing in the literature for other steels. A data acquisition system has been used to collect and compute compliance data provided by the extensometer and from the calibration curve to plot the curves crack depth vs.No.of cycles.

Material tested

The steel used for testing is a commercial 7 mm. diameter prestressing steel wire. Its chemical composition and mechanical properties are included in Table 1.

The steel was patented by cooling from the austenitic condition in a molten lead bath to produce fine pearlite, after which it was cold drawn in six passes to achieve an overall reduction of about 66%. The drawn wires were stress-relieved by normal practice involving exposure at about 400°C for a few seconds.

Specimens used were precracked, for which a starter notch, some 1 mm deep was introduced with a jewellers file and then fatigue precracked to produce defects of about 1.5 mm. when the fatigue and corrosion fatigue crack growth measurements started.

TABLE 1 - Composition and mechanical properties of the steel

%C	%Mn	%Si	%P	%S	0.2%σ_{ps} MPa	σ_u MPa	e* %	K_c $MPam^{1/2}$
0.78	0.67	0.21	0.012	0.022	1400	1620	6.5	93.5

* % elongation at maximum load according to ISO TC17/SC16/1977

Tests performed

Steel wires have been subjected to axial fatigue both in air and in artificial sea water according to ASTM Standard (6). Load amplitude and frequency have been held constant automatically during the test. Three waveforms have been studied: sinusoidal, triangular and square.

The frequency was varied from 0.07 Hz to 8 Hz. in corrosion fatigue tests and from 0.2 to 20 Hz. in fatigue tests in air. The stress range was varied from 250 to 610 MPa, while the R ratio was held constant below 0.1 in corrosion fatigue tests and varied from 0.1 to 0.67 in fatigue tests in air.

All tests have been performed at 20±1°C of temperature. The relative humidity of air was 50±5%. In corrosion fatigue tests, artificial sea water was used (6), the pH measured was 8 and the free corrosion potential about -740 mV with respect to the s.c.e.

RESULTS AND DISCUSSION

From the curves crack depth vs. number of cycles plotted by the system, a numerical differentiation method has been applied to obtain the crack growth rates da/dN at different crack depths. Since the stress range $\Delta\sigma$ was held constant for each test, the stress intensity range ΔK can be calculated for each one of these crack depths from equation (2):

$$\Delta K = \Delta\sigma\sqrt{\pi a} \;\; M\left(\frac{a}{D}\right) \qquad (3)$$

Then, it is possible to plot log (da/dN) vs. log. (ΔK) and check if there exists a linear relationship according to the Paris law. Figure 4 shows the experimental results of crack growth rate vs. stress intensity range for fatigue tests in air and different load amplitudes. As can be seen a relationship of the Paris form is able to describe fatigue crack growth in prestressing cold drawn steel wires, independently of the stress range and crack depth. It can be seen also that fatigue crack growth in prestressing steel wires is independent of waveform, frequency and stress ratio R within the intervals used in the tests. Finally, the figure shows the best fit by a straight line in the log. log. plot leading to the following crack growth law:

$$\frac{da}{dN} = 11 \times 10^{-12} \, (\Delta K)^{2.3} \qquad (4)$$

where a is in m. and ΔK in $MPam^{1/2}$.

Figures 5,6 and 7 illustrate the experimental results for corrosion fatigue tests in sea water obtained with sinusoidal, triangular and square waves respectively. The figures show also the two straight lines parallel to that described by equation (4) in between which 95% of the experimental results obtained in fatigue in air are encountered. As can be seen, the corrosion fatigue crack growth in sea water for prestressing steel wires seems to be independent on frequency, although some dependency on waveform is found.

With sinusoidal waves, the crack growth rate is higher in sea water than in air, with a factor ranging between 7 and 2 depending on the ΔK applied. On the other hand, the results obtained with square waves in sea water lie within the scatter band of fatigue results in air. With triangular waves, the results are intermediate between the sinusoidal and square waves, and in this case the frequency seems to affect the results in the sense of increase the crack growth rate for the lower frequencies.

CONCLUSIONS AND FUTURE WORK

The study of corrosion-fatigue in prestressing steels is approaching the stage where Fracture Mechanics can be used to obtain a more quantitative description of the phenomenon.

1.- Experimental results of axial fatigue crack growth in 7 mm. diameter cold drawn steel wires in artificial sea water have been obtained for the first time, based upon Fracture Mechanics concepts:

a.- Crack growth fits Paris law within a wide range of ΔK values (from 30 to 100 $MPam^{1/2}$).

b.- The influence of frequency, in this interval, is almost negligible.

c.- Regarding wave form, small trends may be inferred: Sinusoidal waves induce higher crack growth rates than triangular ones. Square wave results are similar to those in air.

2.- Work on crack initiation is in progress in spite of difficulties in motoring small crack growth. It is expected that frequency, waveform as well as stress-ratio, will play an important role at ΔK values lower than 20 $MPam^{1/2}$, as figure 6 is suggesting.

SYMBOLS USED

D = wire diameter

e = elongation at maximum load

M = a dimensional factor.

REFERENCES

1. Taylor,M.P.J., and Sharp,J.V., 1978, The Structural Engineer 56A, 69

2. Price,W.I.J., Tricklebank,A.H., and Hambly,E.C. 1982, "Fatigue Considerations in the Design of Concrete Offshore Structures" IABSE Int. Colloq. on Fatigue Proceedings, Lausanne, Switzerland

3. CEB-FIP, 1978 "Model Code for Concrete Structures". Bulletin d'Information n°124/125-F. Paris France

4. Sánchez-Gálvez, V., Elices,M. and Valiente,A., 1982 "Fatigue crack propagation in steel prestressing wires" IABSE Int. Colloq. on Fatigue Proceedings, Lausanne, Switzerland.

5. Valiente,A., 1980 "Criterios de fractura para alambres" Ph.D.Thesis. Universidad Politécnica de Madrid. Spain.

6. ASTM, 1980, "Standard Specification for Substitute Ocean Water" ASTM D1141-75.

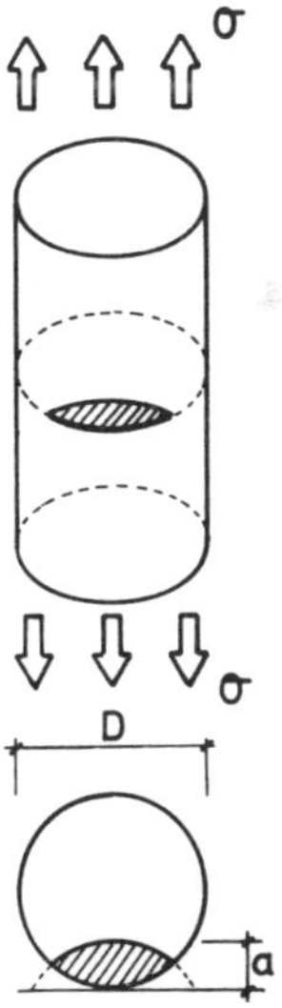

Figure 1 Specimen geometry

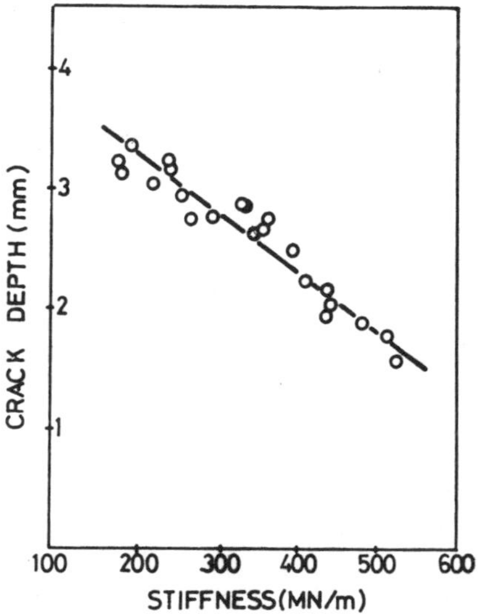

Figure 2 Stiffness vs. crack depth calibration curve

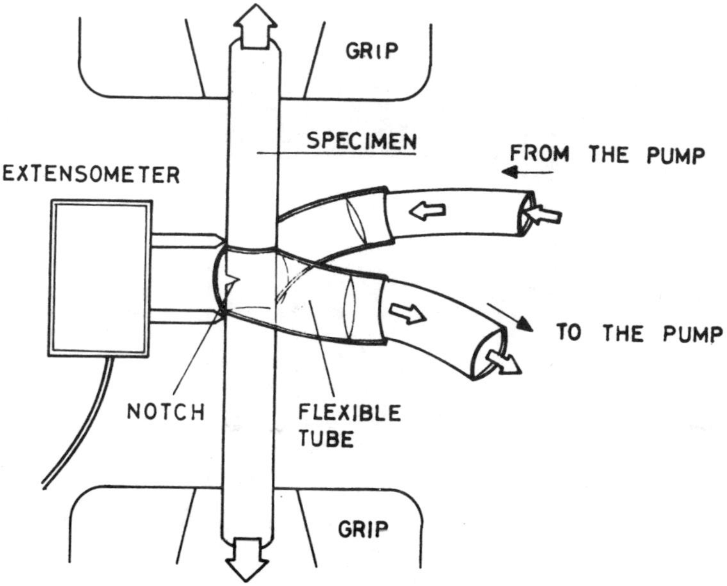

Figure 3 Test arrangement

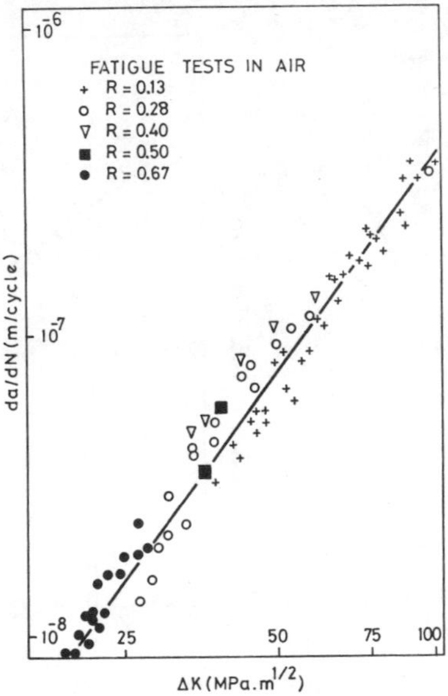

Figure 4 Crack growth rate vs. stress intensity range for fatigue tests in air.

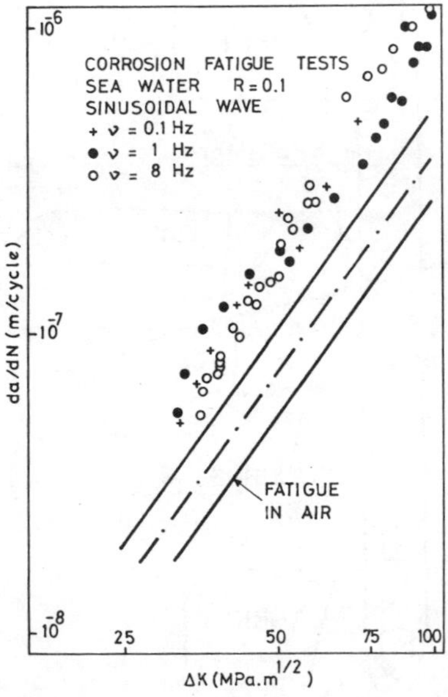

Figure 5 Crack growth rate vs. stress intensity range for corrosion fatigue tests in sea water. Sinusoidal wave.

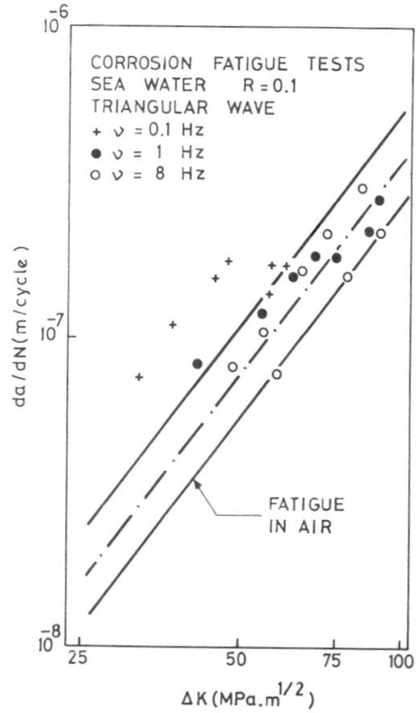

Figure 6 Crack growth rate vs. stress intensity range for corrosion fatigue tests in sea water. Triangular wave.

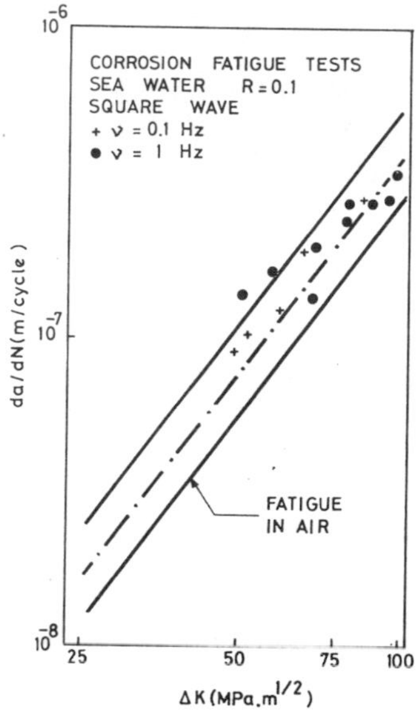

Figure 7 Crack growth rate vs. stress intensity range for corrosion fatigue tests in sea water. Square wave.

USE OF PHOTOELASTICITY IN FRACTURE MECHANICS

J.L.F.Freire* and H.Arai*

A photoelastic method to determine stress intensity factors in plane mixed-mode problems is presented and applied to cracks in finite width bars subjected to tension and to cracklike defects near joints of orthogonal and angular (45°) welded plates subjected to tension and bending.

INTRODUCTION

Fracture Mechanics is known today to be a powerful approach to be used in the design of structures to avoid brittle fracture, fatigue or any other type of failure which depends on crack propagation. For example, the rate of growth of a fatigue crack from an initial cracklike defect in a welded joint and the possibility of its propagation as a brittle fracture can be predicted by Fracture Mechanics if the stress intensity factor (SIF) range and its maximum value can be defined. Therefore, the determination of theoretical SIF for this and other complex geometries becomes a very important subject. Due to its well--known advantages of being a whole field technique, modelling complex geometries and being suitable for three-dimensional application, Photoelasticity may be considered as a very interesting technique for SIF determination.

In this paper, the use of Photoelasticity to determine SIF in mixed-mode problems is discussed and a procedure to determine K_I and K_{II} stress intensity factors for opening modes I and II respectively, is presented with basis on an overdeterministic method previously proposed by Sanford and Dally (1). The developed method is shown to be well behaved in the determination of SIF for cracks relatively close to free boundaries, through its application to the problem of orthogonal and angular (45°) flaws in finite width bars. Finally, the method has been applied to show that SIF related to cracklike defects near welded plates can be determined and compared with SIF of simpler configurations.

* Department of Mechanical Engineering, Catholic University of Rio de Janeiro - PUC/RJ.

EXTRACTION OF STRESS INTENSITY FACTORS FROM PHOTOELASTICITY

Photoelastic methods used in the extraction of SIF for plane problems make use of equations 1 below, based on the Westergaard solution (2), where the term σ_{ox} was included by Irwin (3) to take into account the influence of the far, non-singular, stress field. The notation used in these equations is presented in Figure 1.

$$\begin{aligned}
\sigma_x &= \frac{1}{\sqrt{2\pi r}}\left[K_I \cos\frac{\theta}{2}\left(1-\sin\frac{\theta}{2}\sin\frac{3\theta}{2}\right) - K_{II}\sin\frac{\theta}{2}\left(2+\cos\frac{\theta}{2}\cos\frac{3\theta}{2}\right)\right] - \sigma_{ox} \\
\sigma_y &= \frac{1}{\sqrt{2\pi r}}\left[K_I \cos\frac{\theta}{2}\left(1+\sin\frac{\theta}{2}\sin\frac{3\theta}{2}\right) + K_{II}\sin\frac{\theta}{2}\cos\frac{\theta}{2}\cos\frac{3\theta}{2}\right] \qquad (1) \\
\sigma_{xy} &= \frac{1}{\sqrt{2\pi r}}\left[K_I \sin\frac{\theta}{2}\cos\frac{\theta}{2}\cos\frac{3\theta}{2} + K_{II}\cos\frac{\theta}{2}\left(1-\sin\frac{\theta}{2}\sin\frac{3\theta}{2}\right)\right]
\end{aligned}$$

By employing the basic photoelastic relationship expressed in equation 2, where N is the isochromatic fringe order at the considered point, f is the calibration fringe value, and t is the thickness of the analysed model at that point; recalling that the maximum in-plane shear stress in the point is given by equation 3,

$$\tau_{max} = \frac{N\,f}{2\,t} \qquad (2)$$

$$\tau_{max}^2 = \frac{1}{2}\left[(\sigma_x - \sigma_y)^2 + 4\,\tau_{xy}^2\right] \qquad (3)$$

equation 4 may be obtained by relating the distribution of isochromatic fringe orders in the neighborhood of the tip of the crack to the SIF for the geometry and loading conditions subjected to analysis.

$$\left(\frac{N\,f}{t}\right)^2 = \frac{1}{2\pi r}\left[(K_I \sin\theta + 2\,K_{II}\cos\theta)^2 + (K_{II}\sin\theta)^2\right] + \\ + \frac{2\,\sigma_{ox}}{\sqrt{2\pi r}}\sin\frac{\theta}{2}\left[K_I \sin\theta(1+2\cos\theta) + K_{II}(1+2\cos^2\theta+\cos\theta)\right] + \sigma_{ox}^2 \qquad (4)$$

Several methods have been proposed for the solution of equation 4. Solutions to account for far field non-singular stresses, based on the substitution of the last two terms of the right hand side of equation 4 by a power series were proposed by Smith and Smith (4), Chia and Du (5), Watanabe et al (6) and Watanabe et al (7). A very efficient overdeterministic method for the solution of equation 4 in terms of K_I, K_{II} and σ_{ox} was developed by Sanford and Dally (1), who employed the Newton--Raphson and the least-square techniques. Computer plotted isochromatic fringe distributions and their comparison with the experimental distributions were presented by Sanford and Chona (8), and may be used as a powerful qualitative criterion of acceptance of determined multi-parameter solutions of equation 4 (8).

The method used in this paper is fully presented by Arai (9) and follows the approach by Sanford and Dally (1), except for the allowance of the point by point variation of σ_{ox}. For this purpose, a complete polynomial in x and y is used instead of σ_{ox}, as expressed below in polar coordinates

$$\sigma_{ox} = \sum_{i=0}^{M} \sum_{j=0}^{i} B_{ij} r^{i} (\sin\theta)^{i-j} (\cos\theta)^{i} \qquad (5)$$

where B_{ij} are coefficients to be determined in conjunction with K_I and K_{II} through the use of the Newton-Raphson and least square techniques (9). The choice of M, degree of the polynomial, is not trivial and depends on the geometry and loading conditions of the problem and on the distance between the tip of the crack and a free surface or any other disturbance of the singular stress field expressed by equations 1. To evaluate qualitatively the correctness of this choice, experimental and computer plotted isochromatic fringe distributions may be compared. For this purpose, a computer program was written (9) to determine K_I, K_{II} and B_{ij} and then to plot the calculated isochromatic distributions. Point by point input and output fringe orders are also compared as a measure of the accuracy of the determined solution.

APPLICATION EXAMPLES

Cracks in Finite Width Bars

The objectives of this application example were to compare the experimentally determined SIF for cracks in finite width straight bars subjected to tension with results presented in the literature, and to verify the behavior of the applied method of SIF extraction in problems with high influence of near free boundaries. Eight photoelastic models, as shown in Figure 1, were constructed in a milling machine from polycarbonate sheets (PSM-1, Photoelastic Inc.) 6.35 mm thick. Artificial orthogonal and angular (45°) cracks were introduced by a 0.5 mm thickness circular saw with a 30° sharpened cutting border as proposed by Schroedl and Smith (10). Photoelastic data were collected for at least 65 points for each model in a polariscope with a 10 × field magnification. The data region was limited by two concentric circles with radii 1.0 and 15 mm centered in the tip of the artificial flaw, although most data points were collected inside a circle of radius 6.0 mm. The number of data points D collected for each model, as well as the degree of the polynomial M which best adjusted experimental and plotted fringe distributions are given in Figure 1.

The determined values of K_I and K_{II} were plotted in Figure 2 and may be compared with the photoelastic results of Smith and Smith (4) and with Wilson's results for slanted edge cracks (4). A good comparison involving K_I in both crack geometries may be noticed in Figure 2, but the same cannot be said of the K_{II} values, although the same weak tendency of their variation with a/w was confirmed. The influence of free boundaries in the singular stress field near the crack tip may be noticed through the highly distorted isochromatic fringe distribution presented in Figure 3 for the a/w = 0.8 model, as compared with the low distorted pattern presented in the same Figure for the a/w = 0.5 model. Two computer plotted outputs for model a/w = 0.8 are presented in Figure 4 to show the degree of adjustment of the photoelastic fringe distribution that can be achieved if the polynomial of equation 5 is used in the place of σ_{ox} and M is chosen through the best comparison with the experimental pattern.

Application to Welded Joints

As a design application of the method previously discussed photoelastic models were built to determinate SIF for cracks in orthogonal and angular (45°) fillet welded joints. Although fillet welded joints have been widely used for many metal structures, little information regarding theoretical SIF for the presence of cracks in these joints has been presented in the literature. This prevents the designer from using the fracture mechanics approach to verify quantitatively the safety of welded joints against brittle fracture, and to predict its life if the structure is loaded by varying or cyclic loads, or if it is subjected to environmental embrittlement.

Gurney and Johnston (12) presented a revised analysis of the influence of toe defects over the fatigue strength of transverse non-load-carrying fillet welds (NLCFW) and furnished a number of determinated values of SIF based on finite elements for several geometry variations. Bell et al (13) have recently presented SIF at weld toe defects for NLCFW geometries, and also for T-joint specimens based on finite elements. Although Photoelasticity has been used for the determination of stress concentration factors (14,15) in welded joints, very few authors employed this technique to study welded joint problems with crack like defects. Zachary et al (16) discussed the problem of non--penetrating defects in butt welds to predict their largest acceptable length. A very useful picture of photoelastic patterns for the qualitative assessment of the severity of non-penetrating welds has been presented by Pompa in (17). In a recent paper, Tsai and Park (18) determinate SIF for fillet welded T-joints by applying a computer assisted photoelastic method which makes use of the Sanford and Dally (1) technique of SIF extraction.

Geometries of the three photoelastic models used in this example, as well as loading conditions, are shown in Figure 5. These models were built in two pieces by hand filing PSM-1 sheets with 6.35 mm thickness. Artificial flaws were milled by means of a circular saw 0.3 mm thick without sharpened cutting borders. After this, the two pieces of the models were cemented with a cyanoacrylate adhesive. Overall geometry and flaw location for these models were subject of a previous report (19) which had the objective of studying stress concentration factors for these types of joints. From this report, it is interesting to observe a picture of the isochromatic fringe distribution (Figure 6) of an uncracked fillet welded T-joint subjected to bending, where one can notice the location of the higher in-plane shear stresses (fringe orders) and their small concentration size as compared to the other specimen dimensions.

Regions for data collection were limited by two concentric circles with radii equal to 1.0 and 5.0 mm to avoid the influence of the very near stress field and of the far non-singular stress field. The number of data points D and the degree M of the polynomial, which gave the best fit between experimental and computer plotted fringe distritubions, are given in Figure 5. The determined SIF were compared with those obtained from simpler geometries in the current literature(4,11), and the results of this comparison are presented in Figure 5 as a correction factor named M_k . This denomination is the same one used by Gurney and Johnston (12) and by Bell et al (13), and it is simply the ratio of the determined K_I for the weld geometry and K_I' determined for the simpler geometric similar case, as given by equation 6 below.

$$K_I = M_k K_I' \qquad (6)$$

It is interesting to notice that, for the cases studied in this paper, M_k was always lower than one. This can be justified by observing that the ratio a/w for the welded geometry used for comparison with the simpler similar case was always lower than the real one, due to the increase of w in the welding region. For the orthogonal T-joint model loaded in tension or bending, the appearance of a small K_{II} factor is justified by the non-symmetry of the geometry. This can be noticed through the distorted and tilted isochromatic fringe loops near the crack in Figure 7.

CONCLUSIONS

A procedure to determine stress intensity factors in plane mixed--mode problems from photoelastic data was presented with basis on Sanford and Dally's (1) overdeterministic approach, where a complete polynomial of degree M was used in the place of σ_{ox} . Through the application examples it was shown that Photoelasticity can furnish reliable stress intensity values which can then be used to predict brittle failure or crack propagation for simple or complex geometries such as cracklike defects in fillet welded joints.

REFERENCES

1. Sanford, R.J. and Dally, J.W., 1979, Eng. Fract. Mech. 11, 621.

2. Westergaard, H.M., 1939, J. Appl. Mech. 6, A 49.

3. Irwin, G.R., 1958, Proc. SESA 16 (1), 93.

4. Smith, D.G. and Smith, C.W., 1972, Eng. Fract. Mech. 4, 357.

5. Chia, Y.C. and Du, J.J., 1982, Proc. JSME - SESA Joint Meeting, 428.

6. Watanabe, K., Yoshioka, S., Miyazaki, M., Kitagawa, H. and Hiranu, Y., 1982, Proc. JSME - SESA Joint Meeting, 422.

7. Watanabe, K., Hirano, Y., Hisada, T. and Kitagawa, H., 1982, Proc. JSME - SESA Joint Meeting, 599.

8. Chona, R. and Sanford, R.J., 1981, Proc. SESA Spring Meeting, 273.

9. Arai, H., "Determinação de Fatores de Intensidade de Tensão para Modos de Abertura I e II Combinados através da Fotoelasticidade", 1983, Master Thesis, Mech. Eng. Dept., Catholic U. of Rio de Janeiro - PUC/RJ.

10. Schroedl, M.A. and Smith, C.W., 1975, Eng. Fract. Mech. 7, 341.

11. Hertzberg, R.W., 1976, "Deformation and Fracture Mechanics of Engineering Materials", John Wiley and Sons.

12. Gurney, T.R. and Johnston, G.O., 1979, Welding Research Int. 9, 43.

13. Bell, R., Kirkhope, J. and Vosikovsky, O., 1983, Proceedings of Ninth Canadian Congress of Applied Mechanics, 379.

14. Norris, C.H., 1945, Welding Research Supplement, 558.

15. Gurney, T.R., 1968, "Fatigue of Welded Structures", Cambridge at the University Press.

16. Burger, C.P., Zachary, L.W. and Riley, W.F., 1975, Exp. Mech. 2, 73.

17. Pompa, L., "Design for Welding", 1958, ASME Handbook Metals Engineering - Processes, 255.

18. Tsai, C.L. and Park, S.K., 1983, Proc. SESA Spring Conference, 16.

19. Freire, J.L.F., "Análise de Tensões em Juntas Tubulares Via Modelos Planos", Mech. Eng. Dept., Catholic U. of Rio de Janeiro - PUC/RJ, Report to CENPES - Petrobrás.

MODELS	a/w	M	D
ORTHOGONAL CRACK	0,512	1	214
	0,600	5	83
	0,688	4	82
	0,811	4	65
45° CRACK	0,503	1	106
	0,600	5	67
	0,707	5	75
	0,808	5	65

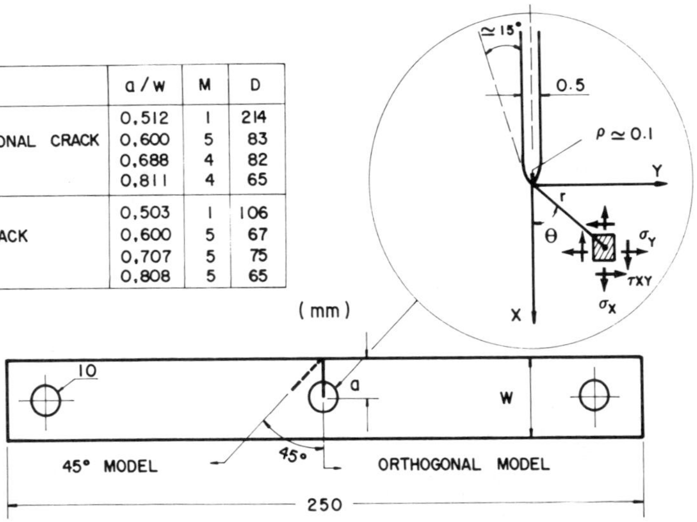

Figure 1 Finite width artificially cracked models

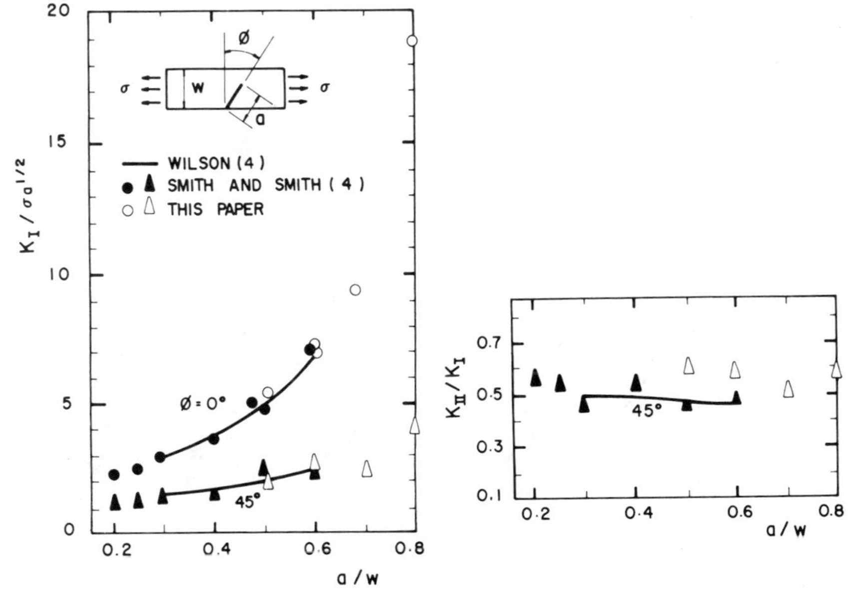

Figure 2 Values of SIF for cracks in finite width models

a/w = 0.8 a/w = 0.5

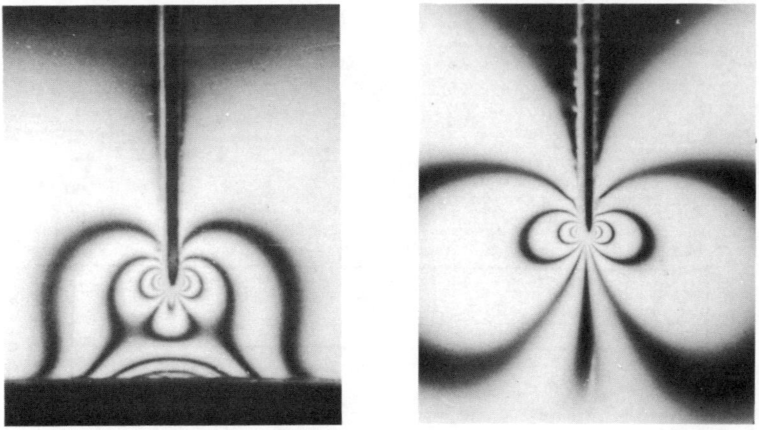

Figure 3 Isochromatic fringe distributions of models a/w = 0.8 and a/w = 0.5

M = 4 M = 0

Figure 4 Final art from computer plotted outputs of model a/w= 0.8 (external load different from the one considered in Fig. 3,a/w = 0.8)

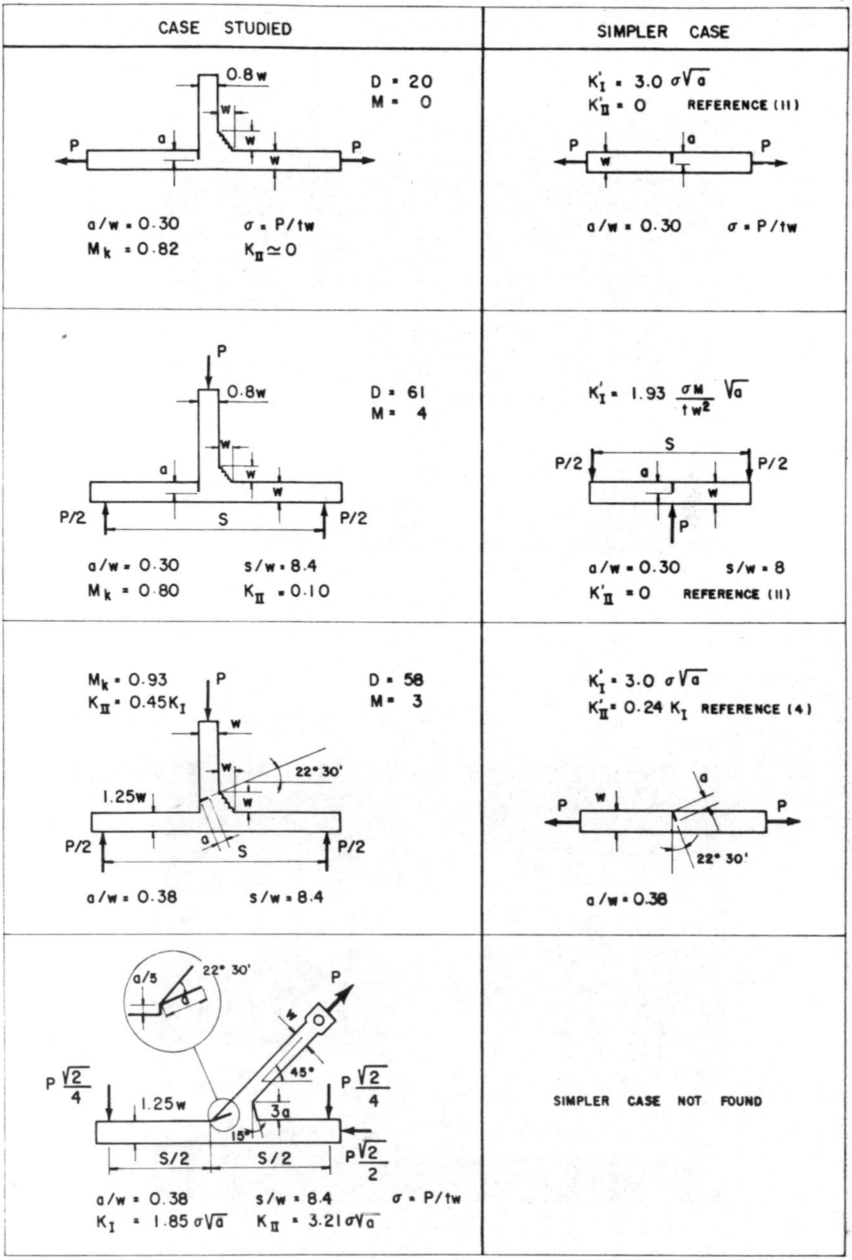

Figure 5 Cracked welded joint models

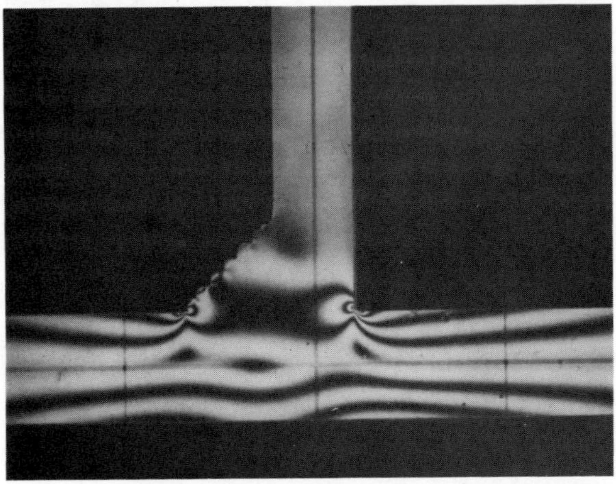

Figure 6 Stress concentration at orthogonal welded joint model under bending

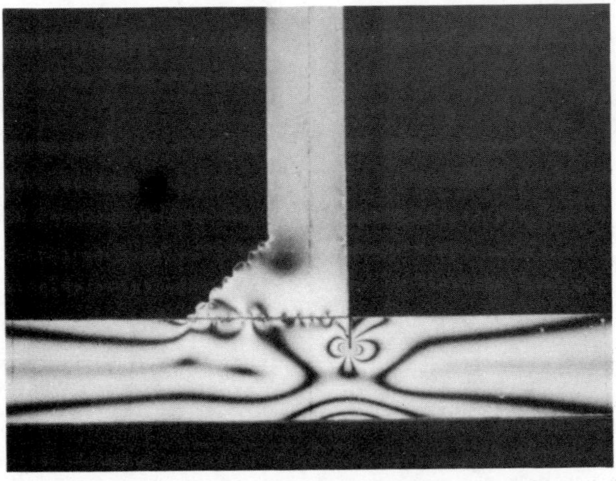

Figure 7 Isochromatics for cracked orthogonal welded joint model under bending

CATHODIC POLARIZATION EFFECTS ON MAGNESIUM CALCIUM DEPOSITS FORMATION AT FATIGUE CRACK ROOTS OF MILD STEEL IN SEA WATER.

G. PHILIPPONNEAU*, S. WIDAWSKI*, M. HABASHI** and J. GALLAND*.

Important ways for corrosion protection are used to increase fatigue lifetime and decrease corrosion rate : one of them is cathodic polarization. Nevertheless, high cathodic current may promote hydrogen embrittlement. On the other hand cathodic current density enhances also local pH at metal surface which permits mineral deposits formation essentially composed of $CaCO_3$ and $Mg(OH)_2$. These deposits may hinder crack closure and hence crack growth rate is decreased.

INTRODUCTION

"OFF-SHORE" plants subjected to sea swell effect and corrosion actions due to sea water are usually protected by cathodic current. Therefore interactions may occur between cyclic stresses and agressive environment. Cathodic protection decreases the corrosion process, but on the other hand, hydrogen diffusion may embrittle steel structure in specific conditions such as cathodic current density or pH values. Under these conditions, initiation of fatigue-corrosion crack is observed and crack growth rate is enhanced.

Fatigue-corrosion is a complex process which depends on many parameters, mechanical and/or electrochemical. PARIS-ERDOGAN relationship [$da/dN = C.(\Delta K)^m$] is not valid and we have to apply other models such as superposition (1) or competition (2). Every model is verified in specific metal-environment couples depending essentially on $\Delta K/K_{Iscc}$ ratio and K_{Ic} value.

---

* Ecole Centrale des Arts et Manufactures, 92290 CHATENAY-MALABRY, FRANCE.
** Centre National de la Recherche Scientifique, 75007 PARIS, FRANCE.

Steel cathodic protection in sea water at potential values $\geqslant$ -980 mV/SCE produces at steel surface calco-magnesium deposits which reduce oxygen adsorption (3) and cathodic current density (4), i.e. hydrogen diffusion (5). When cathodic current interrupts, the deposit decreases, for some time, corrosion rate (6).

In this work, we have studied kinetics of deposit formation and hydrogen permeation flux in synthetic sea water in function of cathodic potential or current, at 5° and 20°C without stirring and at pH $\simeq$ 8. Mechanical properties in tensile tests are performed on cathodically polarized steel to study potential and pH effects.

Fatigue crack growth is measured on mild steel subjected to sea water under different cathodic potential values from the dissolution potential E_D to -1500 mV/SCE. Experimental pH values 4 and 8 are chosen.

After rupture, fatigue cracked surfaces are analysed by E.D.S. apparatus coupled to S.E.M. to measure (Mg/Mg + Ca) ratio in function of the crack length , i.e. in relation with applied ΔK.

EXPERIMENTAL PROCEDURE

Kinetics of deposits formation are measured on normalized mild steel samples (table I) of 3 cm^2 area.

TABLE I - Chemical compositions of mild steel.

C%	S%	P%	Si%	Mn%	Ni%	Cr%	Mo%	Cu%	Sn%	Al%
0.128	0.004	0.004	0.310	1.160	0.025	0.010	0.003	0.030	0.021	0.008

Synthetic seawater is used following ASTMD 1141 recommendations. Sample surfaces are mechanically polished to grade 800 and then cleaned in acetone. To prevent chloride formation in the studied solution, a special cell has been designed. This cell has two compartments separated by sintered glass sheet. It is assumed then that pH value is maintained constant ($\simeq$ 8) during the longest test (80 hours), especially at high applied cathodic potential. Also, to prevent Mg^{++} and Ca^{++} impoverishment, a great cell volume is employed, i.e., about 500 cm^3 of seawater by 1 cm^2 steel surface. Three parameters are studied to evaluate deposit formation kinetics :

a) cathodic polarization time (0 to 80 hours) at a constant current density 0.1 $mA.cm^{-2}$ ($\simeq$1050 mV/SCE) and at 20°C.

b) cathodic polarization potential (-900 to -1100 mV/SCE) at 5° and 20°C.

c) hydrogen permeation flux ϕ evolution with cathodic polarization potential.

Chemical analyses of steel surface are achieved to quantify the ratio (Mg/Mg + Ca) by using spark spectrometry or chemical dosimetry. Also, SEM and X-ray analyses are performed to identify the deposit constitution. DEVANATHAN and STACHURSKY method (7) is employed to measure the hydrogen flux ϕ on specimen disks 0.7 mm thick. All measurements are made in the potential range -1000 to -1500 mV/SCE.

Tensile and fatigue tests are performed on another normalized steel (E 355) which has the following chemical compositions :

TABLE II : Chemical compositions of E 355 steel.

C%	S%	P%	Si%	Mn%	Ni%	Cr%	Mo%	Cu%	Sn%	N %	V%
0.160	0.023	0.019	0.300	1.36	0.048	0.029	0.009	0.445	0.010	0.007	0,011

Tensile tests are performed, after hydrogen charging in seawater, on an INSTRON machine with deformation rate $\simeq 3.10^{-4}$ at room tempe rature. Cylindrical specimens having a diameter of 8 mm and a gauge length of 50 mm are employed. A servohydraulic machine and SENT specimens with 10 mm thickness are used to measure fatigue crack growth while cathodic polarization potential is applied in seawater. Fatigue tests are achieved in the following conditions : constant cyclic load, triangular wave form, R = 0,1 ($R = P_{min}/P_{max}$) and frequency equal to 1 Hz. All tests are achieved at room temperature, with pH$\simeq$ 8 at the beginning of fatigue test, without seawater pumping. Fatigue crack growth is measured by optical microscope with 30 μm precision.

RESULTS AND DISCUSSIONS

Kinetics of calcium carbonate $CaCO_3$ and magnesium hydroxide precipitation at a given cathodic polarization condition ($i = 0{,}1$ mA/cm^2, $E \simeq -1050$ mV/SCE) are shown in figure 1 (8). (Mg/Mg + Ca) ratio firstly decreases when cathodic polarization time increases up to 20 hours and then it becomes constant during 20 to 80 hours hydrogenation time. Magnesium hydroxide kinetics are faster than those of $CaCO_3$. The first $CaCO_3$ crystals are detected after 3 to 6 hours of polarization time. Figure 2 shows the deposit constitution modification in function of cathodic polarization time. After 20 hours hydrogenation in seawater at different cathodic potential values, we measured current density and plotted it versus potential values for two tested temperatures, 5° and 20°C. For 20°C seawater temperature, current density raises linearly with increasing applied potential, figure 3 (8). At 5°C current density is lower than at 20°C, increasing slowly from -950 to about -1050 mV/SCE and then rapidly enhanced up to -1100 mV/SCE. At higher potential values, seawater temperature has no effect on current density. We notice that first $Mg(OH)_2$ crystals are detected at -950 mV/SCE (8). For each applied potential and after 20 hours charging, calco-magnesium deposits are analysed whether by spark spectrometry of by chemical dosimetry. Whilst plotting (Mg/Mg + Ca) ratio versus applied potential at 20°C, we can observe that the relation is roughly linear, figure 4. It seems then that current density measurements may indicate kinetics of deposit variation whether with seawater temperature or applied potential. We can conclude also that, at 5°C, these kinetics are much lower with respect to that detected at 20°C within cathodic potential range -950 to -1050 mV/SCE.

In order to discover how calco-magnesium deposits may modify hydrogen cathodic discharge mechanism and in what manner hydrogen penetration in the steel may be changed, we measured permeation flux at 20°C, in the range of -1000 to -1500 mV/SCE, using DEVANATHAN and STACHURSKY method (7). Flux permeation is measured at steady state, i.e., after 20 hours cathodic polarization. This is due to current variation with time in the transient state and also to current fluctuation during deposit formation (8). Figure 5 shows that hydrogen cathodic discharge mechanisms are complex. It seems that, at low potential values, VOLMER - TAFEL mechanism is active. Nevertheless, at higher applied potential ($\gg$ -1150 mV/SCE) VOLMER - HEROVSKY mechanism is responsible for hydrogen penetration in the steel. We also notice, that current density is independant to applied cathodic potential. This fact is not surprising because at higher cathodic potential values, pH at metal surface reaches 11 to 11,5, i.e. a very basic value, and this result resembles hydrogen discharge mechanism in 0.1N sodium hydroxide solution (9).

Mechanical properties σ_y and σ_{max} of mild steel cathodically polarized during 24 hours in sea water at 20°C are not affected much with applied potential (-1200 or -1500 mV/SCE) or pH value. At pH = 4 or 8 and potential polarization equal to -1200 mV/SCE, mechanical properties are slightly increased by 10% in comparison to those obtained at -1500 mV/SCE at pH $\simeq$ 4. Mechanical properties at -1200 mV/SCE with or without hydrogenation at pH = 4 are equivalent.

Fatigue lifetime decreases approximatly linearly with cathodic polarization potential. At corrosion potential E_D, loss is 72% greater than the value measured in air, while this loss at -1500 mV/SCE is about 78%.

These results suggest that fatigue lifetime in seawater for mild steel is reduced by 2% for each 100 mV cathodic polarization potential in relation to E_D. Figure 6 shows an example of results obtained in seawater at -1000 mV/SCE, pH $\simeq$ 8 and in air. In air, crack growth rate da/dN increases linearly with cyclic stress intensity coefficient ΔK, with $da/dN = 4.9 x 10^{-12} (\Delta K)^{2.9}$. HAAGENSEN and al. results (10) give, on the same steel, but with specimens of 20 mm thickness and 20 Hz frequency : $da/dN = 5.1 x 10^{-13} (\Delta K)^{3.85}$ within ΔK range 7 to 30 MPa$\sqrt{m}$. On the other hand, AUSTIN and al. (11) mentioned that PARIS relationship may be written as $da/dN = 5.32.10^{-11} (\Delta K)^{2.53}$.

With hydrogenation, the curve da/dN = f(ΔK) has a "pseudo-plateau" beginning at $\Delta K_p \simeq 31$ MPa$\sqrt{m}$. ΔK_{Iscc} is estimated as being equal to 28 MPa$\sqrt{m}$. It seems then that at $\Delta K \geqslant$ 28MPa$\sqrt{m}$, we are in presence of fatigue-stress corrosion process (2). At $\Delta K \leqslant \Delta K_{Iscc}$, true fatigue corrosion is active (2). After plotting da/dN versus ΔK for all cathodic polarization values (E_D to -1500 mV/SCE), we observe, figure 7, that crack growth rate at "pseudo-plateau" $(da/dN)_p$ decreases firstly with increasing applied cathodic potential. At E $\geqslant$ -1200 mV/SCE, $(da/dN)_p$ is an increasing function of E. $(da/dN)_p$ versus E, is represented in figure 8a. MAAHN and al. (12) MORGAN and al. (13) results show, in vigorously stirring water at 20°C, that da/dN increases within potential range -800 to -1100 mV/SCE. It seems that stirring is an important factor which governs fatigue crack growth. Stirring may damage or hinder calco-magnesium deposition at crack tip. Without stirring, ΔK_p

decreases continuously with elevated cathodic applied potential, figure 8b. We can conclude that, in our conditions, threshold K_{Iscc} and K_p values are reduced with applying cathodic potential, but there is a critical potential value at which environment agressivity is minimized. Agressivity reduction is due to calco-magnesium deposit at crack tips. da/dN depends on ΔK value ; when ΔK increases crack growth is accelerated. Deposits at crack tip hinder crack closure, hence ΔK is reduced and accordingly da/dN. Reduction ratio depends on deposit adherence and thickness at crack tip. Knowing that, in smooth samples, deposit thickness raises with increasing cathodic applied potential and polarization time (8), and we can expect that da/dN is continuously reduced with higher potential values. This is not the case in fatigue results and one can suspect that adherence quality may vary with applied potential. To verify this hypothesis, VICKERS hardness measurements were performed to appreciate cyclic plastic size r_y'' (14) at crack tips in function of ΔK and for two cathodic potential values, -1000 and -1200 mV/SCE. Figure 9 shows that cyclic plastic size evolution for -1200 mV/ECS is a decreasing function with increasing ΔK values within 15 to 30 $MPa\sqrt{m}$ and r_y'' absolute values are much higher in respect to those measured for -1000 mV/SCE. $r_y'' = g(\Delta K^2)$ for the last potential lies between $r_y'' = \frac{1}{3\pi}\left(\frac{\Delta K}{\sigma_y}\right)^2$ and $r_y = \frac{1}{2\pi}\left(\frac{\Delta K}{\sigma_y}\right)^2$. This result suggests that at -1200 mV/SCE, adherence and thickness of deposits at crack tips are too high to hinder crack closure and hence high compressive stresses are created at crack tip. When cathodic potential exceeds -1200 mV, hydrogen bubbles may be generated at crack tips and the deposit is reduced (15), r_y'' evolution with ΔK agrees with $r_y'' = \frac{1}{3\pi}\left(\frac{\Delta K}{\sigma_y}\right)^2$, i.e. complete crack closure.

It has been shown that pH values require an achievement of precipitation of $CaCO_3$ and $Mg(OH)_2$ and are respectively 8,35 and 9,54 (8). All our tests start at pH $\simeq 8$ and after test: pH $\simeq 4$. pH evolution during the test may affect crack growth rate and also calco-magnesium deposits composition. Fatigue tests are performed at -1200 mV/SCE for the two pH values 4 and 8 and the results shown in figure 10 indicate that da/dN is increased roughly by about two fold at pH = 4 incomparison to crack growth rate at pH = 8. Deposits are observed at surface specimen when pH is either 4 or 8.

After fatigue failure in seawater, deposit composition on rupture surface is analysed by using X-rays analyser (E.D.S.) coupled with S.E.M. (Mg/Mg+Ca)% evolution with ΔK, for two cathodic polarization potentials (-1000 and -1200 mV/SCE) is shown in figure 11. We can observed that potential drop raises with increasing crack length or ΔK. The average drop in ΔK range 15 to 35 $MPa\sqrt{m}$ is about 70 mV, i.e. 3.5 mV by 1 $MPa\sqrt{m}$. This result is in good agreement with MAAHN and al. results (12) in which potential drop is about 4 $mV/MPa\sqrt{m}$ in ΔK range 10 to 30 $MPa\sqrt{m}$ and at -1100 mV/SCE. We can conclude that with this semi-quantitative method we can estimate potential drop evolution with crack length. Deposit composition evolution with pH must be further studied to find out whether this drop is due to crack geometry change or to pH evolution.

CONCLUSION

1- Magnesium hydroxide $Mg(OH)_2$ kinetics are faster than those of calcium carbonate $CaCO_3$ at cathodic polarization potential equal to -1050 mV/SCE.

2- (Mg/Mg + Ca) ratio is roughly a linear function of cathodic potential between -960 to -1100 mV/SCE.

3- Seawater temperature has great effect on calco-magnesium deposit kinetics. At 20°C, cathodic current density measured between -900 to -1200 mV/SCE is also a linear function of cathodic polarization potential, while at 5°C, current density is lowered, between -950 to -1100 mV/SCE.

4- Calco-magnesium deposits modify hydrogen cathodic discharge mechanisms. At cathodic potential equal or higher than -1150 mV/SCE, VOLMER-HEROVSKY mechanism is responsible for hydrogen penetration in the metal.

5- Cathodic potential (-1200 to -1500 mV/SCE) and pH values (4 to 8) do not modify mechanical properties of mild steel much.

6- Without seawater stirring, and in potential range from E_p to -1500 mV/SCE, a "pseudo-plateau" has been observed in $da/dN = f(\Delta K)$ curves. (da/dN) at "pseudo-plateau" has a minimum value at about -1200 mV/SCE. Vickers hardness measurement shows that, at this potential, higher compressive stresses are detected at crack tips than those measured for the other potential values. These high compressive stresses are due to high thickness and good adherence deposits.

7- Decreasing seawater pH value at -1200 mV/SCE increases by two fold da/dN rate, but deposit formation is observed.

8- After fatigue failure in seawater, chemical analyses of deposits on the rupture surface show that (Mg/Mg + Ca) ratio decreases with increasing ΔK values. In relation to point 2, this means that we can estimate the ratio potential drop/ ΔK is about 3.5 $mV/MPa\sqrt{m}$. In these results pH evolution with ΔK is not considered.

REFERENCES

1. WEI, R.P., and LANDES, J.D., may 1969, Int. J. Fract. Mech., 69.

2. AUSTIN, I.M., and McINTYRE, P., july 1979, Metal Science, 420.

3. HUMBLE, R.A., july 1948, Corrosion NACE 4, 358.

4. COMPTON, K.G., LEE CRAIG, H., and SMITH, C.A., march 1974, Int. Corrosion Forum, 85., Chicago.

5. MARETTE, D., HACHE, A., and CUGNIER, M.M., 1961, Bull. Centre Etudes et Recher. Scient. 3, 513, Biarritz, France.

6. HEUZE, B., March 1961, Corrosion et Anticorrosion 9, n° 3, 80.

7. DEVANATHAN, M.A.V., and STACHURSKI, L., 1962, Proc. Roy. Soc. A270, 90, London.

8. PHILIPPONNEAU, G., June 1982, Thèse Doctor Ingeneer, Ecole Centrale des Arts et Manufactures, France.

9. DAFFT, E.G., BOHNENKAMP, K., and ENGELL, H.J., 1965, Corrosion Science 19, 1025.

10. HAAGENSEN, P.J., Oct. 1981, Intern. Conf. "Steel in marine structures", 9.4, Paris, France.

11. AUSTEN, J.M., RUDD, W.J., and WALKER, E.F., Oct. 1981, Intern. Conf. "Steel in marine structures", 5.4, Paris, France.

12. MAAHN, E., Oct. 1981, Intern. Conf. "Steel in marine structures", 5.3, Paris, France.

13. MORGAN, H.G., THORPE, T.W., RANCE, A., SYLVESTER, D.R.V., and SCOTT, P.M., Oct. 1981, Intern. Conf. "Steel in marine structures", 5.1, Paris, France.

14. BATHIAS, C., "La fatigue des matériaux et des structures", 163, Maloine, S.A. Editer, Paris, France.

15. ATTAYA, B.G., and PICKERING, H.W., 1975, J. Electrochem. Soc. 122, 1018.

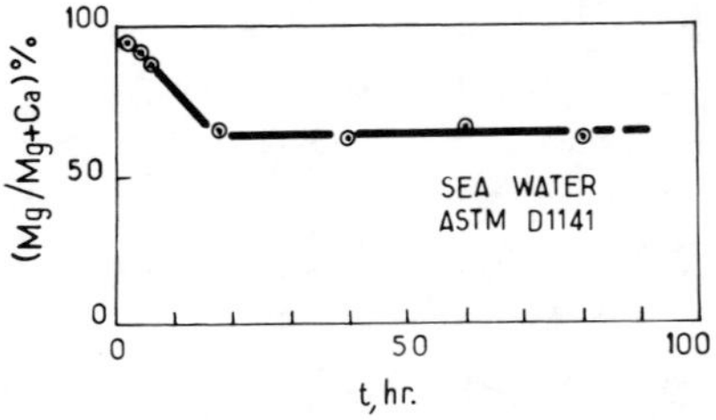

Fig. 1 : (Mg/Mg + Ca) ratio versus time of cathodic polarization (-1050 mV/SCE).

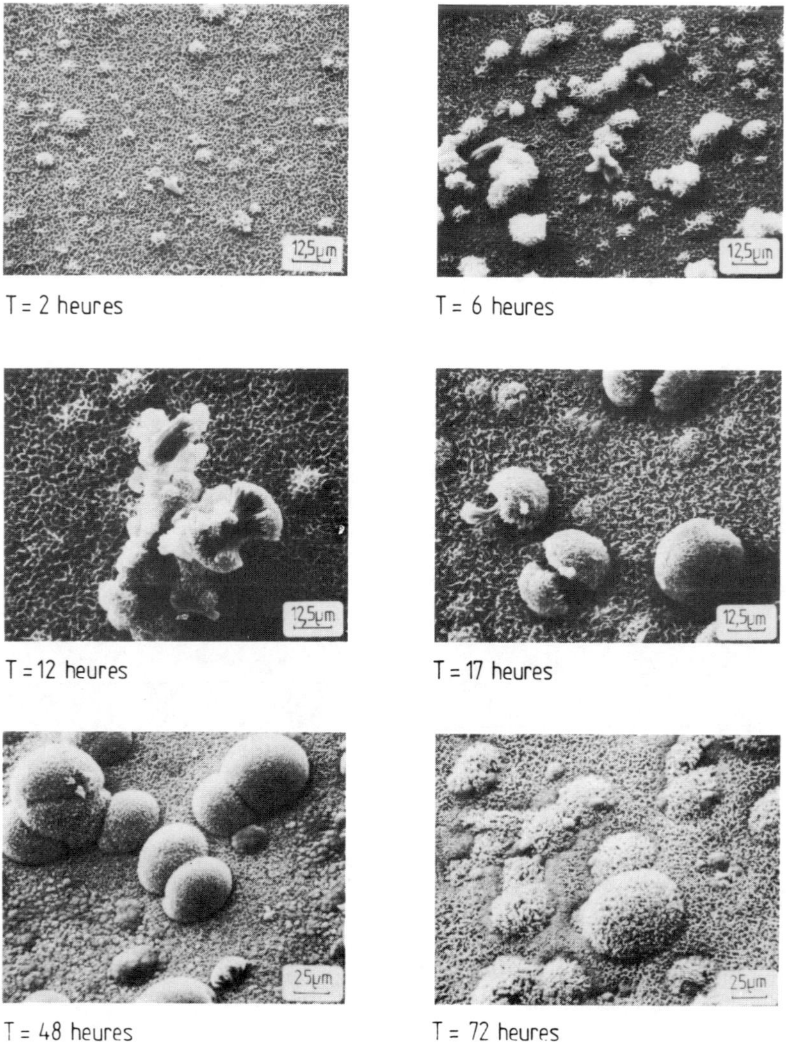

Fig. 2 : Calco-magnesium deposit chemical compositions in function of cathodic polarization potential time at 0.1 $mA.cm^{-2}$.

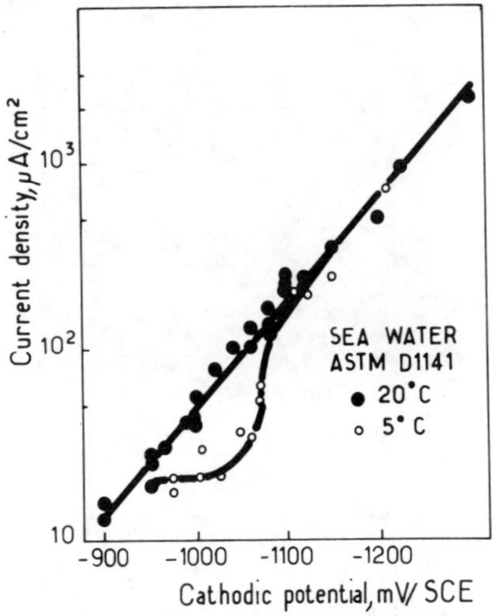

Fig. 3 : Temperature effect on kinetics of calco-magnesium deposit.

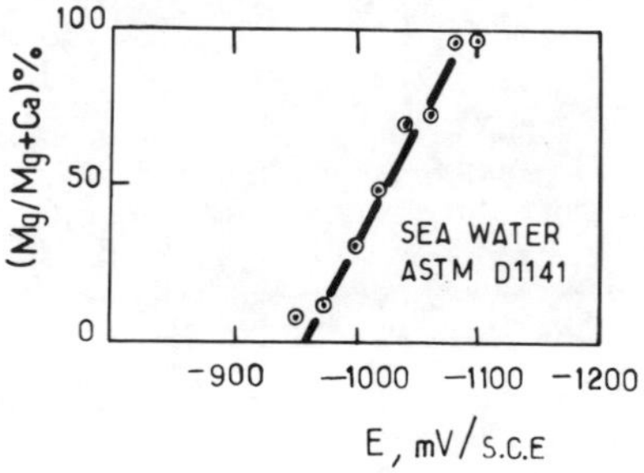

Fig. 4 : (Mg/Mg+Ca) ratio versus cathodic potential in seawater after 17 hours of polarization.

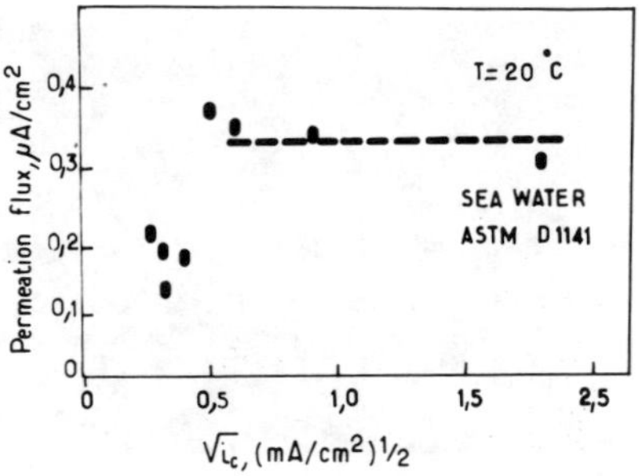

Fig. 5 : Permeation flux versus current density square root.

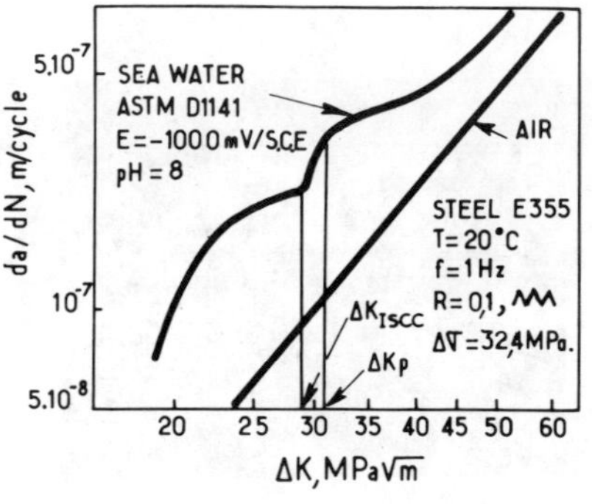

Fig. 6 : Fatigue crack growth rates versus ΔK.

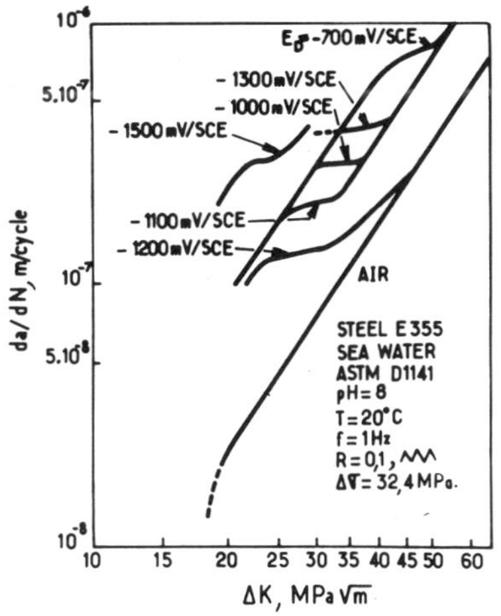

Fig. 7 : Cathodic polarization potential effect on fatigue crack growth rates.

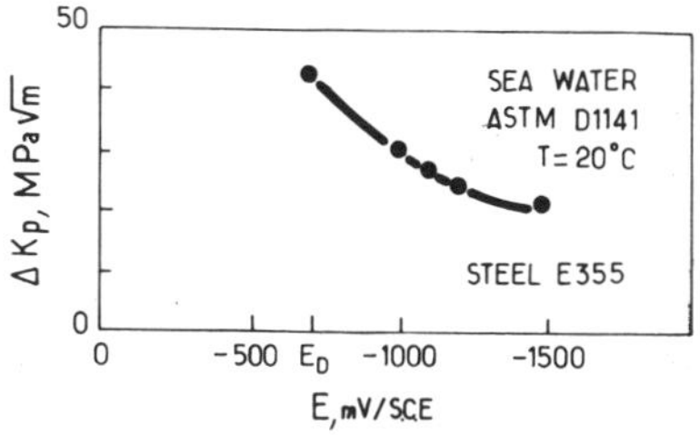

Fig. 8a : Cathodic polarization potential effect on ΔK_P values.

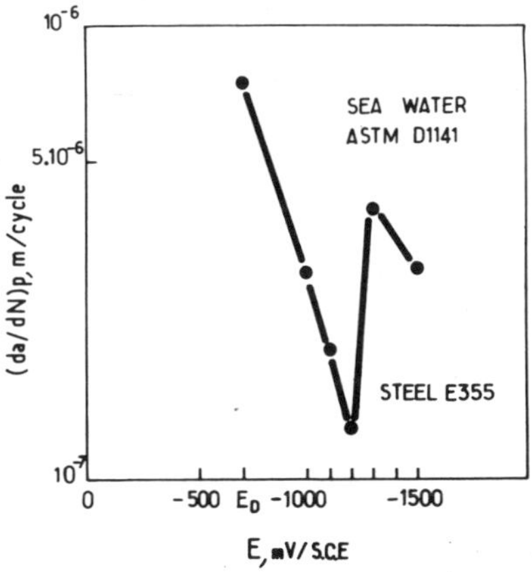

Fig. 8b : da/dN evolution at "pseudo-plateau" with applied cathodic potential.

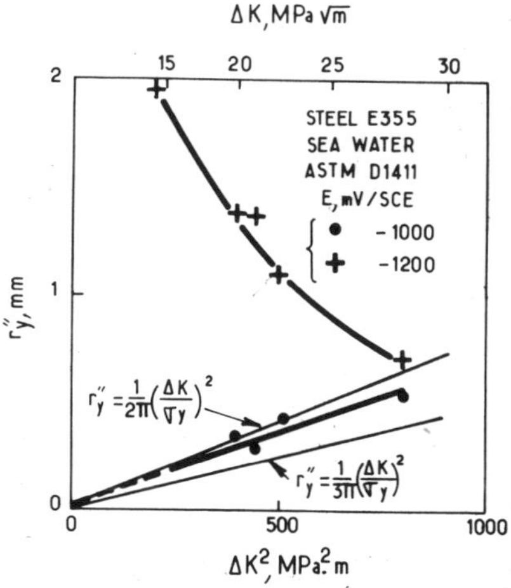

Fig. 9 : Fatigue plastic zone evolution at crack tips at -1000 and -1200 mV/SCE.

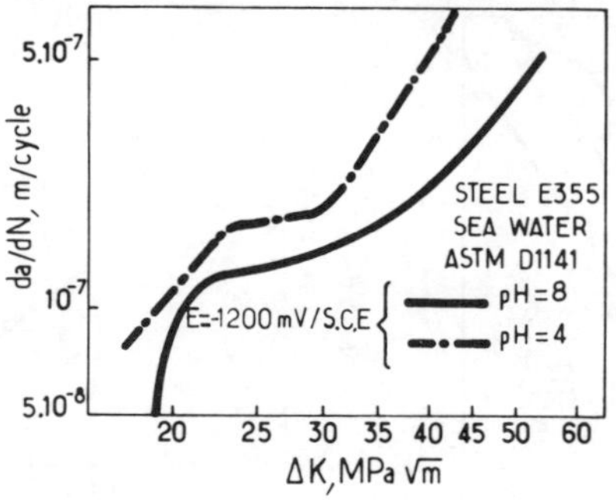

Fig. 10 : pH effect on fatigue crack growth rate of mild steel polarized at -1200 mV/SCE in seawater.

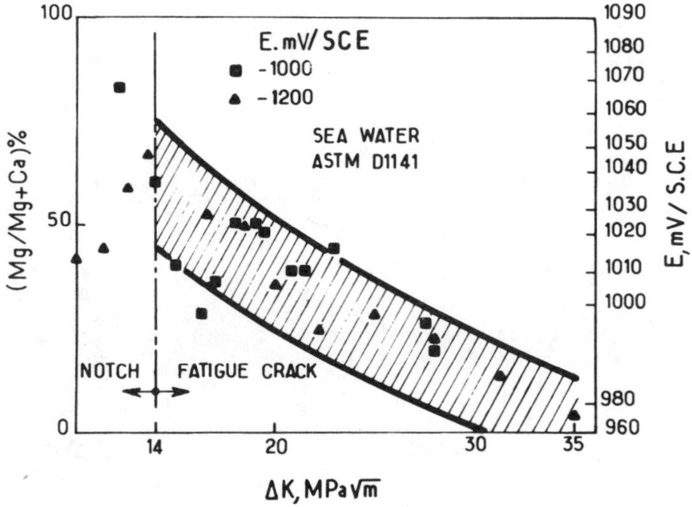

Fig. 11 : Chemical analysis of calcomagnesium deposits versus ΔK values on fatigue fractured surface after cathodic polarization.

SOURCES OF SCATTER IN WELD METAL FRACTURE TOUGHNESS VALUES

Stephen Slatcher, Tor-Bjørn Larsson & Jon Lereim *

The COD toughness of the weld metal in a 100 mm thick manual metal arc weld has been investigated in the as-welded and post weld heat treated conditions. High and low toughness values in the cleavage regime scatter band were found to be associated with different microstructures. Post weld heat treatment improved the toughness of each microstructure. The significance of the microstructural regions of differing toughness is discussed.

INTRODUCTION

The results presented here were obtained in a project, the aim of which was to investigate the effects of a post weld heat treatment on the weld metal fracture toughness of a heavy manual metal arc weldment. The toughness was assessed by Charpy testing, crack opening displacement (COD) testing using specimens of various sizes and containing cracks of various lengths and orientations, and by wide plate testing. The project illustrated the fact that it is impossible to fully describe the COD fracture toughness of the weld metal of a particular weldment by a single value or distribution of values. The measured critical COD values depend on:

(i) The constraint in the testpiece or structure
(ii) The residual stresses acting on the crack
(iii) The microstructures along the crack tip

The constraint depends on the size of the testpiece or structure and on the length and shape of the crack. It is well documented (ref. 1 for example) that decreasing the constraint by reducing the size of the testpiece or by using a shorter crack can lead to larger critical COD values. This effect is very large if the reduction in constraint causes the fracture mode to change from brittle to ductile.

If the weldment contains residual stresses, then the distribution of the residual stresses over the surface of the crack will in some cases affect the externally measurable fracture toughness (ref. 2). Therefore cracks of different lengths, orientations and positions can show different effective toughness values due to residual stress variations in the weldment. Also,

* Det norske Veritas, P.O. Box 300, N-1322 Høvik, Norway.

larger testpieces are capable of holding larger residual stresses than smaller testpieces. Typically the residual stresses vary through the thickness of the weldment, being large and tensile on the surface and compressive in the middle. Superimposed on this residual stress pattern however, there is also a large variation in the magnitude of the residual stresses within each weld bead of a multipass weldment (ref. 3).

The critical COD value is very dependent on the microstructures actually along the crack tip. Thus one can expect large variations in the COD fracture toughness due to microstructural variations in the weld metal and the location of the crack tip in the weld metal. The microstructure of the weld metal in a thick weldment will vary from the root to the face of the weld, there will be slight differences between weld beads at the same depth, and there are also large microstructural variations within each weld bead.

In some cases, the variation in COD fracture toughness is regarded as an "effect" - for example the "thickness effect". In other cases the variation is usually regarded as scatter and the results are treated statistically. However, a statistical treatment of scatter is not sufficient if one wishes to, for example, realistically apply the results of COD testing to the assessment of defects in structures. It is necessary also to understand the physical mechanisms creating the scatter because they may operate differently in the COD testpiece and the structure. As a step towards a full understanding of the variety of different critical COD values obtainable for a weld metal of a particular weldment, a series of COD tests was performed in which the constraint and the residual stresses were the same for each testpiece, but various microstructures were sampled. It is these tests that are reported here.

EXPERIMENTAL PROCEDURE

The weldment examined was a 100 mm thick butt weld with a 60° X-groove, manual metal arc welded in the horizontal position. The parent plate was OX 522 D, a normalized niobium microalloyed steel corresponding to BS 4360 50C, and the electrode was OK Hytrode 7016, which satisfies E7016. The welding procedure, and the chemical analysis of the parent plate and weld metal are given in tables 1 and 2 respectively. Note that two batches of the electrode were used, and that the welding was performed in two different places, but using the same welding procedure. The yield strength of the as-welded weld metal was 460 MPa at +20°C and 650 MPa at -140°C. The PWHT for the weld not to be left in the as-welded condition was 3 hrs 40 mins at 620°C. Three-point bend COD testpieces with the dimensions W=2B=25mm, S/W=4, $a/w \sim 0.5$ were used (W = width, B = breadth, S = loading span, a = crack length). The small size of the testpieces ensured that the residual stresses contained in them were negligible. The testpieces were machined such that the the cracks lay in the centre plane of the welding groove, with the crack tips parallel to the welding direction and at depths of 15, 30 and 50 mm in the weld.

The COD specimens from the electrode batch 1 weldment were tested at temperatures in the range -140°C to +50°C. All the COD specimens from the electrode batch 2 weldment were tested at -140°C. With the exception of a few specimens that had fatigue crack tips marginally too close to the machined notches at the specimen edges, the COD testing and calculation of results was carried out in accordance with BS 5762 (ref. 4).

A lower bound transition curve was constructed for each depth (15, 30 and 50 mm) in the weld metal in each condition (as-welded and PWHT). The 0.2 mm transition temperatures, defined by these six transition curves, are plotted in fig. 1. Clear trends show that the PWHT weld metal has lower transition temperatures than the as-welded weld metal, and that the weld surface region has lower transition temperatures than the weld root. The results of the specimens that failed without any ductile crack extension were then examined in more detail (see fig. 2). It can be concluded that the PWHT improved the mean toughness at -140°C but not the lower bound toughness. Note that at this temperature 29 specimens were tested and the mean values and scatter bands are given in fig. 2. Otherwise, because there are too few data and too much scatter, there are no clear trends.

MICROSTRUCTURAL INVESTIGATION

The microstructure was examined at the mid-point of the crack tip in each testpiece that failed without ductile crack extension. By comparing these microstructures with their corresponding δ_c values it was possible to identify a particular weld metal microstructure that was significantly tougher than all the other observed weld metal microstructures. The tough microstructure was characterized by the fact that the only pro-eutectoid ferrite phase present was equiaxed ferrite, and lay in the region of the weld bead that was refined by successive weld beads. The tough microstructure is illustrated in fig. 3. The less tough microstructures contained other pro-eutectoid ferrite phases and are illustrated in figs. 4, 5 and 6. The proportions of the tough and less tough microstructures at various depths in the weldment are given in table 3.

The data of fig. 2 are replotted in figs. 7 and 8. The mean values and scatter bands are given for -140°C. Fig. 7 contains the data obtained from the as-welded specimens, and fig. 8 those obtained from PWHT specimens. In each figure the microstructures corresponding to the δ_c values are indicated. It may be seen from figs. 7 and 8 that the toughness was not greatly dependent on microstructure at -140°C, but at higher temperatures the distinction between the tough and less tough microstructures was more apparent and the two microstructures had different transition temperatures. The beneficial effect of PWHT on the lower shelf toughness of each microstructure may be readily discerned by comparing figs. 7 and 8, whereas when the microstructures were not distinguished between there was a more confused picture except for the test temperature of -140°C.

SIGNIFICANCE OF MICROSTRUCTURAL TOUGHNESS VARIATIONS

It has been established therefore that in each weld bead of this weld metal there exist tough and less tough regions, and that these regions correspond to readily identifiable microstructures. However, the crack tip in larger COD testpieces and structures would be expected to pass through several microstructural regions of differing toughness. The critical question therefore is how the microstructural regions of differing toughness combine to influence the toughness of larger COD testpieces and structures. The toughness of an individual large testpiece or structure will depend on the microstructure along and immediately ahead of the crack tip. That is to say it depends not only on the proportions of the microstructures present, but also on the size of the regions, their distribution, and their orientation if they are not equiaxed regions. If this dependence could be established, then it would be an important step towards being able to account for scatter in weld metal toughness values. COD toughness distributions could be calculated assuming the positioning of the crack tip in the weld metal was a stochastic process. One could also then begin to establish realistic relationships between the COD toughness distributions for cracks of different shapes, and cracks in different orientations.

For this weld metal there were two clues that suggested how the various microstructural regions might affect the toughness of a large testpiece or structure. One clue was that on the fracture surfaces of six of the wide plate testpieces that failed by cleavage, there were lines that clearly indicated that there was a single initiation site for each of the six plates. The initiation site was found to lie in a less tough microstructure in each case. This observation suggests that, in some cases at least, a "weakest link" theory is appropriate, i.e. the toughness of the structure reflects the toughness of the brittle microstructures along the crack tip. The "weakest link" theory has been partly responsible for the common practice of taking COD testpieces from weldments in the through thickness direction to be sure of including a brittle region of the weld at the crack tip. However, it should be noted that through thickness notched COD testpieces may in some cases give lower bound critical COD values that are higher than the lower bound critical COD values obtained from surface notched COD testpieces (refs. 5 and 6). The second clue may be obtained from the following observation. Although there was no evidence for the toughnesses of the individual microstructures varying with depth in the weld, the proportions of the different microstructures did vary. It may therefore be deduced that it was the proportions of the different microstructures that were responsible for the variation of COD transition temperature with depth in the weld (fig. 1). This could be due to the fact that if the tougher microstructure at the crack tip tended to behave in a ductile fashion at the crack tip, the constraint in the less tough microstructures would be reduced and therefore the necessary cleavage stresses could not be obtained even in the less tough microstructures.

CONCLUSIONS

(i) COD transition temperatures were higher in the weld root than closer to the surface, and higher for the as-welded condition than the PWHT condition.

(ii) There was much scatter in the cleavage regime. The higher critical COD values were obtained when the crack tip lay in a microstructural region of the weld metal consisting of equiaxed ferrite.

(iii) PWHT improved the COD toughness of all microstructures in the cleavage regime, and lowered the 0.2 mm COD transition temperature of all microstructures.

(iv) For the 6 wide plates examined, the final cleavage fracture initiated in a "less tough" microstructure, i.e. not the equiaxed ferrite microstructure.

(v) The variation of transition temperature with depth in the weld is explicable in terms of the varying proportions of the different microstructural regions.

(vi) The "overall toughness" of this weld metal could be improved by increasing the toughness of its less tough microstructures or by reducing their proportion of the whole weld metal.

(vii) When comparing critical COD values obtained from testpieces to those of structures, account must be taken of the constraint, the residual stresses and the crack tip microstructures in both the testpiece and the structure. This is a very complicated task when weldments are being considered, and there is obviously much scope for further work in this field.

ACKNOWLEDGEMENTS

The financial support of Nordforsk, NTNF, Kværner Brug A/S, Norsk Hydro A/S, A/S Norsk Jernverk and Det norske Veritas is gratefully acknowledged. Also, thanks are due to Svenskt Stål for providing the plate material.

REFERENCES

1. Lereim, J., 1982, Paper 13, Second International Conference on Offshore Welded Structures, Welding Institute, London, England.

2. Wu, X., 1983, The Effect of Welding Residual Stresses on Brittle Fracture of Plates with Surface Cracks, Report 38, Inst. för Hållfasthetslära, KTH, Stockholm, Sweden.

3. Fidler, R., 1982, Trans. ASME, J. Pres. Ves. Techn., presented at Pressure Vessels and Piping Conference, Orlando, Florida, USA.

4. British Standards Institution, 1979, Methods for Crack Opening Displacement (COD) Testing, BS 5762 : 1979.

5. Tenge, P. and Karlsen, A., 1979, Paper C5, Colloquium on Practical Application of Fracture Mechanics, IIW, Bratislava, Czechoslovakia.

6. Sumpter, J.D.G., 1982, Int. J. Pres. Ves. & Piping 10, 169.

TABLE 1 - Welding Procedure

Pass Number	Electrode Diameter (mm)	Current (Amp)	Voltage (Volt)	Run Off Length (mm)	Arc Time (sec)	Heat Input (MJm^{-1})
1	3.25	110-115	23	180-220	82	1.2
2	3.25	140	24	200-240	78	1.3
3	4.0	190	24	240-280	80	1.5
4-15	5.0	240	25	190-230	104	3.12
Turn and carbon-arc chisel						
16	4.0	190	24	240-280	80	1.5
17-n	5.0	240	25	190-320	104	3.12
Turn and complete welding						
n-n'	5.0	240	25	190-230	104	3.12

Preheat: 150°C

Interpass temperature: 250°C

TABLE 3 - Proportions of the Tough (Equiaxed Ferrite) and Less Tough Microstructure

	Weld Metal (1)			Weld Metal (2)		
	15 mm	30 mm	50 mm	15 mm	30 mm	50 mm
Equiaxed Ferrite	61 %	46 %	23 %	65 %	15 %	18 %
Other	39 %	54 %	77 %	35 %	85 %	88 %

TABLE 2 - Chemical Composition of Materials in Weight Percent

Material	Depth in Weld	C	Si	Mn	P	S	Cr	Mo	Ni	Al	V	Nb	Ti
Parent Plate	-	0.18	0.47	1.49	0.035	0.016	0.04	<0.01	0.014	0.027	<0.01	0.025	0.005
	15 mm	0.10	0.31	1.18	0.029	0.008	0.02	<0.01	0.016	0.004	<0.01	0.001	0.018
Weld Metal (1)	30 mm	0.11	0.39	1.32	0.028	0.008	0.03	<0.01	0.017	0.004	<0.01	0.004	0.020
	50 mm	0.12	0.42	1.23	0.031	0.010	0.03	<0.01	0.026	0.007	<0.01	0.006	0.020
Weld Metal (2)	30 mm	0.058	0.36	1.31	0.018	0.006	0.01	0.02	0.03	<0.001	0.03	<0.005	0.007

Weld metal (1) was from batch 1 of electrodes

Weld metal (2) was from batch 2 of electrodes

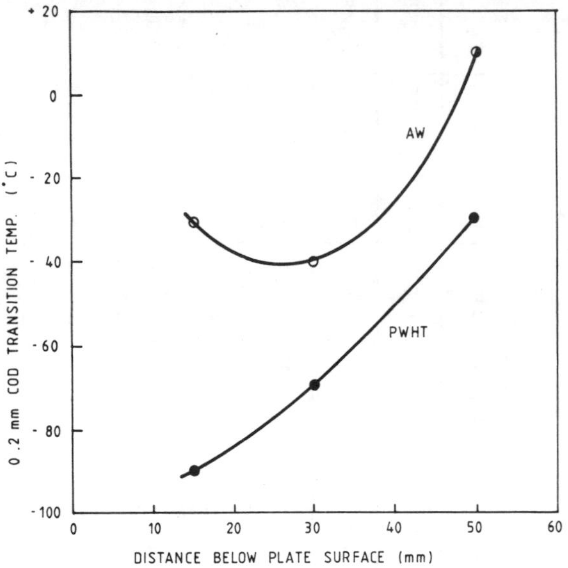

Figure 1 0.2 mm COD transition temperatures

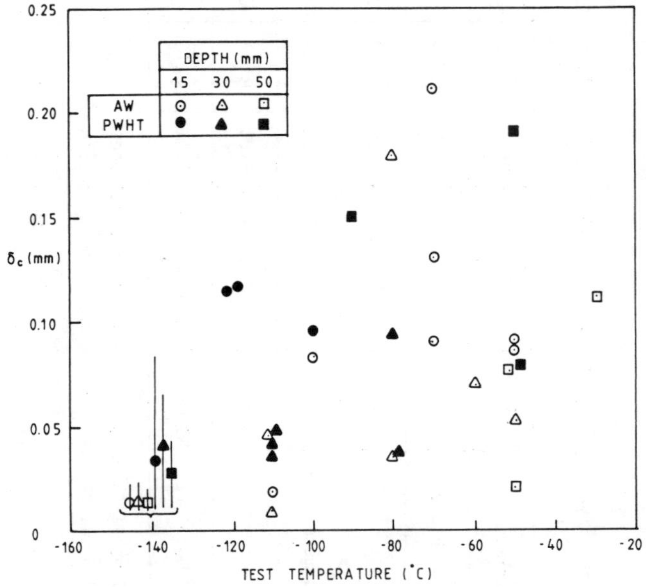

Figure 2 Critical COD values

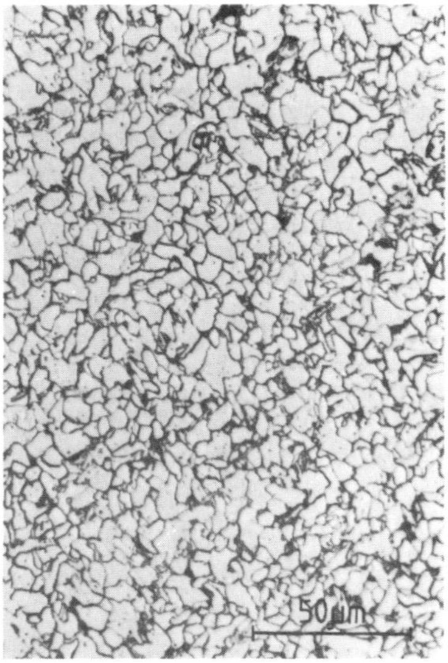

Figure 3 A refined microstructure equiaxed ferrite - tough

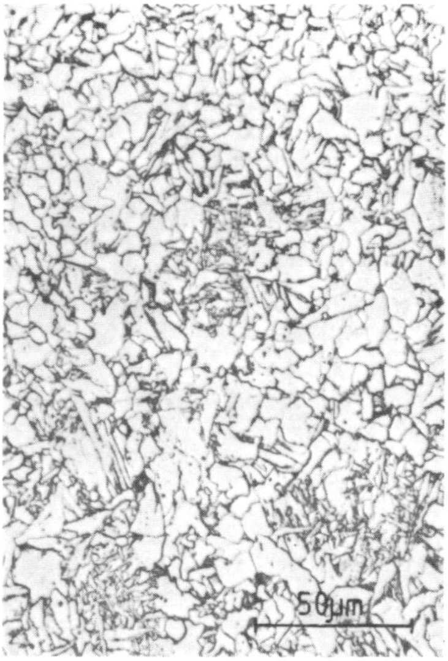

Figure 4 A refined microstructure - less tough

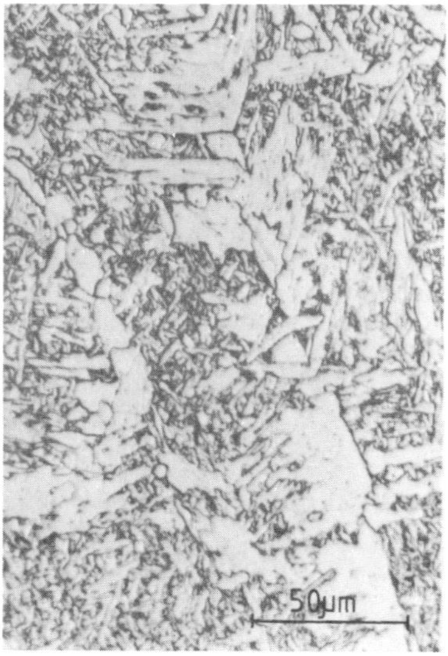

Figure 5 An unrefined microstructure - less tough

Figure 6 An unrefined microstructure - less tough

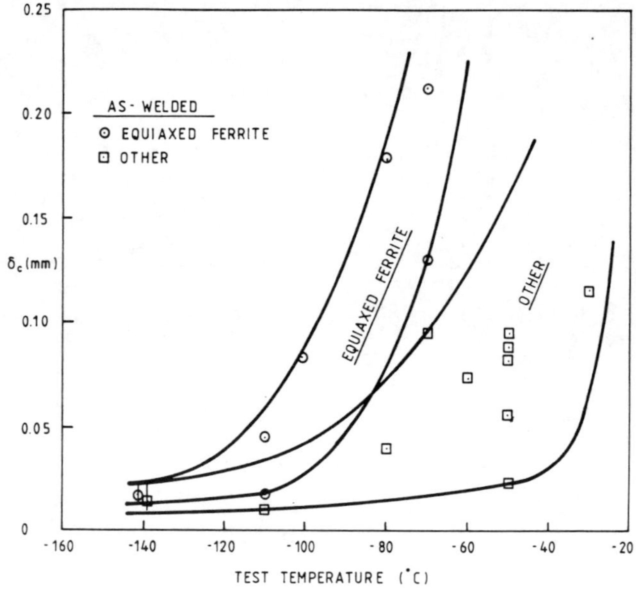

Figure 7 Critical COD values for the as-welded condition only

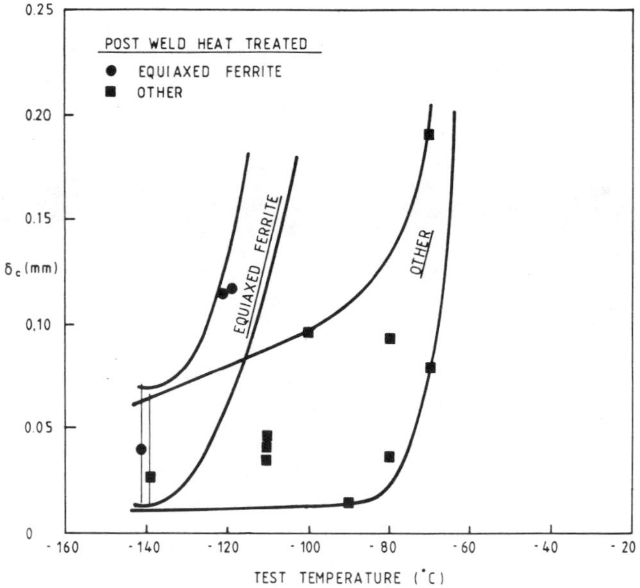

Figure 8 Critical COD values for the post weld heat treated condition only

INFLUENCE OF SILICON CONTENT ON MECHANICAL PROPERTIES AND MICROSTRUCTURE OF AN AWS E8018-C1 TYPE ELECTRODE WELD METAL.

R.Herrera*; L.A.de Vedia*; R.Timerman**; J.C.Gonzales***

This work analyzes the influence of Si content on mechanical properties and microstructure of AWS E 8018-C1 type electrode weld metal in the range 0.1 to 0.5% Si. Optimum combination of strength and toughness in a wide temperature range was obtained with 0.3% Si in the weld deposit, both in the as welded and stress relieved conditions. The influence of PWHT on fracture toughness and microstructure is also assessed.

INTRODUCTION

The use of Ni additions to weld deposits in order to achieve good values of toughness in structural steelwork fracture critical members, has been a common practice for several years. This is the case for example, of "off shore" production platforms. For many such structures, as those operating in the North Sea, a minimum design temperature of -10°C is considered adequate for parts exposed to the atmosphere and splash zones, while for the submerged parts a minimum design temperature of +4°C has generally been adopted (1).

AWS E8018-C1 type electrodes have been extensively used for this application because they have usually given better COD values than AWS E7018 electrodes (2). The effects of adding Ni to the weld deposit have been studied by several authors (3)(4)(5). Although the influence of Ni on mechanical properties and microstructure of weldments is fairly well understood, knowledge on the effects of variations in the Si level of Ni bearing weld deposits is not so adequate. This situation becomes particularly unsatisfactory if account is taken of the fact that AWS Specification

* División Soldadura,Universidad Nac.de Mar del Plata,Argentina

** CONARCO ALAMBRES Y SOLDADURAS S.A., Argentina

*** LEMIT - CIC, Argentina.

for E8018-C1 electrode allows for variations in Si level up to 0.8% maximum in the weld deposit (6).

Silicon is a strong deoxidant and is normally present in sufficient quantity in the electrode wire or as a compound in the covering to provide for effective deoxidation of the weld metal and prevent porosity. The amount of Si required depends upon the degree of deoxidation to be attained, which varies with the level of oxidation generated by the welding process. Work done by Tuliani et al (7) on submerged arc C-Mn steel weld metals containing silicon in the range of 0.09-0.40% showed that optimum combination of strength and toughness could be obtained with less than 0.1%C; 1.2-1.4%Mn and 0.18-0.20%Si in the deposit. The same work concludes that toughness of a weld metal is a complex function of composition, strength and microstructure.

Silicon has also an influence on inclusion type and level, and oxygen content, which in turn influence fracture mechanisms at different temperatures.
The purpose of this work is to study the effects of changes in Si level on mechanical properties and microstructure of welds produced using AWS E8018-C1 type electrodes. In an experimental programme on M.M.A. consumables, three experimental AWS E8018-C1 type covered electrodes were developed that provided Si levels in the weld metal ranging from 0.1 to 0.5%. These electrodes, designated for the purpose of the present investigation as 01, 03 and 05, were employed to obtain the standard all weld metal samples and production type single-V welded joints necessary to carry out this work.

EXPERIMENTAL PROCEDURE

All weld metal chemical composition corresponding to the three electrodes are shown in Table 1.a.- Since there is evidence that all weld metal impact properties may vary with different welding procedures, standard all weld metal samples according to AWS A5.5 -81 and ISO 2560-73 were made with each electrode. Typical welding parameters used are shown in Table 2. Before welding, the electrodes were dried at 400°C for 90 minutes.

To study the change in properties introduced by the use of post-weld heat treatment, half of the AWS samples were kept in the as welded condition while the remaining samples were subjected to a stress relieving treatment for one hour at 620°C.
To take into account any possible effect of dilution and/or dynamic strain ageing at the root region on fracture toughness of weld deposits (8)(9), production type single-V multirun welds were made on 19 mm thick plate with each electrode. Typical welding parameters used in this case are also shown in Table 2.

Welding was done in the flat position; the sequence was such that a backing run was deposited first and, after grinding to sound weld metal from the other side, the weld was completed. In order to make the root region to accomodate the largest possible amount of plastic strain, no external restraint was employed. Thus the test panels were free to move during welding and for this reason had to be preset with a 4 degree angle between them. This value was obtained from previous trials to ensure that the plates reached the same plane after welding. Chemical compositions corresponding to base plate and single-V multirun weld deposits are shown in Table 1.b and c.

In order to see the influence of Si on room temperature weld metal strength and ductility, standard tensile specimens were obtained from the AWS weld deposits in the as welded and stress relieved conditions.

Standard Charpy-V specimens were machined out of the AWS and ISO all weld metal samples and tested at temperatures between -100 and +20°C.

Fracture toughness of the production type single-V welds was assessed by means of COD and J integral testing. For this purpose, full thickness single edge notched three point bend specimens according to BS 5762:79 (10) were extracted from each weld, with the notch in the through thickness direction as indicated by Fig. 1. An initiating fatigue crack, with initial crack depth to width ratio a/W equal to 0.6, was used in all cases. Testing was conducted at room temperature and at -40°C. To obtain the COD and J integral values corresponding to initiation of slow crack growth, designated respectively δ_i and J_i, a multispecimen technique was employed (10) (11). Thus, J_i values were obtained as the intersection of the J-R curve with the blunting line of equation $J=2\sigma_y\Delta a$, where σ_y was the effective yield strength defined as the average between the 0.2% offset yield stress and the ultimate strength (11). δ-R curves were constructed following the recommendations of Apendix A of BS 5762:79. However, in order to make the results compatible with those obtained from the J-R curves, δ_i was determined in each case as the intersection between the δ-R curve and the blunting line of equation $\delta=2\Delta a$ (12).

To account for any possible effect of dilution or strain ageing damage on notch toughness, standard Charpy-V samples notched in the through thickness direction were obtained from the root region of the production type single-V welds. Testing was conducted in this case between -40 and +60°C.

A quantitative metallographic study was made to see the influence of Si on microstructure, inclusion size and level.

RESULTS AND DISCUSSION

The results of tensile tests of standard AWS all weld metal spec-

imens in the as welded and stress relieved conditions are shown in Table 3. It may be seen that an increase in the Si content raises the yield stress and tensile strength. Stress relieving reduces these values but seems to improve ductility up to a Si level of 0.3%.
Charpy curves corresponding to AWS and ISO specimens are shown in Fig. 2.a, b, and c. It is seen that within the testing temperature range, electrode 05 shows a marked reduction in absorbed energy values when compared to electrodes 01 and 03 for AWS as welded specimens, and that the same is true for ISO stress relieved specimens. However, stress relieving seems to produce a general deterioration of impact properties in the transition temperature range of all weld metal specimens, as judged by the 100 Joule transition temperatures indicated in Table 4. This Table shows that the shift in transition temperature is particularly large beyond 0.3% Si in the ISO samples. This observation may be related with the fact that in the ISO weldments, made with three passes per layer, the tip of the notch of the Charpy-V specimens probes a larger proportion of columnar grain structure than in the AWS weldments made with only two passes per layer.

COD and J integral values at initiation of crack growth, obtained with the full thickness specimens extracted from the single-V welds, are shown in Fig.3.a, b, c and d. It is seen that the highest fracture toughness values were exhibited by electrode 03 at both testing temperatures. It is worth noting that fracture toughness increases up to a maximum corresponding to a 0.3% Si level in the weld deposit. Beyond this value, a reduction in fracture toughness is observed.
This reduction is particularly marked at low temperature. Thus, no slow crack growth was observed during testing of the 0.5% Si weldments at -40°C. Failure of the specimens was in this case by cleavage fracture which prevented J integral determination. The corresponding critical COD value was measured and is indicated in Fig. 3.b.

The absorbed energy values of Charpy-V specimens extracted from the root region of the single-V welds are shown in Fig.2.d. It can be observed that increasing the Si content raises the 100 Joule transition temperature as previously found in all weld metal specimens; Table 4.
The effect of silicon on notch toughness varies with temperature. In the transition temperature range an increase in Si content raises the 100 Joule transition temperature and 0.5% Si is enough to completely supress slow stable crack growth in COD and J integral specimens at -40°C. At room temperature, this same level of silicon does not seem to be extremely deleterious, as judged by Charpy and fracture toughness test results.

The preceding analysis singles out the 0.3% Si level as giving the optimum combination of strength and toughness in a wide temperature range, both in the as welded and stress relieved conditions.

The results of the quantitative metallographic study are indicated in Table 5. It is seen that changes in Si level do not seem to have significant effect on grain size. On the other hand, silicon does favour the formation of acicular ferrite at the expense of other microconstituents. Inclusion area fraction also increases with Si content. This seems to be the result of a larger inclusion size rather than the consequence of an increase in inclusions number that remained essentially the same for different Si levels. The changes observed in the microstructure of the columnar regions are shown by the micrographs of Fig. 4.a, b and c. The increase in the amount of acicular ferrite in the as welded specimens due to increments in Si level, is readily visible.
The effect of post-weld heat treatment on microstructure is also seen in Fig. 4.a, b and c. It can be observed that after 1 hour at 620°C, the columnar grains are transformed to structures containing a higher proportion of polygonal ferrite, which may account for the reduction in Charpy energy found in stress relieved specimens. The increment in polygonal ferrite after stress relieving is very large for the lowest Si content and becomes smaller with increasing Si levels. This may be the result of the mild influence Si exerts in rising the A_1 transformation temperature and in shifting to the right the pearlitic and bainitic noses in a C.C.T. diagram. Thus, since the A_1 temperature is already depressed by the presence of Ni, additions of Si tend to supress partial austenization produced by the stress relieving treatment and to maintain the original structure.

CONCLUSIONS

- In Ni bearing AWS E8018-C1 type electrode weld deposits, optimum combination of strength and toughness in a wide temperature range, may be obtained with 0.3% Si in the weld metal, both in the as welded and stress relieved conditions.

- Stress relieving seems to produce a general deterioration of impact properties in the transition temperature range as judged by the 100 J transition temperature shift.

- The observed deterioration of impact properties after stress relieving is accompanied by microstructural changes in the columnar grains leading to structures with a high proportion of polygonal ferrite. This suggests a cautious aproach to post-weld heat treatment of AWS E8018-C1 type electrode weld deposits.

- The effect of Si on notch toughness varies with temperature. In the transition temperature range an increase in Si level beyond 0.3% raises the 100 J transition temperature and drastically reduces fracture toughness. At room temperature, the same level of Si does not seem to be particularly deleterious.

- Silicon favours the formation of acicular ferrite in as welded specimens, but this is not necessarily accompanied by an improvement in toughness.

ACKNOWLEDGEMENTS

This work forms part of a research programme on development of welding consumables sponsored by the Comisión de Investigaciones Científicas de la Provincia de Buenos Aires-Argentina, the Consejo Nacional de Investigaciones Científicas y Técnicas, and the SUBCYT-Argentina. The support received from CONARCO ALAMBRES Y SOLDADURAS is also acknowledged.
The authors are indebted to Prof. R.L.Apps from C.I.T.-U.K. for his helpful suggestions, and to J.L.Trotti; E.S.Surian; J.L. Otegui and D. Mejías for their contributions to experimental work.

REFERENCES

1- H.G.Pisarski; M.G.Dawes "Measurement of crack opening displacement in weldments with particular reference to offshore structures". Conf. on Analitical and Experimental Fracture Mechanics; Rome, June 1980, pp.595-614

2- R.de Haeck; B.Phelps; A.A.Smith "Developing consumables and processes for work on offshore platforms". Welding and Metal Fab. Sept. 80, pp.441-449.

3- J.V. Peck; C.E. Witherell "Welding 3½% Nickel Steel". Welding Journal, May 63, pp. 193-s/ 201-s.

4- R. Thorneycroft; D.E. Jordan; L.W. Crane "Some metallurgical observations on 3½% Nickel steel weld metal with respect to properties at sub-zero temperatures". British Welding Journal, V. 10, May 63, pp. 212-221 .

5- M.W. Hardie; M.G. Hipkins "Low temperature impact properties of submerged arc welds in 3½% Nickel steel". Wel. and Metal Fab., June 66, pp.223-227.

6- AWS A5.5-81 "Specification for low alloy steel covered arc welding electrodes".

7- S.S. Tuliani; A. I. Ceram; R.A. Farrar "The effects of silicon in submerged arc weld metal at low concentrations". Wel. and Metal Fab., Sept. 75, pp. 553-558.

8- R.C. Cochrane; P. Terry; J.G. Garland "Root run toughness in multi-pass manual metal arc welds" Wel. and Metal Fab., May 76, pp. 316-320; July-August 76, pp. 439-448.

9- J.L. Otegui; R.A. Vega; L.A. de Vedia "Influence of dynamic strain ageing on notch toughness of weld deposits". LatinAm. J. Met. Mat., V.3, Nº1, 1983

10- BS 5762:79 "Methods for Crack Opening Displacement (COD) Testing"

11- ASTM E 813-81 "Standard Test for J_{IC}; A measure of fracture toughness"

12- J.D. Landes; J.A. Begley "Test results from J-integral Studies: An attempt to establish a J_{IC} testing procedure" Fracture Analysis, ASTM STP 560, American Society for Testing and Materials, 1974, pp. 170-186.

Table 1.– Composition of materials used in weld test series

Electrode	All weld metal composition [wt %]																		
	C	Mn	Si	Ni	P	S	Sn	As	W	Cu	Co	Cr	Mo	V	Nb	Ti	Al	N	O
01	.050	.80	.13	2.47	.015	.015	.01	<.01	.04	.08	<.01	.05	<.01	<.01	.010	<.01	.01	.009	.070
03	.050	.82	.32	2.52	.014	.012	.01	<.01	.04	.08	<.01	.05	<.01	<.01	.015	<.01	.01	.011	.057
05	.055	.80	.54	2.46	.014	.011	.01	<.01	.04	.08	<.01	.05	<.01	<.01	.015	<.01	.01	.012	.050

(1.a)

Electrode	Weld metal composition [wt %]																
	C	Mn	Si	Ni	P	S	Sn	As	W	Cu	Co	Cr	Mo	V	Nb	Ti	Al
01	.050	.91	.15	2.15	.012	.014	.01	<.01	.03	.07	<.01	.05	<.01	<.01	.010	<.01	<.01
03	.050	.87	.33	2.20	.011	.013	.01	<.01	.03	.07	<.01	.05	<.01	<.01	.010	<.01	<.01
05	.050	.87	.54	2.22	.011	.013	.01	<.01	.03	.07	<.01	.05	<.01	<.01	.010	<.01	<.01

(1.b)

Base metal composition [wt %]				
C	Mn	Si	P	S
.08 – .115	.34 – .62	< 0.10	.010 – .015	.020 – .028

(1.c)

Table 2.– Test welding procedures

Weld preparation	Elec. Dia. [mm]	Pass	Interpass Temp. [°C]	Current [Amps]	Voltage [Volts]	Heat imput [KJ/mm]
AWS A5.5 	4	1 - last	90–110	170	26	1.80
ISO 2560 	4	1 - last	90–110	175	25	1.25
70° Single – V 	4	backing 2 3 - last	Not Controlled	140 160 160	23 26 25 – 26	1.27 1.53 2.4-2.5

Table 3.– All weld metal tensile properties

Electrode	U.T.S. [N/mm^2]		Y.S. [N/mm^2]		Elong. [%]	
	AW	SR	AW	SR	AW	SR
01	56	52.8	48.3	43.9	27.3	29.8
03	60.1	57	51.6	49	29.8	33.7
05	62.8	61.4	53.7	46.4	28.5	27.9

AW: As welded SR: Stress relieved

Table 4.– 100 J transition temperatures [°C]

Electrode	Weld Prep.			
	AWS A5.5		ISO 2560	Single V
	AW	SR	SR	AW
01	-72	-48	-65	-40
03	-72	-38	-58	-33
05	-56	-40	-29	-28

Table 5.– Microstructural details

Electrode	Grain size		Microconstituent			Inclusion level	
	Columnar	Equiaxed	GF	AC	AF	Area	Number
	[mm]	ASTM	[%]	[%]	[%]	[A%]	[1/mm^2]
0'	.0716	11	50.5	30.3	19.2	.0263	10329
03	.0708	9-10	46.7	26.7	26.6	ND	ND
05	.0703	9-10	39.5	20.5	40	.0370	10329

Key
- GF = Grain boundary ferrite
- AC = Ferrite with aligned M-A-C
- AF = Acicular ferrite
- ND = Not determined

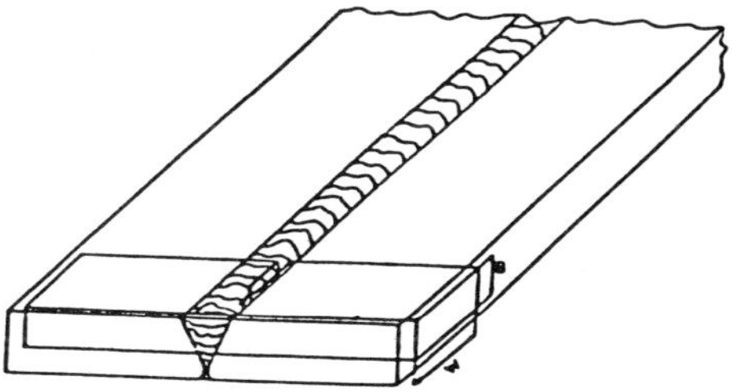

Fig 1 Obtention of COD/J integral test pieces

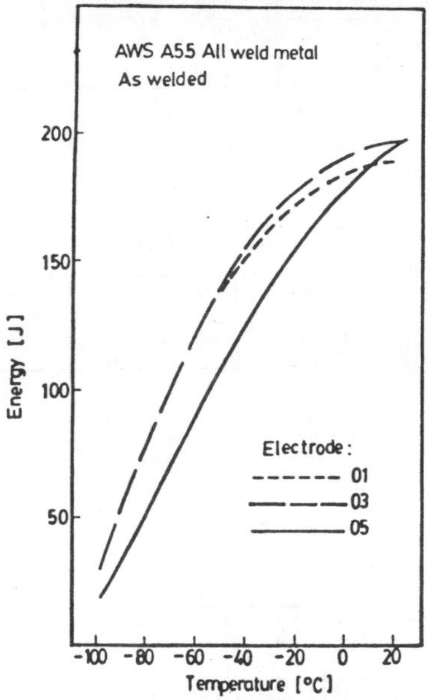

Fig. 2.a All weld metal notch toughness

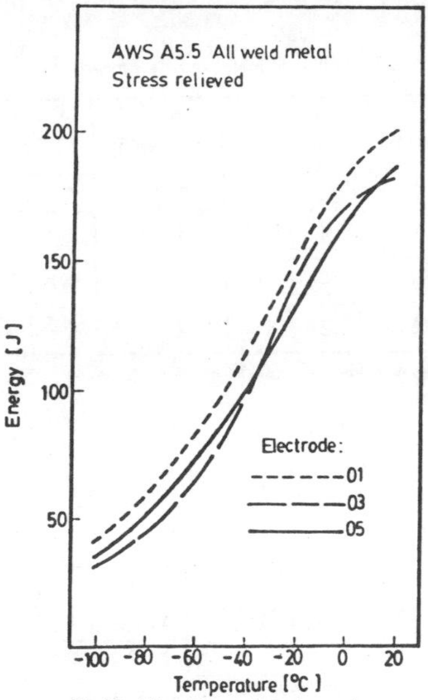

Fig. 2.b All weld metal notch toughness

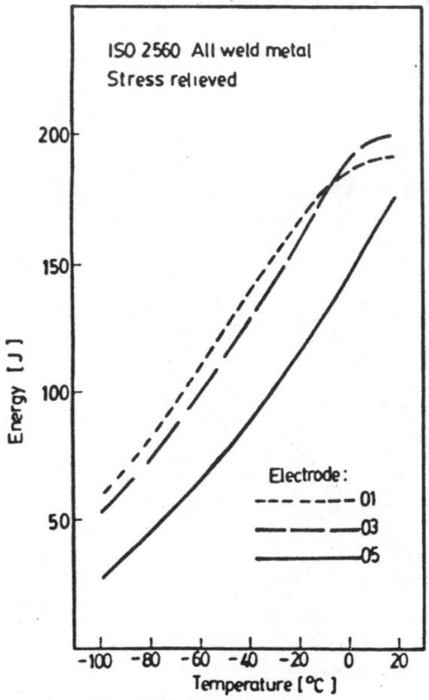

Fig 2.c All weld metal notch toughness

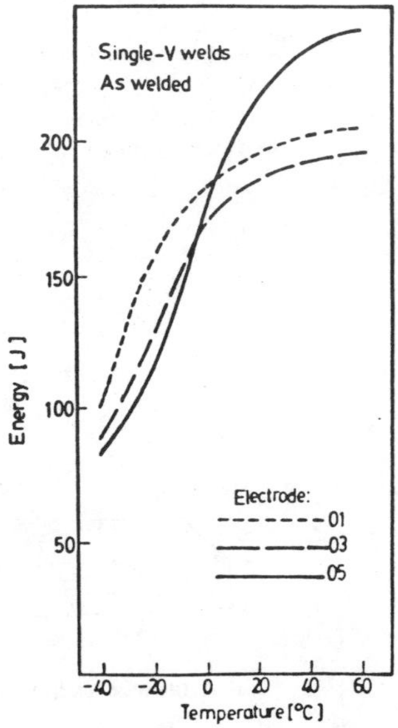

Fig. 2.d Root region notch toughness

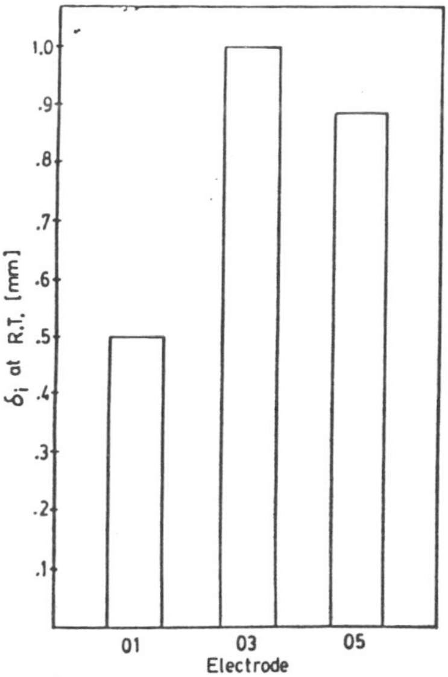

Fig.3.a COD values at initiation. Single–V welds AW condition

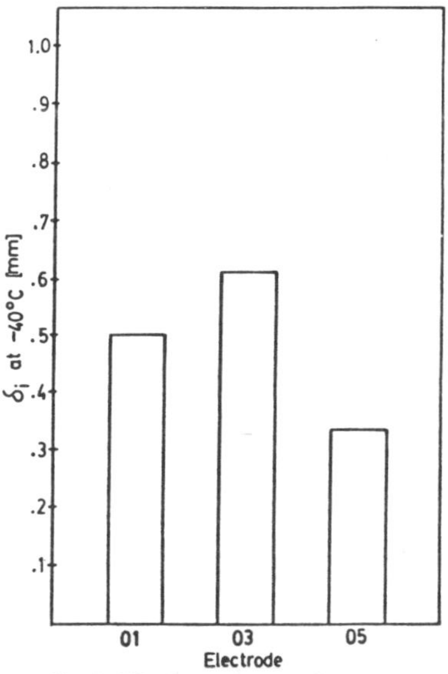

Fig. 3.b COD values at initiation. Single–V welds AW condition

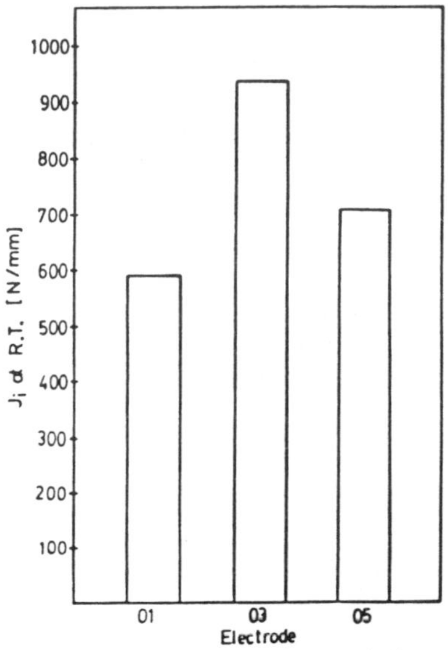

Fig.3.c J integral values at initiation. Single–V welds. AW condition

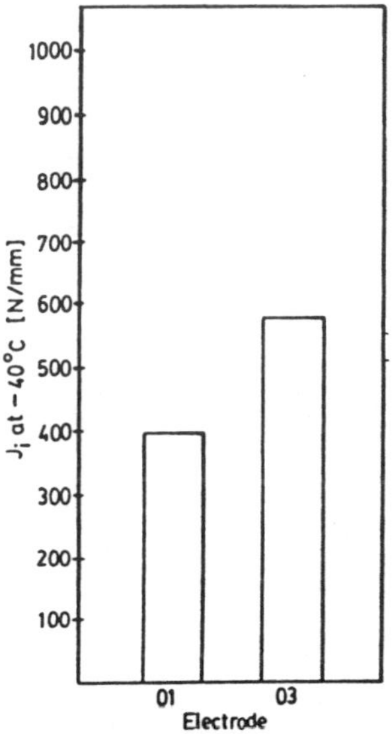

Fig.3.d J integral values at initiation. Single–V welds AW condition

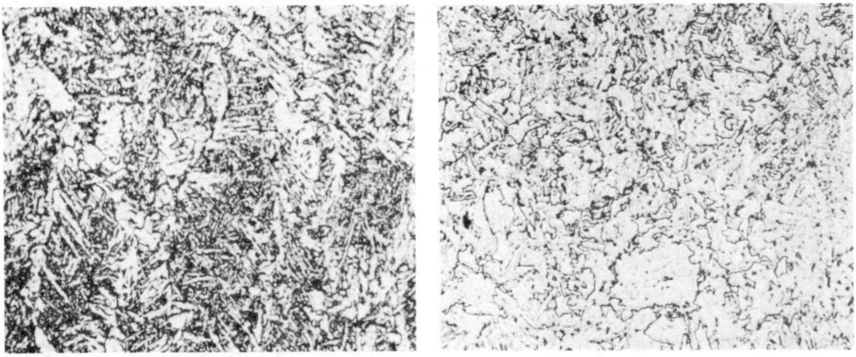

As welded (a) ELECTRODE 01 Stress relieved

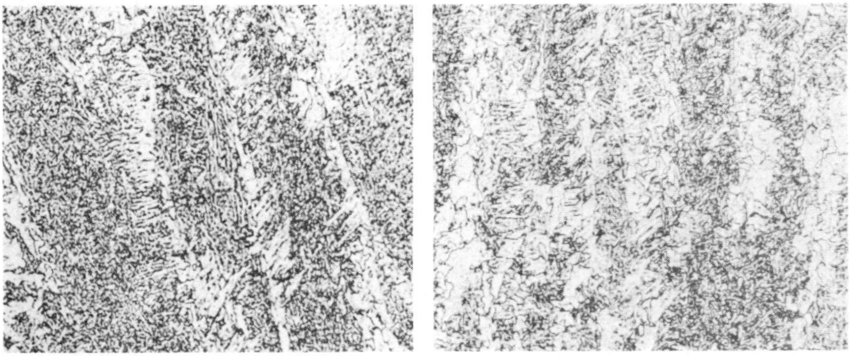

As welded (b) ELECTRODE 03 Stress relieved

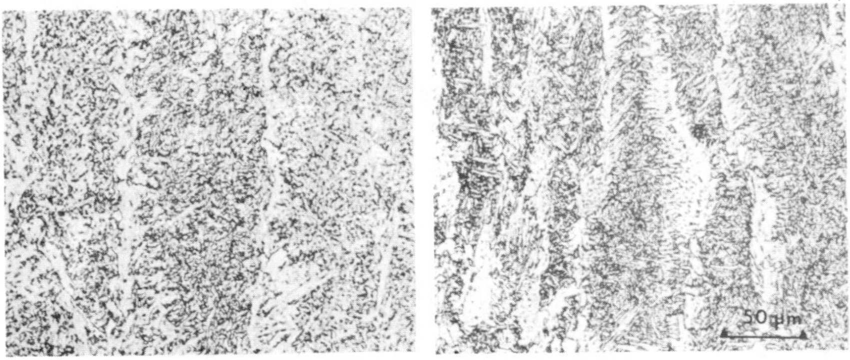

As welded (c) ELECTRODE 05 Stress relieved

Fig.4. Influence of PWHT on columnar grains microstructure for different Si levels 300x Nital etch.

IMPROVED FRACTURE TESTING VIA CRACK TIP MEASUREMENTS

T. G. F. Gray*

Measurements of in-plane and out-of-plane displacements in the crack tip region of loaded SENT specimens are given and analysed to show that such measurements yield a higher quality of information on significant events occurring in a toughness test. The effects of triaxial constraint on yielding transitions and relationships between J and δ are discussed.

INTRODUCTION

The development of fracture mechanics as we now know it has been greatly stimulated by unexpected catastrophic failures in the energy and transport industries in the past and if such failures are less frequent now, this is probably due to the use of improved material selection procedures which include specific testing for resistance to crack propagation. The various experiences of failure in ship structures, thick pressure vessels, bridge girders and aerospace applications have added information about different aspects of the problem to the store of knowledge. However one basic lesson has emerged repeatedly for over a century and that is that a material which performs in a ductile and satisfactory manner in a plain tensile test can turn out to be poorly resistant to the passage of cracks under the particular mechanical and environmental conditions in service.

The particular role of the fracture toughness test therefore is to identify such materials and to measure and index their behaviour in terms which allow the performance of full-scale structures to be confidently assessed and predicted. This problem of measuring and indexing behaviour provided the incentive for the research reported here.

Fracture toughness testing methods

The basic approach used in current procedures is remarkably unchanged from the methods established over 15 years ago by The American Society for Testing and Materials. In essence, a pre-cracked specimen is loaded monotonically to generate an autographic plot of load against displacement, measured at some location, usually distant from the crack tip. The resulting plot is

* Department of Mechanics of Materials, University of Strathclyde.

then examined to find the instant of crack extension from which a relevant index of fracture (K_{Ic}, δ_c, J_{Ic} etc.) can be derived.

The theme of the present paper is that more information of a higher quality can be extracted from a given test if the displacement measurement is moved to a site close to the crack tip where fracture events can be more distinctly observed. Such measurements have greater potential also for monitoring triaxial constraint on the crack tip plastic zone. Triaxiality has long been understood to be a critical consideration in fracture behaviour (see for example, Irwin (1) and Wells (2)) but there has been little attempt to monitor constraint in testing procedures other than through the establishment of semi-arbitrary minimum dimensions for specimens.

Two forms of near-crack-tip measurement were employed in the present study, namely, notch-root-contraction as proposed by the present author (3) and a development of the Moire fringe method described by McDonach et al (4).

CRACK-OPENING GAUGES

Displacement measurements can be used in different ways in fracture testing. Firstly, they can be used to monitor the test in terms of deviation from linearity, without regard to the numerical value of the displacement or its physical significance. "Clip-in" gauges, as prescribed by the ASTM for plane strain toughness testing, function in this way (5). In other cases the actual value of the displacement may indeed be of interest with respect to procedures whereby displacement or energy is used as a fracture index (6, 7). A third role emerged during the early stages of COD testing when gauges operating on the "paddle" or "twisted-strip" principle were used to measure COD directly (Burdekin and Stone (8), Wells (9)). These latter instruments could not however be used to sense opening at a fatigue crack tip and fell out of favour.

Further developments leading to the present COD procedure (7) were based on the observation that in a bend-specimen configuration, theoretical rigid-plastic solutions point to the formation of a fixed hinge-centre in the uncracked ligament so that crack-tip displacements after limit load can be related by simple geometry to clip-gauge displacements which are easier to measure. In practice, however, the relationship between the two displacements is far from simple due to work-hardening, contributions from the pre-limit load phase, the intervention of cracking and other phenomena. Although the basic idea was discussed some 14 years ago by Egan (10) research is still going on (Lin et al (11)). Correlations in non-rotational limit configurations are even more difficult.

Correlations between crack-mouth-opening and load-point movement can also be used to determine J in bend testing as shown by Sumpter and Turner (12).

It is unfortunate in some ways that most of the techniques used to determine CTOD are indirect, as the uncertainties caused thereby tend to obscure the relationship between the two important fracture indices J_c and δ_c. Some of the effects influencing this relationship have been reviewed by Paranjpe and Banerjee (13) but it seems possible that a better understanding would develop given more direct measurement of events in the crack tip and plastic zone regions.

NOTCH ROOT CONTRACTION

The term "notch-root-contraction" (hereafter NRC) refers to the dimple or depression which forms at the tip of a stationary crack at the point where it intersects with the surface. In the case of a plane specimen with a straight-fronted crack it is defined herein as the sum of the maximum dimple depths on either side of the specimen in absolute terms. (The maximum contraction is found precisely at the crack tip in practice).

The significance of transverse contraction as an indicator of toughness was noted over a hundred years ago by Kirkcaldy and there are several allusions in the literature to the concept, as a post-fracture measurement which can be applied to the broken halves of a toughness specimen (see for example, Tipper (14)). It was thought to show less scatter as a measured parameter than absorbed energy. During the early stages of COD test development in the U.K., Burdekin (15), among others, commented on an approximate equality which seemed to exist between critical COD and post-fracture NRC. The measurement was included in a British Standard Draft for Development (16) as an ancillary check which could be made, but was not passed on to the final Standard (7).

Previous work

A surprisingly exact equality between on-load CTOD and NRC was noted by the author in (3) which described some 3-point bend tests employing a double-cantilever NRC gauge and a 'paddle' gauge for CTOD. A plasticity-based explanation of the phenomenon was given, the essential feature being that the opening-mode plastic displacement of material in the interior of the specimen is indicated by thickness-direction movement of triangular wedges of material on the surface (see figure 1). Equality of the opening and contraction displacements is obtained if the 45° slip planes break surface parallel to the crack plane, as they seem to do. Note that this model does not depend on the development of a plane stress plastic zone or a limit-load mechanism but persists from the lowest level of loading in plane strain.

The initial exploratory tests which were largely in the below-general-yield regime, also showed that autographic load/NRC plots can provide sensitive monitoring of toughness tests with regard to triaxial constraint and crack growth. Hence there is a distinct value in the technique aside from the possibility that it indicates CTOD directly.

New series of general yielding NRC tests

Correlation of NRC and CTOD is more difficult to establish with fatigue pre-cracked specimens and under general yielding conditions, due to the aforementioned problem of measuring CTOD directly. However a basis for comparison of on-load NRC and a thoretical formulation of CTOD in a single-edge-notch specimen subject to tension was developed in terms of a closed-form fit to Dugdale model data by Gray (17). Comparative tests were carried out using pin-loaded specimens 62.5 mm wide by 25 mm thick, made from a steel with a relatively flat-topped stress/strain characteristic. The starter notch was machined to a chevron configuration to promote a straight-fronted fatigue pre-crack and some other small improvements in testing technique were made. A hardness machine was utilised to position a small indentation on each side of the specimen near to the crack tip and these served to locate the NRC transducer shown in figure 2 in the correct position.

After the tests, which were in most cases suspended before complete separation, the specimens were subjected to destructive measurements which examined residual crack tip shapes and the nature of any stable crack growth. A typical load/NRC curve is shown in figure 3.

Theoretical CTOD calculations

The dashed curves in figure 3 are based on the strip-yielding zone concept but incorporate a work-hardening term, an arbitrary yield strength elevation factor e to account for the effect of triaxial stress state on yield in the manner of Wells (18) and are further adjusted to compensate for an elastic component of NRC.

The basic relationship between CTOD and load for uniform yield strength in the strip zone is given by (17)

$$\delta = \frac{8}{\pi}\frac{\sigma_Y}{E} \ln \sec \left(\frac{\pi}{2}\frac{\sigma}{\sigma_Y}\right) f\left(\frac{a}{W}, \frac{\rho}{W}, \frac{\sigma}{\sigma_Y}\right) \tag{1}$$

with a subsidiary determination of plastic zone length

$$\rho = a \left(\sec\left(\frac{\pi}{2}\frac{\sigma}{\sigma_Y}\right) - 1\right) f\left(\frac{a}{W}, \frac{\sigma}{\sigma_Y}\right) \tag{2}$$

which also fixes the limit condition when the notional plastic zone has spread completely across the uncracked ligament; in agreement with the determinations of Chell (19) and Ewing and Richards (20) for plane stress, resulting in

$$\frac{\sigma_L}{\sigma_Y} = \left(1 - \frac{a}{W}\right)^2 \tag{3}$$

(Note the plane strain limit loads are substantially higher for $\frac{a}{W} < 0.6$, see (20) and Rice (21)).

The work-hardening characteristic was determined via an incremental cyclic test, expressed in terms of a law of the type $\varepsilon/\varepsilon_o = (\sigma/\sigma_o)^n$ and a representative yield strength in the strip zone was calculated through the equation

$$\sigma_Y = \frac{\sigma_o}{(\varepsilon_o B)^{1/n}} \frac{n}{n+1} (\delta)^{1/n} \tag{4}$$

(See Appendix)

Equations (1), (2) and (4) were then solved iteratively with σ_o as the starting value for σ_Y.

At very low levels of NRC, in thick specimens especially, the gross elastic transverse contraction due to Poisson's ratio contributes significantly to the measured NRC but of course has no correlation with COD according to the model in figure 1. This contraction was shown experimentally to lie between the gross and nett stress transverse compliances, i.e. $\nu P/(WE) <$ NRC elastic $< \nu P/(W - a)E$. As this implies a very small correction it was considered reasonable to measure it directly through the initial linear elastic slope of the load/NRC traces and add it to the values derived from equation (1) in order to allow comparison with the raw autographic trace. (Neglect of this elastic term in the earlier tests (3) led to a spuriously low estimation of the triaxial elevation factor e at low NRCs).

Solution of the equations was programmed for a computer-driven plotter which was used to draw load/CTOD curves directly on to the autographic record for comparison. The elevation factor was then altered to give reasonable coincidence of 'plane-strain' and 'plane-stress' theoretical CTOD curves with appropriate segments of the NRC trace. The implications of the transitional change in elevation factor will be discussed later.

Post-test comparisons

Harrison and Milne (22) have expressed doubts about NRC measurement on the grounds that it may be a 'surface' phenomenon which is poorly correlated with internal deformations. This possibility was investigated by surface grinding the deformed specimens in parallel planes down to the mid-thickness and measuring the resulting crack profiles using a projection microscope. A typical set of profiles is shown in figure 4.

It is not certain that a close correlation between off-load CTOD and NRC should be expected as the mechanism shown in figure 1 may not be entirely reversible. In some of the present tests, there had been some stable crack growth at mid-thickness and in any case the problem of defining the exact point to measure CTOD makes interpretation difficult. However consistent measurements in a given specimen emerged when the point of measurement was taken at a point one COD width back from the blunt tip and comparison with residual NRC measured from the autographic trace is made on this basis in table 1 below.

TABLE 1 - Comparison of internal residual CTOD and NRC

a/W	0.21	0.3	0.42	0.54	0.55
CTOD average in central third mm	0.17	0.51	0.42	0.54	0.55
NRC mm	0.19	0.56	0.38	0.42	0.45
Comments	-	0.3mm SCG	-	0.3mm SCG	SCG and blunting

The CTODs were some 20% less at the surface than in the central third but this again may not apply to on-load measurements.

Stable Crack Growth (SCG)

Small amounts of crack growth were discovered on sectioning several specimens (as can be seen on figure 4) and further crack tip regions were discovered which exhibited negligible residual strength (a condition which is identical to crack growth as far as the strip-yielding model is concerned). Some indication of such events could normally be identified on the autographic trace although the amount of crack growth could not be assessed. The discontinuities corresponding to crack growth most often took the form of horizontal jerks in the trace (clearly seen during the test if load-control was used) but occasionally a short upward step would appear (see figure 5). The NRC transducer therefore gives a sensitive indication of crack growth activity.

Interferometric measurement of crack tip surface profiles

The technique for recording displacement fields is described in detail elsewhere (4). Briefly, a 1000 lines per mm epoxy cross-grating is bonded to the specimen surface over the crack with one of the grating directions parallel to the crack plane. When the specimen is strained, a 50 mm dia. region of the crack tip can be interrogated using a reference 'grid' produced by the interference of a laser beam pair and the resulting fringe pattern can be photographed directly (see figure 6). The opening-mode displacement sensitivity is one micron per fringe. An enlargement of the photograph is analysed by locating the x coordinates of the intersection of given fringes with the crack edge. A computer plotting tablet is used for this and the resulting data can then be drawn out automatically in terms of crack tip surface profiles (see figure 7). Figure 8 gives a typical comparison of on-load NRC (less elastic factor) and surface CTOD as measured by interferometry.

The method is hardly suitable for routine testing at the present stage but it is being used semi-routinely for CTOD testing of material or specimen shapes where CTOD cannot be measured through clip-gauge techniques. It is particularly suitable also for the calibration of hinge-centre correlations as the rigid portions of the crack border can be identified and the relative rotations measured with great accuracy.

Summary

Three separate methods have been applied to investigate the relationship between CTOD and NRC in single-edge-notch specimens subject to tension and loaded to general yield and the point of stable crack growth. The results confirm the earlier finding of a one-to-one relationship between the parameters.

YIELD TRANSITIONS

The load/CTOD relation is clearly sensitive to yield strength and the procedure whereby the apparent constraint is determined by matching the theory to the test results requires discussion. The assumption underlying this procedure is that the load/CTOD relation depends more on the effective yield strength of the material in the ligament than on the precise topography of yielding. Given that the work-hardening influence is accounted for separately, the remaining apparent strength elevation should be caused by triaxiality.

Attempts to relate J and δ through the strip yielding formulation $J = \sigma_Y \delta$ are based on a similar reasoning - if in a given case a fixed yield strength serves to relate corresponding J and δ values which have been determined independently by whatever means, then the strip yield model is valid for that case, and the derived value of σ_Y is implicitly 'effective'. The danger of basing such a determination on a spot value from a loading curve (e.g. $J_c = e\,\sigma_Y\,\delta_c$) without regard to the preceding path should be clear from fig.3. Equally it is unrealistic to expect a fixed elevation factor to persist over a complete loading curve, as the yielding constraint is likely to alter during the test. Robinson's suggestion (23) that the J/δ relationship is material and/or geometry dependent is therefore correct but need not cause difficulties. As long as the apparent elevation factor truly reflects the prevailing constraint and not other factors, then it is highly relevant to the practice of toughness evaluation.

Experimental results

The yield strength elevation factors determined in the present test series are therefore held to be real indicators of triaxial constraint and as shown in table 2, a consistent pattern was found over a range of notch depths, whereby the initial constraint factor was high in the region of the plane strain factor of two reported by Boyle and Wells (24) and relaxation followed to a level somewhat above unity.

TABLE 2 - Yielding Transition Data

a/W	initial e	final	start ρ/B	finish	transition P/PL	final
0.21	2.1	1.3	0.1	1.3	0.85	1.18
0.3	2.0	1.2	0.12	1.43	0.67	1.18
0.42	1.8	1.35	0.19	0.93	0.73	1.19
0.54	1.7	1.23	0.14	1.3	0.53	1.09
0.55	1.9	1.25	0.16	0.87	0.61	1.14

The start and finish points of the transitions are best indexed in terms of calculated plastic zone size to thickness ratio (columns 4 and 5). Transitions began when the strip-yield-zone lengths were 10% - 20% of the thickness and were virtually complete when the plastic zones were approximately the same size as the specimen thickness.

The data in column 6 shows that the trace inflexion which has been identified as the start of transition is not due to the intervention of limit load as the loads were much below the theoretical limit condition. Note also from column 7 that the final load levels were higher than the limit load (already corrected for work-hardening). This indicated that the yielding constraints identified via the Dugdale model are confirmed independently by the limit load criteria.

Further confirmations of the plastic zone size can be obtained from post-test NRC contour information. Given that the x dimension of the 'zero' plastic NRC contour indicates the extent of the notional strip-yield-zone length, the plastic zone dimensions agree reasonably with the values in table 2. The pattern of yielding indicated is similar in form to the plane-strain limit models of refs (20, 21) although there is clearly an element of plane stress deformation associated with the stretching mode.

Implications for J/δ relation

These results show that if the constraint changes during the course of loading and if the point of transition can be altered by geometric effects (principally thickness change), then different final values of J could be associated with the same final deformation state as characterised by δ. The question then arises whether crack initiation is better characterised by an index of the mechanical state at that instant (e.g. δ_c) or by an index which effectively reflects the deformation history up to that point (J_c). Of course these distinctions disappear if the J_c calculation is based on an experimentally based formulation which implies constant constraint up to the critical point (e.g. ref 12).

One answer to these imponderables is to monitor the cracked body using a technique which allows direct determination of both parameters. The Moire application previously described is in theory capable of such a task. Mackenzie and others (25) have shown that J can be measured directly by integrating work/energy terms round a path as in the original Rice formulation. This requires three orientations of displacement measurement at each load level (x, y, 45°) and the path must be drawn to track through material where the stress/strain law is known, but the results for small-scale yielding at least are encouraging. The amount of laborious fringe analysis implied is a drawback of such a method but on-line video-processing of the three fringe patterns could be used to produce an instantaneous readout.

Other configurations

Indexing of triaxial constraint in this case depended on comparison with the predictions of a strip-yield model for a specific geometry. For other configurations of test specimen, similar formulations would clearly be helpful. Reference (17) gives formulations for a central internal notch, a DENT specimen and a circumferentially cracked cylindrical bar. (19) gives a solution for a SENB specimen and Terada (26), a solution for the popular compact tension specimen. Finite element solutions which yield a relationship between load and CTOD (and preferably also plastic zone size) are equally applicable. Work-hardening adjustments similar to equation (4) will further facilitate comparison in these cases. Miyamoto and Kageyama (27) also give results for an internally cracked plate where the yielding occurs on plane strain strips inclined on either side of the crack plane.

CONCLUSIONS

Two forms of displacement measurement which focus attention on the near-crack-tip region have been applied to SENT fracture toughness specimens loaded to general yield. The results have been analysed and compared to demonstrate several features of such measurements, namely:

1. A direct relationship between plastic NRC and CTOD.
2. Sensitive indication of stable crack growth.
3. A capability to index triaxial constraint by comparison with the strip yield model and by measurement of plastic zone length.

NRC measurements are shown to be as simple to make in routine toughness testing as crack-mouth-opening displacements. The interferometric method described has a potential for calibration of load/CTOD/J relationships and hinge-centre determination. This gives scope for the use of a greater variety of fracture specimen configurations.

A theoretical procedure for gauging the influence of work-hardening on autographic plots and limit loads has been checked against experimental data.

The influence of triaxial constraint on yielding and its resultant effect on J/δ relationships has been highlighted and the importance of indexing constraint in toughness testing has been shown.

SYMBOLS USED

a = crack length

B = thickness of specimen

δ = crack-tip-opening-displacement (CTOD)

e = yield strength elevation factor

E = Young's Modulus

ε_o = reference strain in work-hardening law

J = path independent integral (29)

n = index in work-hardening law

ν = Poisson's ratio

ρ = plastic zone length in Dugdale Model

σ = gross applied stress

σ_o = reference stress in work hardening law

σ_L = stress at limit condition

σ_Y = yield strength

W = width of specimen

REFERENCES

1. Irwin, G. R., 1960, J Basic Eng, 417.
2. Wells, A. A., 1963, Brit. Weld. J, 563.
3. Gray, T. G. F., 1971, I.J.Fracture, 8, 3.
4. McDonach, A. M., McKelvie, J., Mackenzie, P. & Walker, C. A., 1983, Exp. Techniques, 7, 6, 20-24.
5. "E399-81 Standard Test Method for plane-strain toughness of metallic materials" in "Annual Book of ASTM standards - pt.10", ASTM, Philadelphia 1982.
6. "E813-81 Standard test method for J_{Ic} a measure of fracture toughness" ASTM loc.cit.
7. BS 5762:1979 "Crack opening displacement (COD) testing", British Standards Institution, London.
8. Burdekin, F. M. and Stone, D. E. W., 1966, J. Strain Anal., 1, 2.
9. Wells, A. A., 1967, "Fracture control of thick steels for pressure vessels", Anglo-German Welding Conf., Dusseldorf, Weld. Inst., Abingdon.

10. Egan, G. R., 1969,"The compatibility of K_{Ic} and COD tests", Welding Institute, Abingdon, Report E24/3/69.

11. Lin, I.-H., et al, 1982, I.J.Fracture 20, 1, R3.

12. Sumpter, J. D. G. and Turner, C.E., 1976, "Method for laboratory determination of J_c" in "Cracks and Fracture STP 601", ASTM,Philadelphia.

13. Paranjpe, S. A. and Banerjee, S., 1979, Eng.Fract.Mechs., 11, 3 - 53.

14. Tipper, C. F., 1962, "The Brittle Fracture Story", Camb. Univ. Press.

15. Burdekin, F.M., 1967, Brit. Weld. J., 14, 12, 649 - 659.

16. DD19, 1972, "Methods for Crack Opening Displacement (COD) testing", BSI, London.

17. Gray, T. G. F., 1977, "A closed form approach to the assessment of practical crack propagation problems",in "Fract.Mechanics in Engineering Practice", editor P. Stanley, Applied Science Publishers, London.

18. Wells, A. A., 1969, Eng.Fract.Mechs. 6, 399 - 410.

19. Chell, G. G., 1976, I.J.Fracture, 12, 1, 135 - 147.

20. Ewing, D. J. F. and Richards, C. E., 1974, J.Mech.Phys Solids., 22, 27 - 36.

21. Rice, J. R., 1972, "The line spring model for surface flaws" in "The Surface Crack", editor J. L. Swedlow, ASME.

22. Harrison, R. P. and Milne, I., 1979, Phil.Trans. Roy.Soc., Series A, 299, 145 - 153.

23. Robinson, J. N., 1976, I.J.Fract., 12, 5.

24. Boyle, E.F. and Wells, A.A., 1973, "A finite element study of plane-strain fracture criteria under elastic-plastic conditions", Dept. of Civil Eng., Queen's University, Belfast.

25. McKelvie, J., MacKenzie, P., Walker, C.A. and Gray, T.G.F., 1983, "Measurement of J for Arbitrary Geometry and Load using a Moire method". Tech. Note, Centre for Industrial Innovation, University of Strathclyde.

26. Terada, H., 1982, I.J.Fract., 20, R15.

27. Miyamoto, H. and Kageyama, K., 1982, "The application of the theory of the continuously distributed dislocations to the elastic-plastic analysis of a cracked body", Bull. Fract. Mechs., 1, Science University of Tokyo.

28. Onat, E. T. and Prager, W., 1954, J. Appl.Phys. 25,291.

29. Rice, J. R., 1967, "A path independent integral and the approximate analysis of strain concentration by notches and cracks", ARPA SD 86 Report E39, Brown University.

30. Heald,P.T.,Spink,G.M.,Worthington,P.J.,1972,"Mat.Sci.& Engin.",10,129.

APPENDIX

Effect of work hardening on yield strength in strip zone

If the opening mode plastic strain at any point along the strip is assumed to be proportional to the opening displacement v at that point, the restraining stress across the strip is given by

$$\sigma(v) = \sigma_o \left(\frac{v}{g\varepsilon_o}\right)^{1/n} \qquad (5)$$

where g is a convenient gauge length, often taken to be equal to the specimen thickness (28).

The J integral value for such a work-hardening strip is given by (29)

$$J = \int_o^\delta \sigma(v).dv$$

$$= \frac{\sigma_o}{(\varepsilon_o g)^{1/n}} \frac{n}{n+1} \delta^{\frac{n+1}{n}} \qquad (6)$$

whereas for a strip with uniform yield strength σ_Y ,

$$J = \sigma_Y \delta \qquad (7)$$

Hence a 'representative' uniform yield strength, which would give the correct value of δ in a work-hardening model, can be determined by equating (6) and (7) giving

$$\sigma_Y = \frac{\sigma_o}{(\varepsilon_o g)^{1/n}} \frac{n}{n+1} \delta^{1/n} \qquad (8)$$

Equation 8 tends to underestimate the work-hardening effect especially at low CTOD values ($\delta < \varepsilon_Y B$) where the non-linear law gives smaller stresses than the Dugdale rigid-plastic assumption.

Note also that for linear work-hardening, equation (8) becomes $\sigma_Y = (\sigma_o + \sigma_u)/2$ as assumed by Heald et al (30).

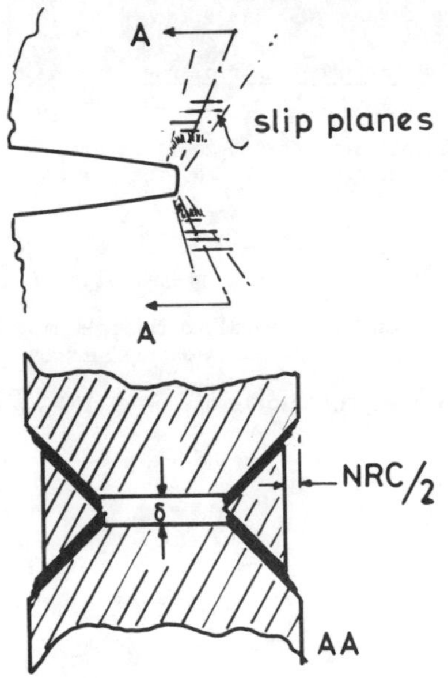

Figure 1 NRC Mechanism

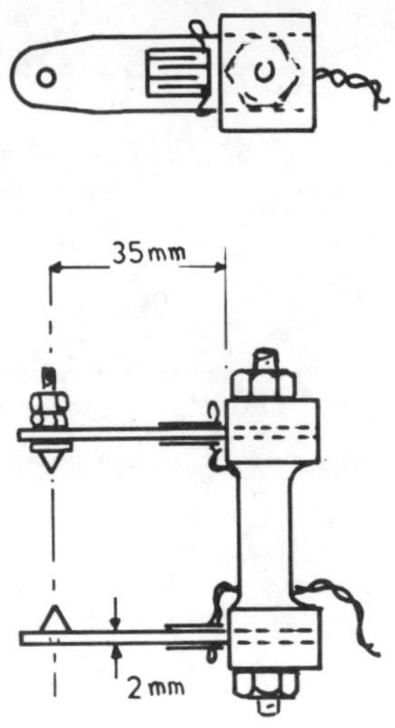

Figure 2 NRC Transducer

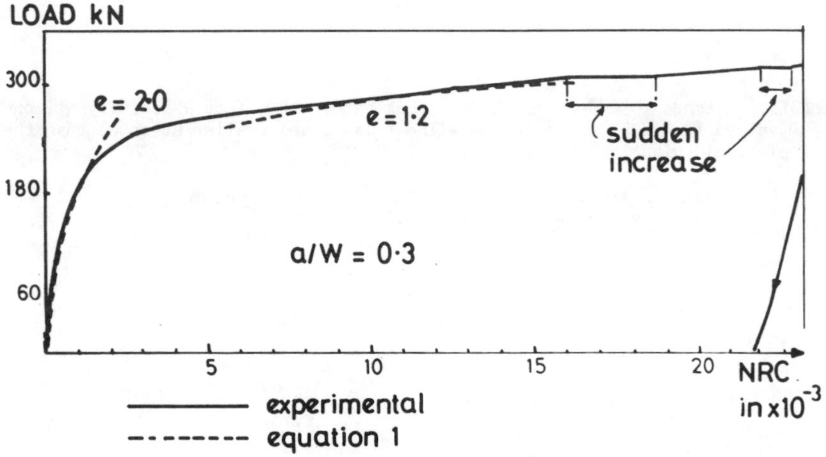

Figure 3 Comparison of NRC and CTOD from strip-yield theory

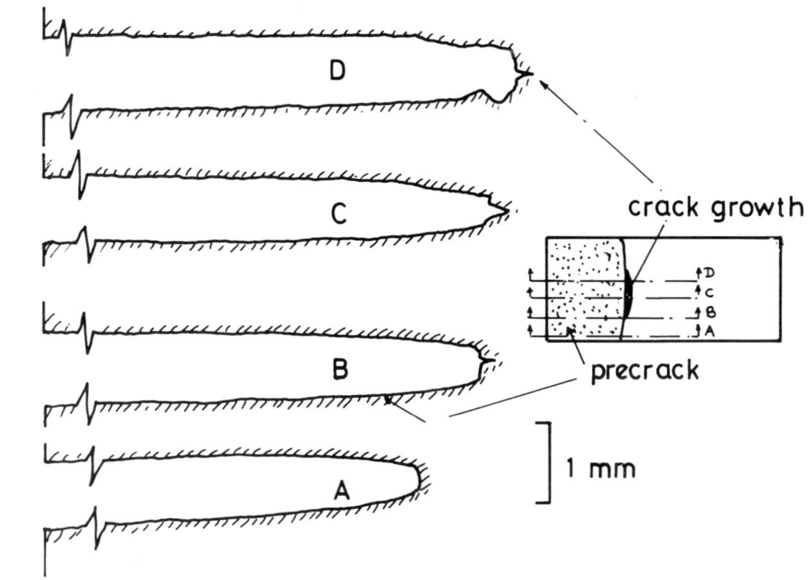

Figure 4 Crack tip profiles taken from cross-sections (autographic trace for this specimen in figure 3)

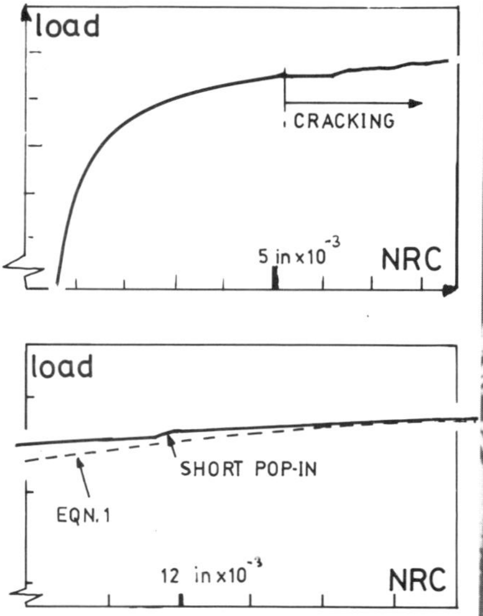

Figure 5 Trace discontinuities due to SCG

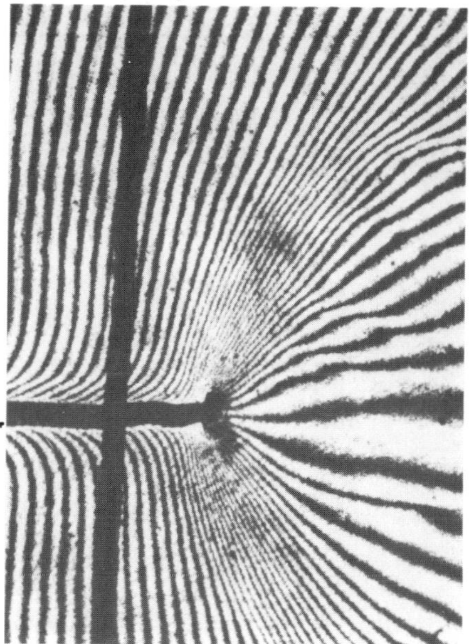

Figure 6 y displacement fringe pattern

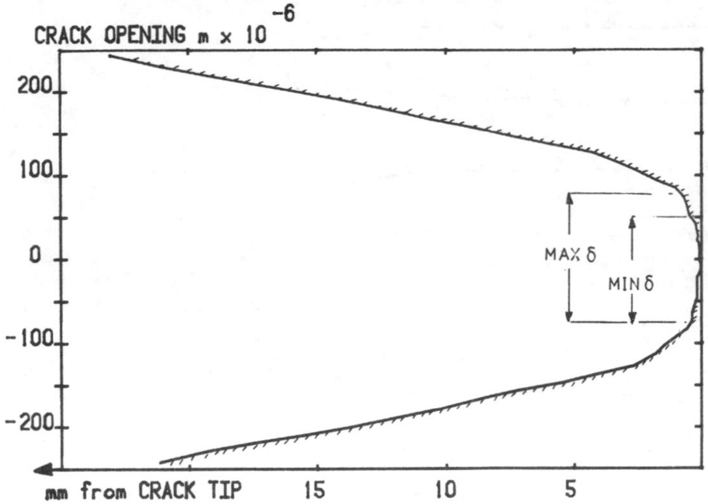

Figure 7 Computer plot of crack profile from fringe photo

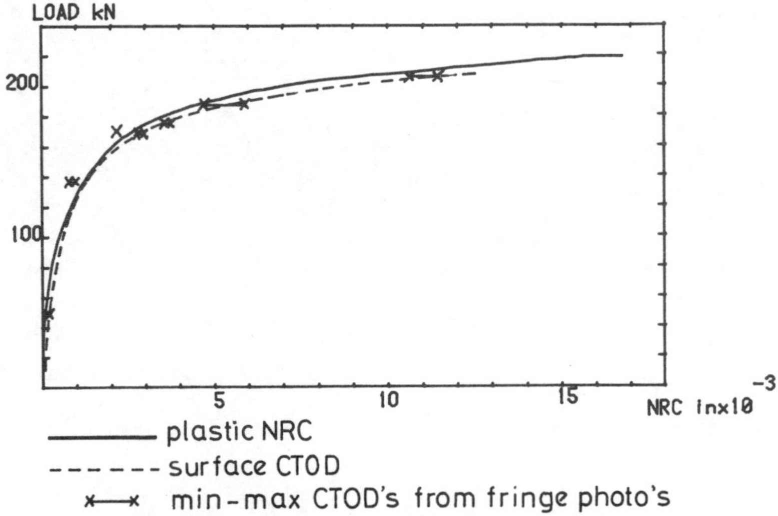

Figure 8 Comparison of optical COD with plastic NRC

NUCLEAR REACTORS

IODINE STRESS CORROSION CRACKING IN ZIRCALOY

A.H.P.Andrade* and R.M.N.Pelloux**

The subcritical growth of iodine-induced cracks in unirradiated Zircaloy plates is investigated as a function of the stress intensity factor K. The testing variables are: crystallographic texture (f-Number),microstructure (grain directionaly), heat treatment (stress relieved vs recrystallized plate), and temperature. The iodine partial pressure is 40Pa.

INTRODUCTION

The Zircaloys have been developed for improved corrosion resistance up to 623K and their typical use is in fuel cladding of LWR nuclear plants. Cladding tubes for PWRs is used in a cold-worked and stress-relieved condition (CWSR). Annealed Zircaloy generally is used for BWRs cladding and others parts of the reactor system.

The Pellet-Cladding Interaction (PCI) phenomenon which affects the Zircaloy cladding of LWR fuel rods is a manifestation of stress corrosion cracking (SCC) with the causative agent being most likely iodine. During SCC, cleavage of Zircaloys is prominent only on planes near the basal planes. Thermodynamic data by Cubicciotti et al (1) leads to the conclusion that solid iodides on the Zircaloy surface are involved in the mechanism of iodine-induced SCC. It is shown also that ZrI_4 must be the gaseous species involved in any mechanism in which vapor transport of Zr is important.

* Comissão Nacional de Energia Nuclear - São Paulo, Brasil
** Massachusetts Institute of Technology, Cambridge, USA

Two metallurgical parameters which can have an influence on SCC of Zircaloys are crystallographic texture and heat treatment condition.

The crystallographic texture, i.e. the development of a preferred orientation of the grains in the final product is one consequence of the fabrication process of the zirconium-based alloys. The concept of an f-parameter introduced by Kearns (2) can be used as a quantitative index of the effective texture, where the single f-number represents the effective fraction of basal poles aligned in any one reference direction.

Syrett et al (3) showed that the greater the tangential texture of the Zircaloy fuel cladding, the greater the susceptibility to SCC. Knorr and Pelloux (4) found that texture has a strong influence on K_{ISCC}.

This work was undertaken to determine the kinetics of iodine-induced crack growth in Zircaloy, using a fracture mechanics approach. Crack propagation occurs by a mixture of cleavage and ductile tearing (fluting) in CWSR materials but may involve intergranular processes in unirradiated, recrystallized materials (5).

MATERIALS AND TEST METHODS

Double cantilever beam (DCB) type of specimen from plate material was used in this work. They have dimensions of 12.7 mm width by 12.7 mm height (2h) by 40.6 mm total length with a machined notch 16.5 mm long. The specimens are machined from different orientations in the plate. In the designation of orientation, the first letter gives the direction of specimen loading (i.e., crack opening) while the second letter indicates the direction of crack growth. Table 1 shows the chemical composition of these plates.

The fabrication schedules of the plates were controlled in a way which resulted in two different initial textures. Plate "S" texture representated that which results from standard commercial plate rolling procedure. The texture consists of one with basal planes parallel to the rolling plane and basal poles in the normal-transverse plane tilted approximately 40 degrees to the transverse direction from the normal direction. Plate "P" is warm cross-rolled to give a normal (0°) texture; (0002) pole figures for both materials are shown in (4). Texture f-numbers are listed in Table 2.

The plates were subjected to two different heat treatments. The grains of the CWSR material are flattened with the smallest grain dimension measured through the plate thickness; for both plates that grain dimension is 4-6 µm. The dimensions in the longitudinal direction are in the range of 20-25 µm and in the transverse direction 12-15 µm. The grain size for the recrystallized plate is 8-10 µm.

SCC growth tests were conducted at 298, 373, and 583 K in highly purified argon + 40Pa iodine flowing gas environment. The gas purification system illustrated in Figure 1 was able to deliver a partial pressure of iodine of minimal water vapor and metal iodides content. The system was built with materials known to be inert to iodine attack. The test chamber was made with glass and gold-plated stainless steel to prevent volatile metal iodides from the test environment. The chamber has mechanical feed-through to permit the application of an external load to the specimen on a universal testing machine.

Stress intensity factor for DCB-type specimen can be calculated using the expression:

$$K_I = (2p/Bh^2).(3h(a+.6h)^2 + h^3)^{\frac{1}{2}} \qquad (1)$$

To perform a SCC test using this specimen, the fatigue pre-cracked specimen is exposed to the environment and loaded to an initial displacement. The load drops due to crack growth and the crack length a is measured on the side of the specimen as a function of time. The crack tip velocity can be calculated from the slope of the crack length versus time plot. Stress intensities corresponding to each measured velocity are obtained from the expression above if the corresponding a and p are known.

RESULTS

Iodine-induced stress corrosion crack growth was observed for all orientations tested and at all temperatures investigated.

The general appearance of da/dt vs. K behavior at 583K of the S-plate material for three different orientations is shown in Figure 2. A low-K region (regime I) exhibited strong K dependence SCC growth, and a high-K region (regime II) where the K dependence of da/dt is weaker. The data obtained by Cox and Wood (6) at 573K is plotted in this figure for comparison.

Figure 3 shows the effect of the heat treatment on the crack growth behavior of specimens of S-plate, NL orientation. For the same K value, the crack growth rate was higher for the stress--relieved material. At low K values there was some evidence of intergranular cracking in the recrystallized material.

Figure 4 gives the crack growth rate as a function of K for specimens of CWSR S-plate material (NT orientation) tested at 298, 373, and 583K. Scanning electron microscopy revealed a tendency for extensive "fluting" in the transgranular fractures at room temperature and also at 373K.

DISCUSSION

The hypothesis of an adsorption-type mechanism which reduces the Zr-Zr bond strength in certain crystallographic directions at the crack tip is a reasonable explanation for the predominantly transgranular crack propagation in the iodine-induced SCC of Zircaloy. The study done by Krishnan et al (7) provides a better understanding of the chemisorption process of iodine on clean zirconium surfaces. Their results show that iodine chemisorbed on zirconium is chemically more stable than combined in the zirconium iodides. So, iodine can initially react with exposed zirconium surface and the solid iodide available to be transferred to fresh zirconium surface, when the metal is strained. Possible mechanisms of transference are surface diffusion of iodides species or vapor transport as ZrI_4 gas.

Due to the mostly crystallographic transgranular cracking of iodine-induced SCC of Zircaloy, it is not surprizing that texture influences the velocity and morphology of crack propagation as shown by our results. Hence, texture that aligns basal poles toward the tensile stress axis should increase the rate of subcritical crack growth at a given K value. The crack growth rate for the P-plate, NT orientation (f_N = 0.70) is the highest among those specimens tested at 583K. Also, the rates of crack growth for specimens of S-plate in both NL or NT orientation (f_N = 0.56) are higher than that for the TL orientation (f_T = 0.33) as shown in Figure 2.

Independently of the texture effects, the microstructural directionality of the grains also affects the rate of crack growth. The grains tend to become elongated in the rolling direction during fabrication leading to anisotropy of the crack growth rate, i.e. the velocity of cracks in specimens of NL orientation (crack growth parallel to the rolling direction) are higher than those for specimens in the NT orientation (crack growth normal to the rolling direction) for all values of K in tests at 583K.

As shown in Figure 3, the crack velocities for SR Zircaloy are higher than those for recrystallized Zircaloy at a given K value. In a qualitative sense, this is consistent with the higher mechanical strength and lower ductility of the SR material. In addition, the extrapolation of the curves corroborates the results of (4) who have found that K_{ISCC} for CWSR Zircaloy is lower than for the recrystallized material.

In a number of iodine-containing environments(8), the SCC growth in Zircaloy appears to start as an intergranular chemical process and changes to a transgranular propagation process. In this work some evidence of intergranular cracking is observed in the recrystallized material at low K values (near K_{ISCC}) as shown in Figure 3. The crack growth rates for intergranular processes are much slower than for transgranular cracking. Intergranular cracking seems to require a combination of a suitable K value and heat treatment condition (recrystallized material).

There is often a significant occurrence of fluting and other ductile processes during tests at lower temperatures (Figure 4); this is indicative of the high stress levels (high K values for a given crack depth) reached in the experiments since the fluted regions are associated with high local tensile strain (8). The flute spacing for a specimen tested at room temperature, for instance, is about 5 μm whereas the grain size is relatively small (15-25 μm). The occurrence of fluting requires considerable expenditure of strain energy in the process of crack propagation leading to a much slower growth rate as evidenced in Figure 4. This result is in conflict with results by (6) who have found little or no difference in crack velocity for Zircaloy tested in iodine between 298 and 573K. It is also apparent in Figure 4 that the extrapolated K_{ISCC} value is displaced to higher K values as the temperature increases.

SYMBOLS USED

LWR = Light Water Reactor

PWR = Pressurized Water Reactor

BWR = Boiling Water Reactor

p = Load (kg)

h = One-half the specimen height (m)

L = Longitudinal direction in the plate

N = Normal direction in the plate

T = Transverse direction in the plate

REFERENCES

1. Cubicciotti,D.,Jones,R.L.,and Syrett,B.C.,1980,"Stress Corrosion Cracking of Zircaloys",EPRI NP-1329.

2. Kearns,J.J.,1965,"Thermal Expansion and Preferred Orientation in Zircaloy",WAPD-TM-742.

3. Syrett,B.C.,Cubicciotti,D.,and Jones,R.L.,1979,"Some Observations on the Influence of Tube Manufacturing Technique on Iodine Stress Corrosion Cracking of Unirradiated Zircaloy", Proc. of the ANS Topical Meeting on LWR Fuel Performance, Portland, Oregon, p.113.

4. Knorr,D.B.,and Pelloux,R.M.,1982,Metal.Trans.A 13,73

5. Videm,K,and Lunde,L.,1979,"Stress Corrosion Crack Initiation and Growth and Formation of Pellet-Clad Interaction Defects", Zirconium in the Nuclear Industry (Fourth Conf.) ASTM STP 681,p.229.

6. Cox,B.,and Wood,J.C.,1977,"The Mechanism of SCC of Zirconium Alloys in Halogens",Proc.Int.Conf. on Mechanisms of Environment Sensitive Cracking of Materials,Guildford,U.K.,Eds.P.R. Swann et al.,The Metals Society,London,p.520.

7. Krishnan,G.N.,Wood,B.J.,and Cubicciotti,D.,1980,J.Electrochem. Soc. 127,2738.

8. Cox,B.,1975,Rev.Coatings&Corr. 1,367.

TABLE 1 - Chemical Composition of Zircaloy Plates

Chief Alloying Elements	S-Plate(Zircaloy 4)	P-Plate(Zircaloy 2)
Sn	1.52w/o	1.51w/o
Fe	.20w/o	.14w/o
Cr	.11w/o	.10w/o
Ni	35 ppm	.05w/o
O	1160 ppm	1310 ppm

TABLE 2 - Kearns' f-Number for Zircaloy Plates

	S-Plate(Zry 4)		P-Plate(Zry 2)
f-Number	SR	RX	SR
f_N	.56	.59	.70
f_T	.33	.32	.19
f_L	.09	.09	.09

S-Plate: SR-Stress Relieved at 785K for 4 hours
RX-Recrystallized at 898K for 4 hours

P-Plate: SR-Stress Relieved at 770K for 4 hours

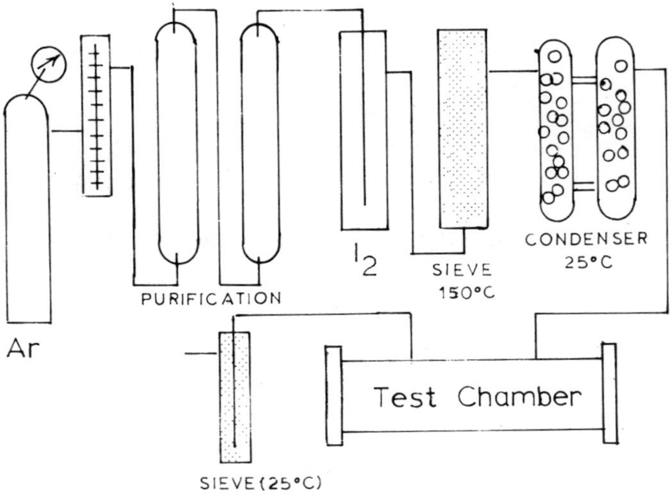

Figure 1 Diagram of the flowing gas (Ar + 40Pa I_2) system

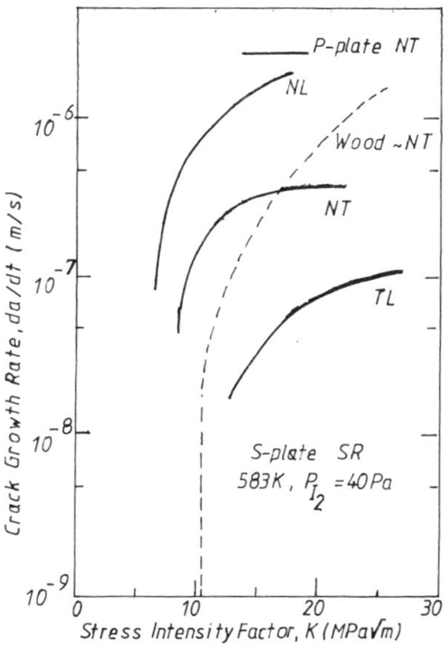

Figure 2 da/dt vs K behavior at 583K

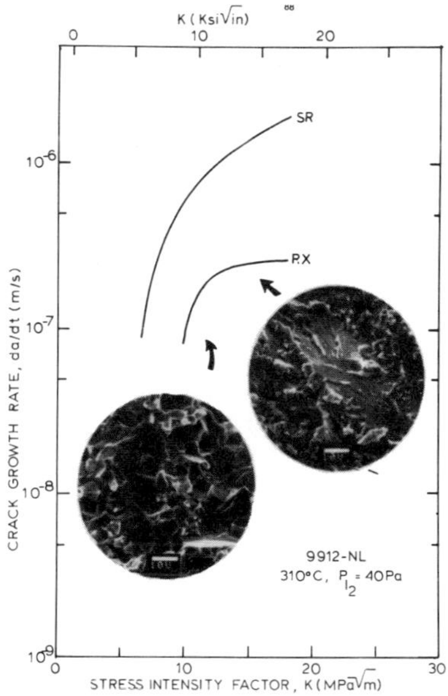

Figure 3 Effect of heat treatment on crack growth of S-plate

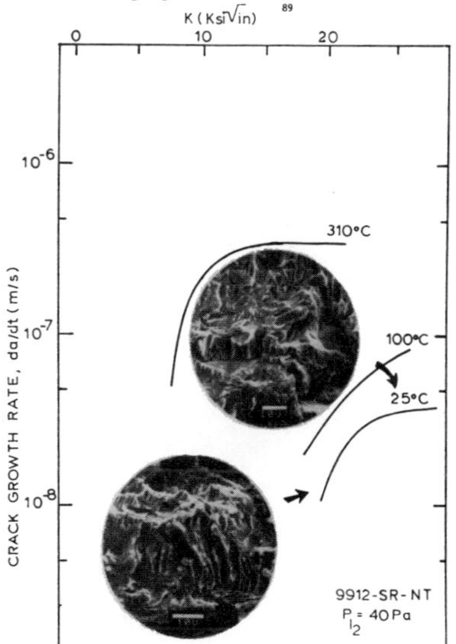

Figure 4 Effect of temperature on crack growth of S-plate material

COLD FORMING DEGREE AND HEAT TREATMENT ON WStE 26 DISHED HEADS

H.J. Hamel * and F.P. R. Correa *

For the first heads of vessels for nuclear use in Brazil the problem of determination of cold forming degree and the effects of cold deformation on the mechanical properties as well as the heat treatment criteria are discussed.

INTRODUCTION

The nuclear program established between Brazil and Germany foresees in its initial phase a participation of the national industry for the manufacture of about 30% of the necessary components.

This manufacture is partially based on know-how coming from respective German partners. Not in all cases the common technology used in Germany can be used in Brazil. Therefore, adaptations to the existing technology have to be made.

One example for this adaptation process will be given in this paper which describes the results of qualification for cold forming of heads for vessels for the application for components of nuclear power plants in Brazil. In Germany normally this process is done by hot forming.

The aim of this paper is to show that heads manufactured by cold forming have a sufficient high resistance against brittle fracture. Dimensional influences on the properties will also be discussed.

Basic considerations

Type of heads investigated. The type of heads to be discussed is of the "Klöpper"-type and is produced by cold spinning (Fig.1).The existing specifications require a normalizing in case of carbon steel dished heads, when the cold forming degree is greater than 5%. Three problems had, therefore, to be solved during manufactur-

*Department of Materials of Nuclen

ing of the heads:

1. Determination of degree of cold deformation
2. Effects of cold deformation on the mechanical properties
3. How far heat treatment is really necessary

Materials and dimensions of heads. The heads were made from WStE 26, a fine grained, normalized C-Mn steel. The final dimensions of the heads and the chemical composition of the plates are given in Table 1.

TABLE 1 - Dimensions and Chemical Composition of the Dished Heads

Dished Head No.	Dimensions (Da x S), mm	Chemical Composition, % C	Mn	Si	P	S	Cu	Al	Cr
1 to 4	Ø856 x 8	0,12	1,02	0,22	0,012	0,008	Tr.	0,029	0,02
5,6	Ø502 x 6,3	0,13	1,03	0,22	0,014	0,008	0,003	0,027	0,02

Tr= traces

Determination of degree of deformation

"Klöpper" heads give, due to the manufacturing process the most complex situation for calculation of degree of deformation applied as various types of deformation are superposed.

For a quantitative evaluation of the influence of cold forming by spinning on the mechanical properties the degree of deformation had to be determined. Various methods for determination of the degree of deformation exist. Some are only applicable for a special type of deformation like bending or dishing where reduction in wall thickness is negligibly small. For the more complex spinning process, however, the reduction in thickness direction has to be considered. It could be shown by others (1) that the V.Mises relation describes best the relations during spinning of "Klöpper" heads using the logarithmic degree of deformation. The effective deformation according to V. Mises is :

$$\varphi = \sqrt{\frac{2}{3}\left(\varphi m^2 + \varphi t^2 + \varphi s^2\right)}$$

where, acc. to Fig. 2, φm is the "meridional" or radial deformation, φt, is the "tangential" or circumferential and φs is the "normal" or in thickness deformation.

For the determination of φm and φt a grid of points with a distance of 50 or 25mm respectively apart was marked on that surface of the plates which later will be the outer one of the head. At these points also the initial thickness φs was measured by an ultrasonic method. After deformation the distance of the grid points were measured again and the thickness measurement repeated.

During the qualification process of various heads the deformation has been measured and the results are shown in Fig. 3 where the meridional deformation is plotted against the reduction in wall thickness for carbon and stainless steel.

The results represent the highest values of deformation found at each head. The values of φm are between 17 and 27%,which is in agreement with other authors (2) regarding this forming process with comparable wall thickness and radius. The reduction in wall thickness reaches 9% for carbon steel and 15% for stainless steel.

The investigations showed that the area of highest deformation is close to the edge of the heads. Thus this area was determined for the test coupons for the following mechanical tests as indicated in Fig. 4.

Effects of cold deformation on the mechanical properties

Sampling. The results of the first six dished heads manufactured for qualification were controlled. The dimensions and chemical composition were already given in Table 1. Tests for the mechanical properties of the initial plates were carried out on two sampling locations: top and bottom of the plate. The test coupons for the evaluation after cold forming were taken from the edge region (initially bottom of the plate) as indicated in Fig. 4.

Mechanical tests

Tensile tests. One tensile test at room temperature has been performed at each coupon according to DIN 50145. Specimens were manufactured acc. to DIN 50125 and the following properties were determined:

tensile strength (σ_u), yield strength ($\sigma_{0,2}$) and elongation after fracture (Lo=5 x do) (A5). The comparison of the test results between initial plates and the dished heads can be found in Table 2.

Notched bar impact tests. The notched bar impact tests were performed acc. to DIN 50115 at 0°C using one set of three Charpy V - notch specimens and the absorbed energy (Av) in Joule determined. The results are also included in Table 2.

Evaluation of the tests. Due to applied degrees of deformation above 17% the normal change in properties is that tensile values increase and toughness values decrease. Figure 5 gives a summary of the test results. The yield strength increased between 13 and 43% and the tensile strength 9 up to 22% above the initial values while the elongation after fracture decreased between 17% and 41% and the notch toughness values decreased down to 49% of the initial value.

It can be noted that for all cold formed heads the situation in comparison to the initial properties is as follows: the yield strength increased but as it was not limited by an upper limitation it is accepted as it is. The notch toughness decreased but is above the specified values. The tensile strength increased above the specified values while the elongation decreased slightly below the specified value.

As can be seen from the results the monitoring of toughness properties of cold formed heads is a very important step during manufacturing as brittle fracture especially in carbon steel components can be caused. One way to restore the original properties is to apply a heat treatment. To decide whether a heat treatment is necessary or not the technical rules and regulations are normally checked as they represent the know-how gained during in-service life of components. The German AD-rules (3) allow under certain conditions, which are:

service temperature > -10°C, design temperature < 120°C and wall thickness ≤ 8mm, that heads can be used without heat treatment after cold forming. Applied to the present case of the six heads presented in Table 2 with s < 8mm heat treatment was, therefore, not carried out. Additionally it has be shown (Fig.6) that the notch toughness was still above the specified value.

TABLE 2 - Mechanical Properties of WStE 26 Initial Plates and Dished Heads

Head No.	Plate No.	Initial Plate $\sigma_{0,2}$ (N/mm²)	Initial Plate σ_u (N/mm²)	Initial Plate A5 (%)	Initial Plate Av(J) mean values	Dished Head $\sigma_{0,2}$ (N/mm²)	Dished Head σ_u (N/mm²)	Dished Head A5 (%)	Dished Head Av(J) mean values
1	1	t294 b306	435 429	37 36	71 74	397	525	24	69
2	1	294 306	435 429	37 36	71 74	418	513	24	75
3	1	294 306	435 429	37 36	71 74	437	521	22	38
4	1	294 306	435 429	37 36	71 74	420	516	22	74
5	2	314 318	441 444	32 32	97 97	391	501	25	80
6	2	314 318	441 444	32 32	97 97	359	485	26	76
specified value		≥255	360-480	≥25%	≥31		t= top b= bottom		

Heads with greater wall thickness than 8mm were also investigated. Cold spinning of 9.5mm thick plate resulted in an effective deformation 20%. In this case as can be seen from Fig. 7 the resulting toughness properties were unacceptably beyond the specified values. These results confirm the requisition of heat treatment acc. to the respective rules (3). In order to determine the influence of heat treatment on the toughness properties stress-relieving and normalizing were carried out. The results are also included in Fig. 7. It can be seen that in this case already stress-relieving at 550°C gave an increase in toughness, while normalizing restored fully the toughness properties. The stress relieving will not always give acceptable results. Experience has shown that the stress relieving temperatures between 530 and 580°C are sometimes not sufficiently high to increase the toughness properties above the specified value. Therefore, the normalizing treatment is the more effective treatment.

Hardness measurements which to a certain extent can be converted into tensile values, were also carried out including the determination over the cross section. The results given in Fig.8 support the results that stress relieving has only a small effect on the surface hardness decrease while normalizing decreases the hardness more significantly and give a more homogeneous hardness distribution over the cross section.

Conclusions

From the results it can be concluded that strain-hardening as a result of the cold forming process decreases the toughness properties of the heads. In order to obtain components with acceptable properties made of C-steel the following rules should be applied in Brazil for this type of heads ("Klöpper"-type) and forming process.

1. For wall thickness $\leqslant$ 8mm:

   Service temperature $>$ -10ºC
   Design temperature $<$ 120ºC

   No heat treatment is required. The AD-rules can be followed.

2. For wall thickness $>$ 8mm:

   Normalizing heat treatment shall be applied.
   Stress-relieving can be accepted if by individual testing of each head acceptable values can be obtained.

SYMBOLS USED

Av = absorbed energy

A5 = elongation after fracture (%)

φs = normal deformation

φt = tangential deformation

φm = meridional or radial deformation

φ = effective deformation

$\sigma 0,2$ = yield strength (N/mm^2)

REFERENCES

1. Oehler, G. 1961. Mitteilungen aus der Forschungsgesellschaft für Blechverarbeitung 3/4, 25-37.

2. Pawelsky, O. Hagedorn, U.E., Lochmann, L., 1979. Bänder, Bleche, Rohre 5.194-197.

3. Guidelines for Pressure Vessels - AD Merkblatt HP 7/2

(1) Edge

(2) Knuckle

(3) Arch

$\vec{m}$ = meridional or radial direction

$\vec{t}$ = tangential direction

$\vec{s}$ = normal direction

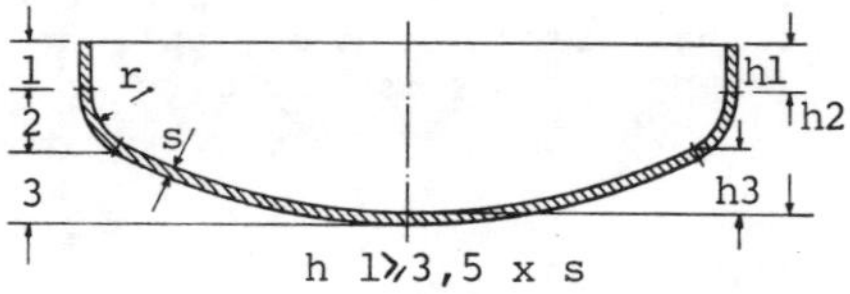

Figure 1 Dished heads of the "Klöpper" type according to DIN 28011

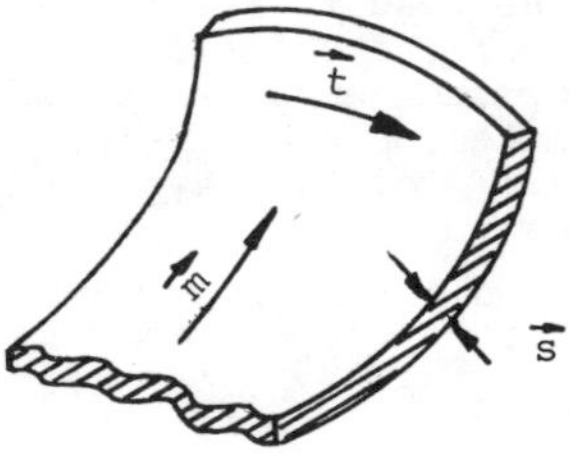

Figure 2 Definition of the direction in a dished head of the "Klöpper" type

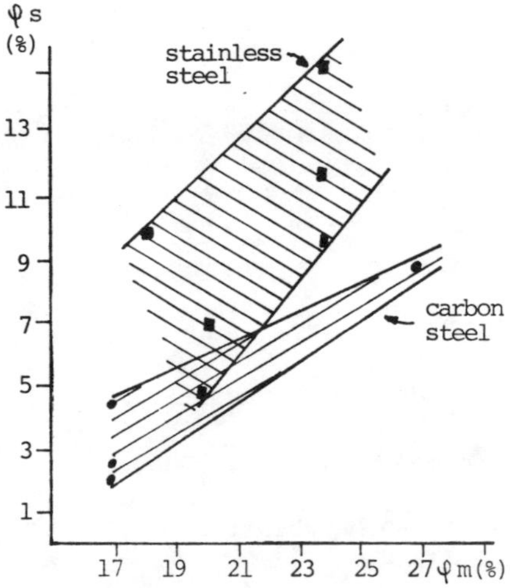

Figure 3 Correlation between φs and φm for dished heads cold formed by spinning

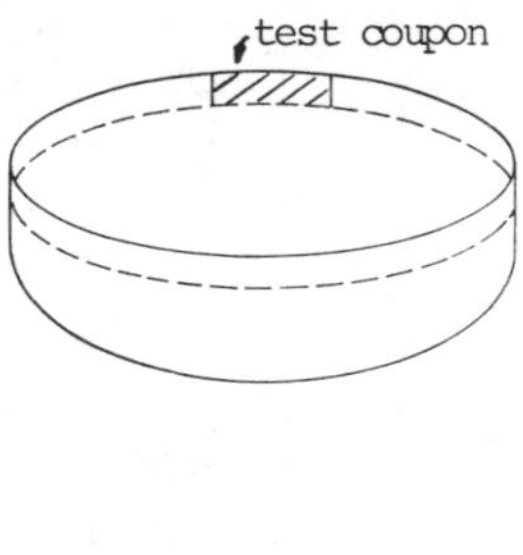

Figure 4 Location of test coupon on dished head

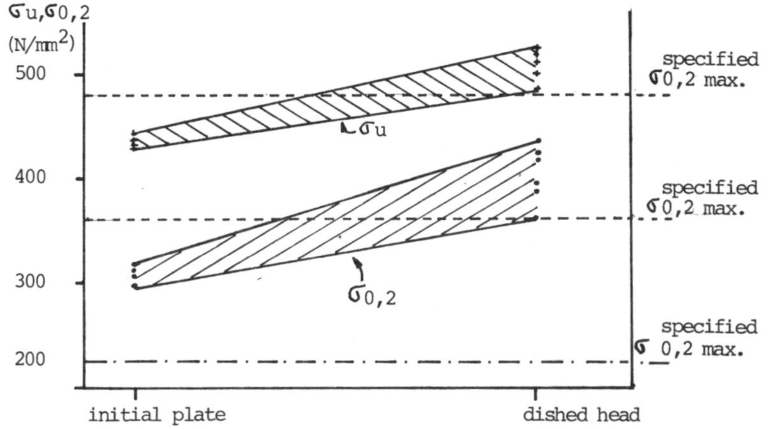

Figure 5 Changes of σu and σ 0,2 after cold forming of WStE 26 dished heads.

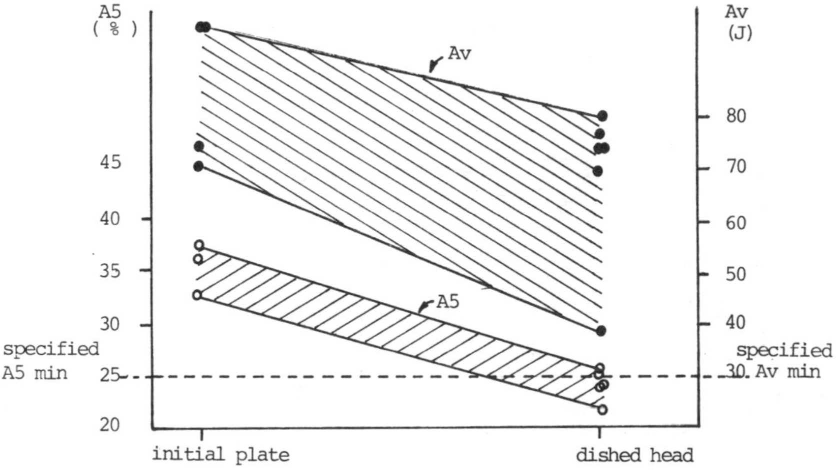

Figure 6 Changes on A5 and Av after cold forming of WStE dished heads.

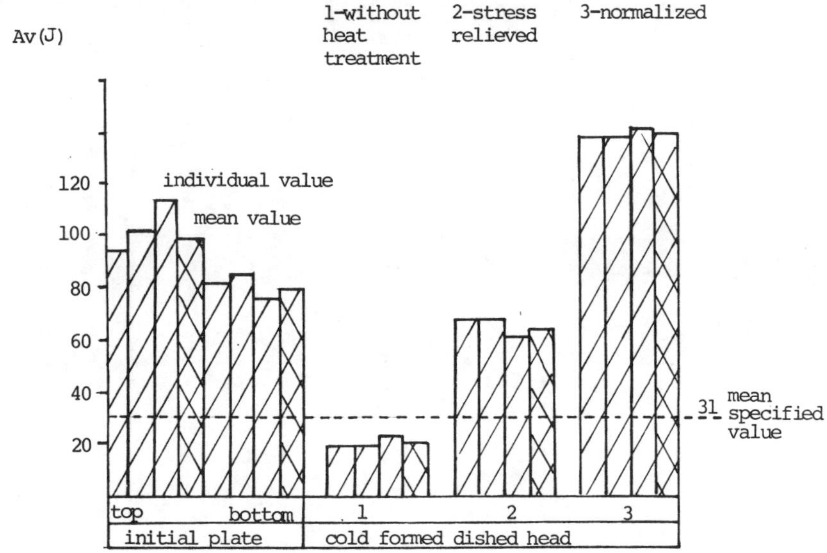

Figure 7 Effect of heat treatment on absorbed energy (ISO-V-0°C) of WStE 26 dished heads with thickness of 9.5mm

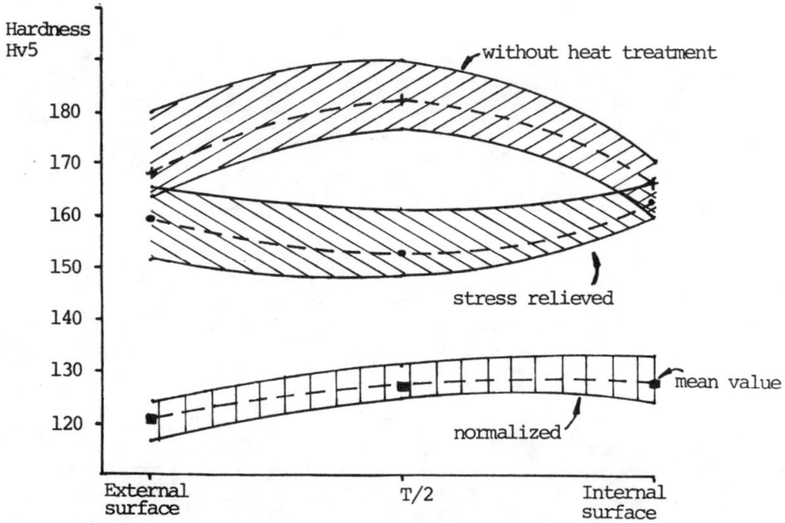

Figure 8 Effect of heat treatment on hardness of WStE 36 dished head with thickness of 9.5mm

DUCTILE CRACK GROWTH IN NUCLEAR AUSTENITIC STAINLESS STEEL PLATES: INFLUENCE OF CRACK ORIENTATION AND STEEL MICROSTRUCTURE

P. BALLADON* AND J. HERITIER*

Fracture toughness at room and elevated temperature of wrought austenitic stainless steels used for the fabrication of pressurised water reactors and liquid metal fast breeder reactors is determined by mean of J-R curve analysis. The influence of microstructure, second phases in the austenitic matrix and crack orientation is examined.

INTRODUCTION

304, 316, 304 L and 316 L austenitic stainless steel plates of various thicknesses are commonly used for the fabrication of pressurised water reactors and liquid metal fast breeder reactors.

These plates generally contain defects essentially due to decohesion between the matrix and the inclusions during and after hot rolling. When used in nuclear power plants, these plates are submitted to different loading sequences (monotonic and cyclic) and the preexisting defects may grow; if crack growth continues to instability, failure of the structure may occur. A way to prevent such accidents is to use J-R curve analysis and this method was developed to examine the influence of crack orientation and steel microstructure on ductile crack growth.

This method has been widely used for A 508 and A 533 grade steels, (1), (2), (3), for high strength structural steel (4), for rotor steels (5) and for austenitic stainless steels (6) (7).

The ductile tearing resistance of a material is usually determined according to the ASTM E 813-81 standard (standard test for J_{1c}, a measure of fracture toughness).

Ductile crack growth initiation and ductile tearing resistance of austenitic stainless steels are strongly dependent on inclusion content, shape and distribution (8).

* Creusot-Loire, Centre de Recherches d'Unieux, B.P. 34, 42701 FIRMINY CEDEX (FRANCE).

The present paper describes the results obtained for different grades, heats, products and inclusion contents of wrought austenitic stainless steels.

In particular the influence on fracture toughness of the distribution of defect planes compared with the rolling plane in the case of plates and forgings is examined.

EXPERIMENTAL PROGRAM

Materials

The materials studied are industrial austenitic stainless steels of 304L and 316L grades with controlled nitrogen content. Table 1 gives the chemical analysis of the heats and the form of the products (plates and forgings). Such steels are used for nuclear plant construction and the compositions of the heats are balanced so that the amount of residual δ ferrite is 1 to 2 per cent after quenching from 1075°C. The tensile properties appear in table 2.

Specimens

The specimens used for determining J-R curves were compact tension type of 15, 25 and 50 mm thickness. Some of them were modified compact tension type 20% side-grooved. Their location in plates and forgings and their orientation appears in table 3. Some of the specimens were located in the short-long direction, i.e. where the crack plane parallel to the rolling plane. In this case fracture toughness is particularly sensitive to the microstructure of the steel (inclusion and second phase content (8)).

Test program

Fracture toughness testing was performed at room and elevated temperature on:

- as quenched samples.
- samples aged after quenching. Two temperatures of aging treatments were used: 650°C, which mainly produces carbide precipitation and 850°C which leads to the formation of σ-phase from δ ferrite.
- samples machined in a plate which was thermomechanically treated by controlled hot rolling.
- samples with different crack orientations with respect to the rolling direction.

The detailed experimental program appears in table 3.

Experimental methods

Two testing methods were used for determining J-R curves according the ASTM E 813-81 standard: the multi-specimen method (interrupted loading) and the single specimen compliance method (unloading compliance).

J_{1c} and $\frac{dJ}{da}$ are determined following the ASTM standard with some differences, mainly for the blunting line equation which is taken as $J = 4\sigma_f.\Delta a$ in most cases, and for validity conditions which are not generally satisfied. Results obtained with plain specimens are compared with these obtained with side-grooved specimens using the mean of the three maximum values of the "nine point measurement method of Δa", other works showing that J-R curves drawn by this way with plain specimens were the same as those determined from side-grooved specimens.

TABLE 1 - Chemical analysis

HEAT	C	Mn	Si	S	P	Ni	Cr	Mo	N	Grade
A1 (plate)	0.023	1.71	0.39	0.0025	0.030	12.1	17.7	2.30	0.065	316 L
A2 (plate)	0.026	1.70	0.49	0.002	0.023	12.3	17.4	2.37	0.065	
A3 (forging)	0.025	1.81	0.49	0.002	0.027	12.2	17.2	2.38	0.074	
A4 (TT plate)	0.019	1.76	0.37	0.006	0.018	12.29	17.40	2.42	0.064	
B1 (plate)	0.022	1.75	0.37	0.011	0.027	12.3	17.7	2.43	0.067	
B2 (plate)	0.029	1.80	0.50	0.012	0.032	12.6	17.5	2.35	0.077	
B3 (plate)	0.027	1.75	0.53	0.015	0.027	9.5	18.9	-	0.066	304 L

TABLE 2 - Tensile properties (as received state)

HEAT	ROOM TEMPERATURE		350°C		550°C	
	σ_y (MPa)	σ_{UTS} (MPa)	σ_y (MPa)	σ_{UTS} (MPa)	σ_y (MPa)	σ_{UTS} (MPa)
A1	295	590	175	445	155	425
A2	275	555				
A3	255	584				
A4	517	692				
B1	285	570			140	450
B2	260	555				
B3	264	588	145	435		

RESULTS

J_{1c} and $\frac{dJ}{da}$ values appear in table 3.

Influence of inclusion content and crack orientation

Materials were studied in the as-annealed state at room and elevated temperature. Figure 1 shows the results obtained at room temperature in LT, TL and SL orientations.

One can conclude from this figure that toughness and ductile tearing of stainless steels at room temperatures are strongly dependent on inclusion content related to steel making practices:

- results obtained on heats A (low sulfur and low inclusion content) are in the same scatter band for all the orientations and give the higher J-R curves.

- results obtained on heats B (higher sulfur and higher inclusion content) are in the same experimental scatter band for LT and TL orientations, J values for a given crack growth being lower than those of heats A (about 50%), but the most detrimental effect of inclusion content can be seen in the SL orientation, where J values for a given ductile crack growth are lower by about 75%, compared to those obtained on heats A.

Some tendencies are seen at elevated temperature (figure 2). This last figure compared to figure 1 also shows that J-R curves are strongly lowered when the temperature increases (J decreasing by 50% for 1 mm ductile crack growth at 350°C and by 65% at 550°C).

Figure 3 is related to the J-R curves obtained at room temperature on one heat of set B with three different crack orientations (LT, SL and 30° with respect to SL). One can see that for an initial angle of crack plane of 30° versus - rolling plane orientation the crack grows in mode 1 and does not change its propagation plane for the rolling plane, which however presents the lowest resistance to crack propagation. The J-R curve in the 30° direction is in the same experimental scatter band as those in the LT direction.

Micrography of figure 6 shows the structural aspect observed in the crack initiation and growth area of a specimen taken from the heat B3. One can see the elongation of austenitic grains due to blunting and the presence of decohesions at the matrix-inclusion interface, particularly in the area around the crack tip corresponding to the plastic process zone where damage appears as cavities which coalesce as a result of local stresses and strains.

Influence of aging treatment

Aging 100 h at 850°C precipitates mainly intergranular carbides and σ-phase in δ-ferrite (8). Figure 4 shows that for heat B1, which exhibits only intergranular carbides after aging, J-R curves of the as-annealed and as-aged materials are in the same experimental scatter band. However for heat A1, where the amount of δ-ferrite is higher (1%), precipitation of σ-phase occurs and produces a detrimental effect on ductile tearing resistance in the TL orientation.

TABLE 3 - J_{1c} and dJ/da results

Heat	State	Test temperature (° C)	Orientation	J_{1c} (KJ/m^2)	dJ/da (MPa)
A1	annealed	20	LT	1560	980
			TL	1560	980
			SL	1080	630
		350	SL	580	640
		550	SL	260	460
	aged 850°C-100h	20	TL	480	370
A2	annealed	20	CR	1670	
A3	annealed	20	TL	1493	756
B1	annealed	20	LT	780	500
			TL	690	390
			SL	260	135
		550	TL	240	92
	aged 850°C-100h	20	TL	590	360
B2	annealed	20	LT	600	440
			SL	250	210
			30°/SL	700	360
B3	annealed	20	TL	780	200
		350	TL	300	190
A4	as received	20	TL	40	91
		350	TL	31	63
	aged 650°C-1000h	20	TL	47	56
		350	TL	31	15

Influence of hardening by thermomechanical treatment

J-R curves obtained at room temperature and at 550°C on the thermomechanically treated plate both in the as received state and after aging 1000h at 650°C appear on figure 5. J_{1c} and $\frac{dJ}{da}$ values are markedly reduced compared with those obtained for heats A in the as-annealed state (90% for J_{1c} and 50 to 80% for $\frac{dJ}{da}$ depending on the temperature). These low values for the ductile tearing resistance can be explained by the influence of monotonic strain-hardening which gives a layer structure as can be seen in figure 7, but also the presence of σ-phase resulting from the transformation of δ-ferrite during the thermomechanical treatment (9). This hard and brittle phase in the form of platelets elongated by rolling makes crack propagation easier by decohesion with the austenitic matrix. Aging 1000h at 650°C does not affect J_{1c} but lowers $\frac{dJ}{da}$ (respectively 40% and 50% at room temperature and 550°C).

CONCLUSIONS

Ductile crack growth testing on austenitic nuclear stainless steels leads to the following conclusions:

1/ Crack initiation and growth (J_{1c} and $\frac{dJ}{da}$) are strongly dependent on inclusion content and shape, more generally on the presence of embrittling second phases (mainly σ-phase). In most cases the presence of a second phase decreases J and $\frac{dJ}{da}$ (except in the case of small intergranular carbides).

2/ Crack growth initiation and ductile tearing resistance are lower in the SL direction compared with LT and TL directions. The difference increases with increasing inclusion content and when the second phases appear as platelets in the crack plane.

3/ Ductile tearing resistance in the presence of a growing crack from a defect in a 30° angle plane versus rolling plane is not decreased compared with fracture toughness in the LT or TL directions. Moreover such a crack does not change its growth orientation towards the plane of least crack growth resistance (SL).

4/ The presence of second phases at the crack tip leads to the formation of cavities by decohesion at the matrix inclusion interface and so makes crack extension easier by coalescence of these cavities.

REFERENCES

1. Lautridou, J.C., Thesis presented at "Ecole Nationale Supérieure des Mines de Paris", June 1980.

2. Andrews, W.R. and Shih, C.F., ASTM STP 668, 1979, pp. 426-450.

3. Vassilaros, M.G., Joyce, J.A. and Gudas, J.P., ASTM STP 700, 1980, pp. 251-270.

4. Joyce, J.A. and Gudas, J.P., ASTM STP 668, 1979, pp. 451-468.

5. Landes, J.D. and Shaffer, J.H., ASTM STP 700, 1980, pp. 368-382.

6. Bamford, W.H. and Bush, A.J., ASTM STP 768, 1979, pp. 553-577.

7. Tobler, R.L., Read, D.T. and Reed, R.P., ASTM STP 743, 1981, pp. 250-268.

8. Balladon, P., Heritier, J. and Rabbe, P., ASTM STP 791, 1983, pp. II - 496-513.

9. Balladon, P., Heritier, J., 16th National Symposium on Fracture Mechanics, Colombus, 1983.

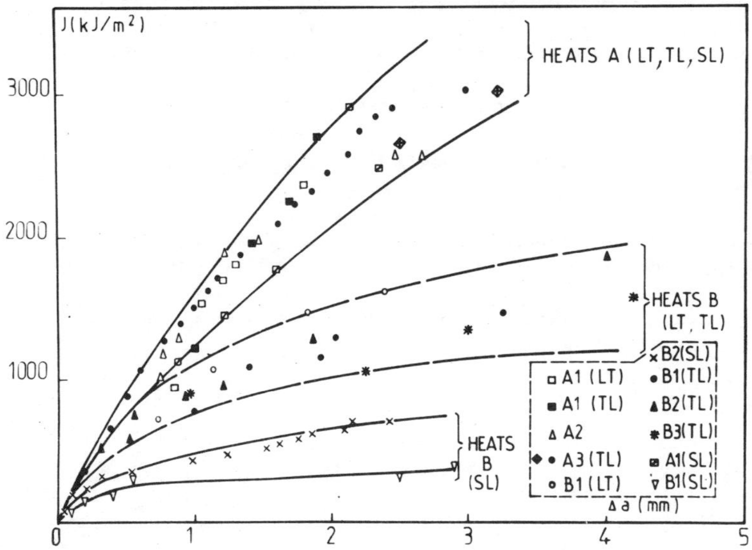

Figure 1   J-R curves at room temperature (as-annealed).

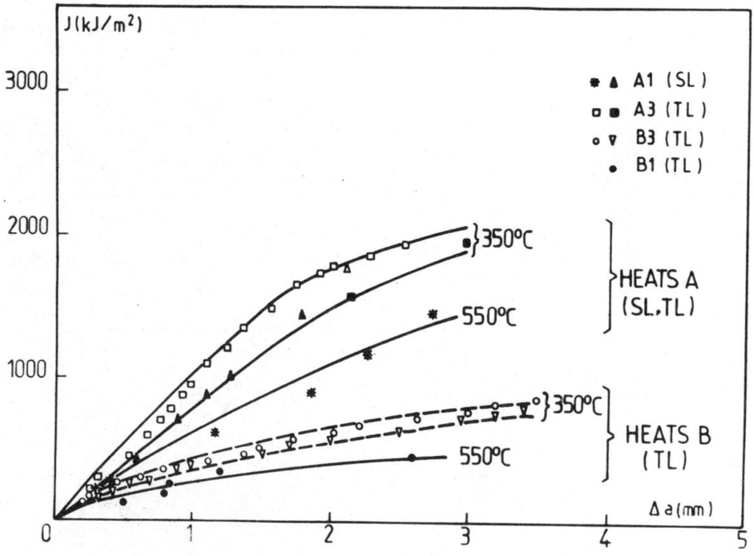

Figure 2 J-R curves at elevated temperature (as-annealed).

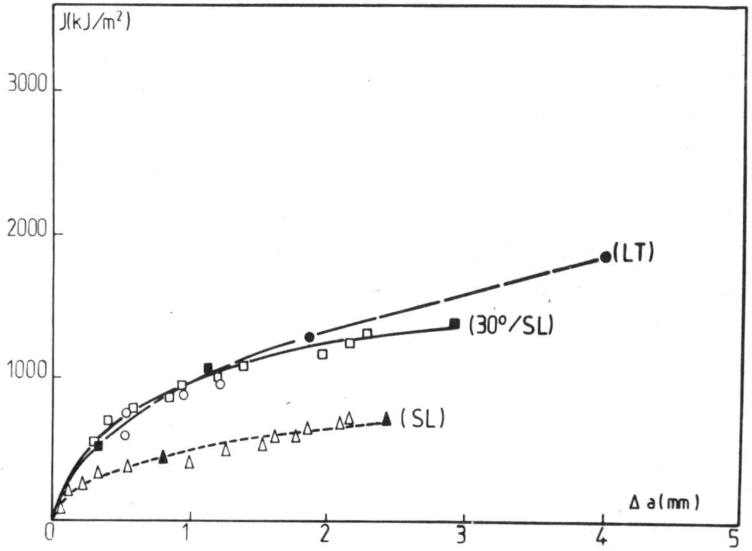

Figure 3 Influence of crack orientation at room temperature.

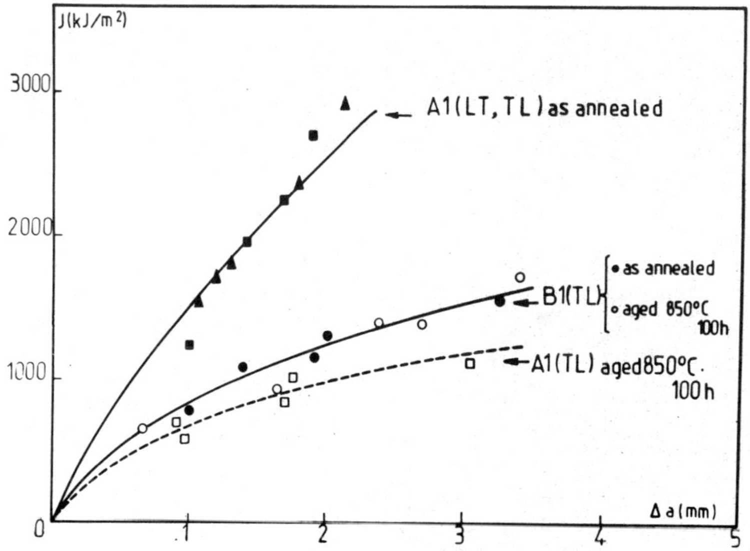

Figure 4 Influence of aging treatment at room temperature.

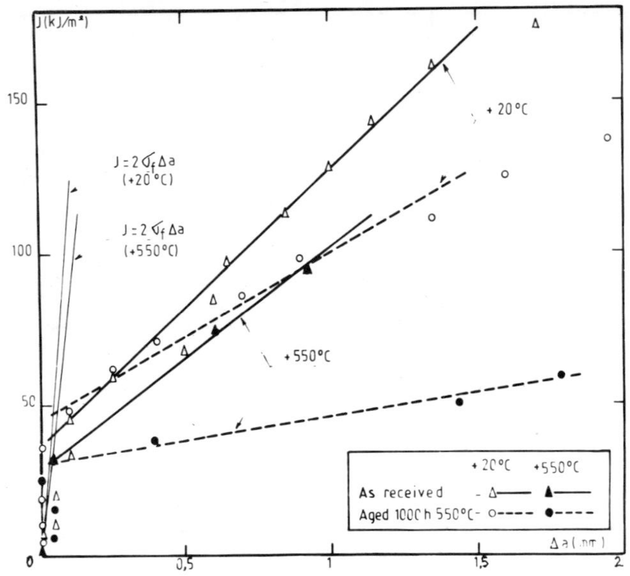

Figure 5 Influence of thermomechanical treatment.

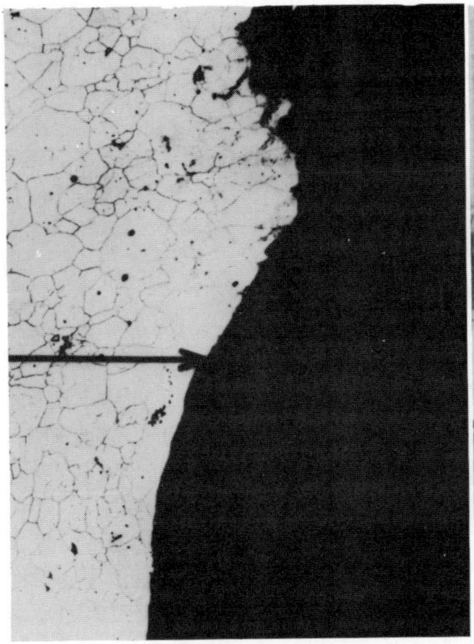

Figure 6 Micrography of crack tip.

Figure 7 Crack growth for a specimen of TT plate.

PROVISIONS AND ACTIVE MEASURES TO PRECLUDE GUILLOTINE BREAKS IN PIPING SYSTEMS OF PRESSURIZED WATER REACTORS

H.Dorner, E.Michel*

The conditions and active measures which preclude a spontaneous failure of pipings are shown. With the basic safety concept a quality standard is achieved characterized by high-grade material properties, a structure that is adequate to the loads to which the components will be subjected in service and is amenable to inspection, precise load and stress evaluation, optimized manufacturing and operation monitoring. The possible failure types are described and the safety against failure is assessed.

INTRODUCTION

Right from the beginning of the reactor technique, leak postulates were required in the safety related systems for the safety analysis. Also from the start it was accepted that the high quality of the pressure retaining walls of reactor components precludes the possibility of large-area breaks. Therefore the assumption of a double-ended guillotine break or of an equivalent longitudinal opening in the biggest pipings connecting the components was considered plausible from the view of thermodynamics as a conservative upper boundary for the possible spectrum of outflow openings. For the primary circuit of the Pressurized Water Reactor, these outflow cross sections and appertaining opening times were originally only postulated for demonstrating the effective functioning of the emergency core cooling system and for designing the containment and its internals. At a later stage the postulate of the double-ended opening of pipings was also used as a design basis for secondary measures such as hydrodynamic loads on internals, determination of jet and reaction forces which necessitated limiting structures (pipe whip restraints). This extension of a design postulate was not in every case the best solution and to some extent it even led to non safety directed developments like overemphasis on leaks of a large cross section and above all impediments to the accessibility of components as a result of pipe whip restraints. Thus operation monitoring and in-service inspections are restricted.

*Division Reactor Components, Kraftwerk Union Aktiengesellschaft Erlangen, Federal Republic of Germany

During the last years the leak and rupture postulates have been considered and discussed on a broad basis. The conclusion was, that it makes more sense to preclude breaks by an adequate basic safety of the pipings than to limit the consequences of breaks by secondary protective measures.

The following possible failure types have to be studied to prove that breaks in pipings can be precluded:

- brittle fracture
- ductile fracture
- fatigue and crack development
- crack propagation
- corrosion

The starting basis to assess these failure types and the actual safety margins against failure are on the one hand the applied material and component quality and on the other hand the stresses occuring during operation. The criteria for this starting basis result in the basis for the safety against failure (basic safety) and are laid down in the basic safety concept. Hereafter the quality features as laid down in the basic safety are described first and finally the above mentioned failure types are studied.

BASIC SAFETY

Material Quality

High-grade material properties are realized. Extreme ductility, good homogenity and low defect frequency are achieved especially by limiting the contents of certain trace elements and the application of optimized manufacturing technologies. Forged base material is exclusively used for the main coolant, steam and feed water lines. A uniform material is used for pipings and connected components to avoid pressure retaining weld joints of different materials.

As the technological properties can only be measured by a destructive material testing, it has to be ensured, that values determined at the sampling locations also exist at every point in the component. This requirement is fulfilled by the provisions of the specifications in which the experience from research programmes of several years duration and the statistics obtained from the manufacturing processes have gone. The uniformity of the mechanical-technological properties and the fulfillment of specified minimum requirements as regards the base material, seam weld and heat affected zone has been demonstrated in the course of the certification of the material and the filler metals, and in many acceptance tests of the base material as well as procedure qualification, production and welding material tests. The supervision of manufacture by independent experts has shown, that these techniques and processes yield reproducible results in all respects. It has been demonstrated in the course of materials qualification and in-service inspections that the technological properties do not undergo any inadmissible changes while the component is in service.

Mechanical Design

The main reason why mechanical design is of importance to the basis of safety down into its smallest details is that it has a major influence in particular on the fulfillment of the requirements in respect of examinability, the assurance of the ability to withstand permissible loads and the ability of the manufacturer to master the manufacturing and fabrication techniques involved. With a mechanical design that is amenable to inspection and is adequate to the loads to which the component will be subjected in service, it is possible to remain with certainty within the safety margin to the failure limit because the preconditions for maintaining an adequate safety margin can then be fulfilled in practice. Pipings constructed in accordance with the basic safety concept are characterized by the following essential features:

- The number of seam welds is minimized and they are away from the areas with relatively high stresses. Only seamless pipes and elbows are used.

- The material strength layout is optimized and locally unfavourable stress conditions are avoided by constructional measures, as for example permitting only very low edge displacements and placing reinforcement into the base pipe at cut-offs (nozzles).

- Adequate design features ensure an unrestricted non destructive examination with a sufficient flaw detectability.

- The thermal expansion of the system is influenced as little as possible by a suitable supporting concept by which forces resulting from a restricted thermal expansion are kept to a minimum.

Examinations and Defect Condition of the Component

The entire volume of each component is examined by the manufacturer and by independent experts appointed by the authority. The test and examination requirements as regards detection of flaws are laid down in standards and specifications. These requirements are the outcome of long years of experience in testing and examination by independent inspection organizations and of detailed qualification of the testing and examination techniques applied.

With the ultrasonic examination flaw detectability is governed by the reference reflectors used as model flaws to define the recording threshold. In addition to these model flaws, further allowance is made for influences such as angular orientation and poor reflection characteristics (roughness) of the flaw and for the signal-to-noise-distance achieved. The latter is a measure of how distinctly a flaw indication stands out above the background signal level. The techniques employed in flaw detection are capable of determining the longitudinal extension of the flaw to an accuracy of within 5 mm (twice half the search unit pitch).

Experience with examination programmes and repair work has shown that, thanks to the multiple in depth examination of the parts, a flaw with the dimensions 3 mm deep and 20 mm long is certain to be detected.

Loads on the Components

In order to be able to predict the load on any point of the component during the entire service life, two factors must be known:

a) the totality of the loads (load collective)
b) a suitable calculation procedure.

Re a) The Load Collective. The values characteristic for the loads, like internal pressure, temperature transients and external forces are theoretically evaluated during the planning. All load cases to be expected during the service life are considered. Constraints resulting from differences in thermal expansion and thermal stresses as a result of local or general changes in the temperature of the coolant are covered by the design stress analysis for all normal operation cycles and for all conceivable off-normal operation modes.

For ensuring the load collective which has only been evaluated theoretically an experimental check is desirable. The commissioning period of a nuclear power plant is convenient for this purpose because all load cases except emergency and faulted conditions are tested to ensure the functionability of the plant.

Thanks to the helpful cooperation of the owner, the load collective was able to be experimentally verified during the commissioning period of the nuclear power plant Grafenrheinfeld in addition to the measurements already at hand. The entire primary circuit was equipped with more than 300 observation points especially for strain, temperature and pressure measuring additional to the 40 measuring points of the normal operational instrumentation. The full range of loads were picked up during the total commissioning time of nearly one year and the results of measurements have been recorded on tapes, which have stored 3000 million test data. The test data is recorded in such a way that a direct subsequent processing with computer programmes is possible. The experimental check ensures that the load collective on which design stress analysis calculations are based is exceeded neither quantitively nor as regards magnitude. The individual load transients during operation of the system are recorded and counted so that it is impossible for the load collective to exceed the loads on which the analysis is based.

Re b) Calculation Procedures. With the calculation procedures available today stresses and strains can be very precisely determined at all locations of the pipings.

- Internal pressure. The stresses resulting from internal pressure are calculated using an analytical method from the formula valid for cylinders. Areas of stress intensification in bends or discontinuities are allowed for by use of stress coefficients or stress intensification factors taken from ASME or KTA. It has been demonstrated by finite element analysis and stress and strain measurements that these factors are conservative.

- Temperature. Changes in the temperature differences (cold/hot, different operation conditions) cause different degrees of thermal expansion in the system materials. In order to be able to analyse and calculate these stresses the piping system is represented as a calculation model with the aid of the finite element method. The special characteristics of the bends as regards elasticity and stress intensification are taken into account. These calculations yield the equivalent forces acting in the pipings, from which in the next step stresses are calculated, again making allowance for stress coefficients. Temperature gradients towards the centre line of nozzles or normal to the wall of the pipes are calculated using finite element analysis. The stresses arising out of the temperature gradients are taken into account.

- Accidents as a result of external impacts. The movements and the resultant stresses in the pipings in the event of an earthquake, aircraft crash and explosion pressure wave are determined in great detail. Using the time histories corresponding to the site-specific or KTA floor spectrum, a finite element shell model of the reactor building is calculated, containing also the masses of the components. In this way, the time history of the movement of the points of the building on which the piping system is supported is obtained. These time histories are inputted into a detailed finite element model of the pipings. The output of these calculations are the time histories of the deformations and equivalent forces. The maximum values are extracted from these time histories to ensure an adequate conservative margin. The corresponding stresses arising from service and accidents are then superimposed. Stresses due to aircraft crash and explosion pressure wave are calculated in a similar manner.

- Vibration due to operation. The vibration of the pipings is measured during the commissioning of each new plant. Experience has shown the vibration amplitudes to be negligibly small and to have no effect on the fatigue strength of the material.

Operation Monitoring

In-service inspection is carried out to check the condition and the behaviour of the component after having been subjected to loading in service and during pressure testing. By means of this, flaws remaining after fabrication can be observed in their behaviour and the occurence of new flaws can be recognized safely and early enough. Good accessibility, easily removable insulation elements and adequate equipment for mechanized examinations provide the conditions for a quick and easy performance with low personnel exposure to radiation. On the reactor coolant lines, rails are arranged in the area of the elbows, that run in the necessary distance round the pipes and are swivelable so that both the seam welds and the elbows can be mechanically examined.

In-service non-destructive examinations are performed as specified in the RSK-Guideline and the KTA Safety Standard. This means the following examination scope:

- visual inspection of the pipings every 4 years

- full volumetric examination of the weld region (seam weld plus adjacent base material region at least 20 mm to each side of the seam) for longitudinal and transverse flaws by means of ultrasonic examination using angle probes

- 50 % of the welds are examined within each inspection interval of 4 years, i.e. all welds within 8 years

- relatively high stressed areas of the base material such as elbows have to be representatively included in the examination scope. This can be done also by reducing the examination scope on seam welds usual up to now.

The in-service inspection ensures that a component condition that could make the component susceptible to fracture is detected in good time.

FAILURE TYPES

With the fracture mechanics a useful tool is available today to be able to assess the safety against failure. The methods of the fracture mechanics are based on established theories and have been experimentally confirmed. They take into account brittle and ductile material conditions, static and dynamic loads with and without the influence of a corrosive ambient. On the basis of world-wide cooperation there is general agreement on which procedures should be employed to give conservative assessment of any material flaws present in order to be able to assess their performance throughout the entire service life of the component.

Brittle Fracture

By the application of tough materials which show a ductile fracture behaviour during the full operation range (temperature range occuring during operation) the possibility of a brittle fracture is excluded from the beginning. The results of the acceptance tests show that the specified toughness values (nil ductility temperature NDT $\leq$ 0 °C, energy absorbed at the notched bar impact test at 0 °C $\geq$ 34 J as smallest single value, $\geq$ 41 J as average value, at 30 °C $\geq$ 68 J and at the upper plateau $\geq$ 100 J) are minimum values and that the actual values as determined in acceptance testing are considerably higher both for the weld metal and for the base material. The absolutely ductile condition of the material to be used is guaranteed by the optimum toughness values together with the high quality of fabrication and processing; thus brittle fractures are excluded.

Ductile Fracture

A failure as a result of ductile fracture is only possible by inadmissibly high loads, both from internal pressure as well as from external forces (including forces from restricted thermal expansion) and by inadmissibly large defects. Thermal stresses and other secondary stresses have no influence, as they are self-limiting, but they have to be taken into account when considering the safety margins for other failure types. Inadmissibly high internal pressures are prevented by the operational instrumentation which is redundantly installed, and by the redundant safety and relief valves, which open at preadjusted pressures. The external mechanical loads are considered in the experimentally ensured load collective. Periodical expansion and movement measurements ensure that additional loads caused by unexpected effects such as building settlement are recognised.

It remains to be investigated as to how large a defect in the pipe wall must be to cause a rupture in the lines under the given loads. For this the critical through-wall crack length has to be determined. The load from the stress out of axial or circumferential forces and from the bending stress is added together. When the sum of these stresses reaches the flow stress, failure of the pipe is predictable. A comparison of the calculation model with experiments show the conservativeness of the theory.

The critical through-wall crack length has been evaluated at 500 mm for the seam weld subject to the highest stress in the reactor coolant line considering the safe shutdown earthquake. The comparison with the flaw found to be still just acceptable (30 mm long, 4.2 mm deep) during acceptance testing in figure 1 shows that there is a considerable safety margin.

Fatigue and Crack Formation

For the assessment of the crack formation as a result of alternating stresses (fatigue) the sum of the primary, secondary and peak stresses has to be taken into account. The stress amplitudes with their corresponding numbers of load alternations are determined for the various load cycles during the life period (pressure and temperature changes). The different load cycles are added with the aid of the damage hypothesis of Miner and the usage factor is determined

$$\sum \frac{n}{N} = \text{usage factor}$$

n = actual number of load alternations

N = permissible number of load alternations

The permissible numbers of load alternations can be taken out of the fatigue curves in the ASME-Code. Safety against crack formation is given when the usage factor does not exceed the value of 1.

For all points of the large pipings of the pressurized water reactor it is proved that the usage factor is smaller than 1. A failure as a result of fatigue could only then occur when the crack propagation caused by load alternations on an already existing defect is so high, that a critical size for a ductile fracture is reached.

Crack Propagation

On the already mentioned example of the seam weld subject to the highest stress in the reactor coolant line, the propagation of a flaw found to be still just acceptable (30 mm long, 4.2 mm deep) during acceptance testing under the specified load collective is shown. Crack propagation is determined using the propagation rates under aqueous conditions given in ASME-Code, Section XI, Appendix A. For the sake of conservativeness, all stresses are taken to be constant over the entire wall. The propagation of the flaw under the specified load collective is 2 mm in the length and 1 mm in the depth. This crack would take 47 times the complete load collective to propagate to the critical depth of about 90 % of the wall thickness. At this point it would break through the remaining wall and produce a stable leak with a length of 100 mm. A full scale representation is also shown in figure 1.

This stable leak would take many years to grow very slowly to its critical through-wall crack length of 500 mm. Only then could a guillotine break be expected. If it is set aside, that defects which are of a size to produce a stable leak, would have been discovered with the in-service inspection long before, the leak would be detected by the different leak monitoring systems installed in the reactor building, long before it could achieve a critical size.

Corrosion

The formation of flaws caused by inadmissible ambient influences i.e. corrosion, is precluded by suitable water chemistry, by the selection of suitable materials and by the design. Such influences would be particularly dangerous if they were able to cause damage in the intervals between in-service examinations.

The entire inner surface of the reactor coolant lines is clad with a stabilized austenitic CrNi steel, in which the stabilizing additive (Nb) makes sensitization impossible under normal thermal load conditions. Sensitization, however, is one of the pre-conditions for the occurence of intergranular stress corrosion cracking. Thanks to the high quality of the reactor coolant, which is subject to constant monitoring, both inter-crystalline and trans-crystalline stress corrosion cracking may be ruled out.

The steam and feedwater lines are protected from further corrosion by a magnetite protective layer under the existent conditions (temperature, clean water). The feedwater has additives of ammonia to achieve an index of pH > 9.5 and hydrazine to absorb residual oxygen. The protective layer might crack during start up and shut down. However, it is built up again during operation and the former corrosion protective effectiveness is achieved. Stress corrosion cracking can be excluded as there are no chemical conditions which lead to this corrosion type.

On the outside the pipings are surrounded by removable insulation to allow visual inspection and non-destructive examination. The ambient medium is dry air. Local moisture as a result of leaks, is detected in good time and can be reliably localized.

REFERENCES

1. Bartholomé,G., Steinbuch,R., Wellein,R., 1981 "Exclusion of the Double-Ended Circumferential Fracture of the Main Coolant Piping", 7. MPA-Seminar, Stuttgart, Federal Republic of Germany.

2. Bartholomé,G., Kastner,W., Keim,E., Wellein,R., 1983 "Exclusion of Failure of the Pressure Retaining Coolant System", Part 2: "Application to the Primary Coolant Piping", IAEA-SM-269-7, Stuttgart, Federal Republic of Germany.

max. permissible defect during acceptance testing

growth of max. permissible defect under the complete load collective

defect size which cause a stable leak

critical through-wall crack length

Figure 1 Defect Sizes in the Circumferential Weld of the Reactor Coolant Line

SURFACE CRACKS IN WELDS OF 7020 T 6 ALUMINIUM ALLOY

Z. MILOSEVIC, C. BATHIAS*, A. PELLISSIER TANON**

200 mm wide, 3 mm thick welded plates of aluminium alloy 7020 T 6 were tested in monotonic loading at room température. Semi-circular cracks of various depths and lengths were electro-eroded in the middle of the weld.
The experimental investigations were made at imposed cross bar displacement (speed 0.1 mm per min) and the following parameters were measured :
- Crack front evolution during stable crack growth by colour tinting
- Opening at the flaw middle point
- Real load line displacement excluding grip deformation
- Acoustic emission at the plate back face
We deduced :
- Critical opening values for initiation, leak and total rupture
- Total crack front growth
- Opening versus crack growth curves for various flaw configurations and the slope (d(opening)da)
- Compliance measurements and crack size calibration

INTRODUCTION

Crack growth, leak and total rupture measurement and prediction for part-through cracks were generally determined on thick plates. Even in cases of extended plasticity the remaining ligament is sufficient to permit crack growth measurement over a wide amount of crack growth before shear fracture by fatigue marking, compliance measurements etc...

For thin plates, an equivalent through crack is generally calculated but crack front geometry from initiation to the leak point is not generally determined and back face necking is not taken into account.

With an equivalent through crack condition an R curve approach using the K factor is possible, but the aim of this report is to understand the ligament behaviour in both through and longitudinal directions so an opening criterion is used.

Ligament deformation and rupture mechanism

Ligament deformation was measured by a strip of strain gages disposed every 2 mm on the ligament back face. The remaining ligament is yielded early for a small load level prior to any crack initiation.

Laboratoire de recherches sur les défaillances d'origine mécanique et physico-chimique - E.R.A. 910 du CNRS - UNIVERSITE DE TECHNOLOGIE DE COMPIEGNE
FRAMATOME - PARIS LA DEFENSE

As explained by Shih (1) the crack propagation starts by flat fracture mode under plane strain conditions before shear rupture. This stable crack growth is of considerable importance and will be discussed in the next paragraph. Shear fracture appears when the remaining ligament at the flaw deepest point falls below a critical depth related to crack opening.

This critical depth varies from δ to 2δ, where δ is the middle point crack opening as shown in figure 5.

This finding and the occurence of fracturing at 45° shear bond reveals that the final instability takes place when the slip mechanism of figure 4 takes over the tearing mechanism. This is equivalent to saying that a plastic necking mechanism takes over the crack tearing propagation mechanism when the fracture process zone of intense strain concentration, which size is of the order of the crack tip opening stretch spans the ligament.

Crack front geometry during stable growth

Crack front evolution is obtained by ink tinting. The ink is introduced into the flaw by a syringe and, by using different superposable colours, the total geometry is obtained. Figures 6 & 7 give an example of two colour ink marking and figure 7 shows schematically the crack front evolution from initiation and total rupture. Both a and c direction propagations were measured for various initial flaw configurations given in the following table :

2c \ a	1.2 (a/t = .4)	1.8 (a/t = .6)	2.4 (a/t = .8)
10	2 plates	2	2
20	4	4	4
40	2	2	2
80	2	2	2

Determination of load versus opening curves and critical opening values

Flaw middle point opening is measured by a clip gage displacement record. A typical record is represented in the figure 9 where I is the point of initiation obtained by ink marking, acoustic emission and compliance measurements. A is the leak point ; from A to B the initial semi-circular crack is through the thickness and grows in the c direction to the point B of unstable rupture. Figure 10 gives the influence of flaw length on load versus opening records δp (or A) opening values decrease with increasing flaw length, but no significant influence of flaw depth on δp was found.

With increasing crack length, the back face remaining ligament will support more strain. As crack growth is a function of crack tip deformation, leak will occur earlier for a longer crack.

On the other hand, δr (or B) increases with increasing flaw length. Short flaws have no significant crack growth in the c direction before instability, so the corresponding opening value at instability will be smaller than the critical opening value of a long flaw with high subcritical crack growth.

Limit load

Figure 13 shows experimental values of limit load versus initial flaw length load versus opening show that leak occurs at the maximal load so the following simple model was adopted in first approximation :

$$P_1 = \sigma_y (w\,t - t/12\,c\,(3\,t^2 + 16\,c^2))$$

(The bracket is an expression of the surface of the uncracked part of the plate cross section)

For $c = c_o$, the model suits experimental values for flaw length under 20 mm, after this value the difference is significant and is due to subcritical crack growth on the longitudinal direction for long flaws, which does not appear for short flaws. For such cases c must be corrected by real crack length. The minimal crack length which induce c direction crack growth before leakage was found to be 19 mm for our specimen geometry.

Opening versus crack growth (Δa) curves

These curves have been deduced from load versus opening records and ink marking values. Linear behaviour of opening during crack propagation is observed over a wide range of crack growth. For each flaw geometry the slope $d\delta / d(\Delta a)$ (or $d\delta / da$) is constant.

$d\delta / da$ was found independent of initial flaw length, but strongly dependent on initial flaw depth.

Therefore, opening values must be corrected by initial depth to caracterize crack growth in the through direction. $\delta/2a$ curves are shown in figure 16 $\delta/2a$ represents the tangent of half opening angle and was found to be constant for small initial flaw length ; but for deeply cracked specimens the deviation is high. This behaviour results from the fact that the rate of crack opening $d\delta/da$ differs little from the value of δ/a at initiation for the shallowest cracks but more for the deepest cracks. On the other hand the ratio $\delta/2a$ at initiation was found to be constant for both small and deep cracks at constant crack length.

Compliance measurements

Compliance measurements were made by the partial unloading technique. Figure 17 shows a detail of an unloading step. The compliance is deduced from the slope of the unloading line.

A measure is taken into account if no significant difference between unloading and reloading (dotted line) appears.

The "hump" after reloading is probably due to the influence of impurities in the weld.

Five to six unloadings of less than 10% of the current load were made for welded specimens and about fifteen unloadings for the non welded plates. Thus the compliance versus opening curves were deduced in order to find opening values at initiation. The compliance increases with crack growth, initiation can thus be deduced from the tangency between the curve and the line of initial compliance.

Figures 18 and 19 show the influence of initial flaw depth and length on the compliance versus opening records.

For long flawlength and particularly for non welded specimens a large crack growth in the c direction appears prior to rupture. measurements by unloading provides continious information on propagation in both a and c direction. This continuity will permit the solution of cases where the condition of plane strain is not fulfilled.

For exemple for deep cracks or non welded material ink marking is not successfull because no plane fracture exists (for through propagation). For this cases it is possible to find the equivalent through crack length at the same compliance value determined for a part-through crack.

Figure 20 shows a compliance versus opening curve for a non welded plate with both a and c propagation. For longitudinal growth it is possible to measure crack propagation optically on both plate faces and so the compliance versus c curve can be found and by extrapolating this curve for small compliance values, an equivalent through crack length is calculated.

Following the same idea, for long cracks where both propagation directions can be marked it is also possible to determine an equivalence between the equivalent through crack size and the real surface crack dimensions by extrapolating for exemple the upper curve of figure 22.

Acoustic emission

Acoustic emission was also measured to detect crack growth initiation. Figure 24 shows two acoustic emission records for welded and non welded plates with the same crack dimensions and the corresponding load at initiation.

Thus initiation opening values detected by :

- δ versus δa curves
- Ink marking
- Acoustic emission
- Compliance measurements

for various initial flaw dimensions were determined and figure 23 shows the curve of opening at initiation versus the shape factor a/2C for the different techniques.

Finally load versus load line displacement curves were recorded by the apparatus represented in figure 3 to exclude the influence of grip deformation. These curves shown in figure 25 for different flaw lengths will allow the calculation of J integral from (4) and (5).

Critical load line displacements decreases with increasing flaw length. As the leak point opening decreases with increasing flaw length the corresponding maximum load will be lawer and so will be the elastic total deformation and δr.

Conclusions

This experimental study allows a better understanding of part through crack growth and rupture, and the determination of the main parameters.

Total crack front evolution was termined for different flaw configurations. Critical opening values for initiation, leak and total rupture were determined and therefore their evolution with flaw geometry.

Opening versus a curves where determined and an attempt to characterize stable growth with a crack opening angle was made.

Compliance measurements were used to determine crack initiation and to calculate an equivalent through crack length when a δ approach is not valid.

Theoritical investigations will cover different points :

- determination of opening versus Δa relation using a Strip Yield Model (2), (3)

- derivation of this S.Y.M. to introduce $d\delta/da$ and a tearing Modulus based on opening or crack opening angle

- J integral calculation form load versus load line displacement records (4), (5) and will be presented in a following paper

NOMENCLATURE

a = crack depth

a_o = initial crack depth

c = crack half length

c_o = initial crack half crack length

P =load

r = ligament depth excluding necking

δ = middle crack opening

$\delta_{p,A}$ = opening at leak point

$\delta_{R,B}$ = opening total rupture

Δa = crack extension in the thickness direction

Δc = crack extension in the longitudinal direction

$\mathcal{E}$ = compliance

σ = applied stress

y = yield stress

Subcripts :

e = elastic

i = initiation

n = current point

REFERENCES

1. Shih, C.F., "An engineering approach for examining crack growth and stability in flawed structures", NUREG/CP 0010

2. PELLISSIER TANON, A., "Fracture mechanics in structural design", International Conference on Application of Fracture Mechanics to Materials and Structure, Freiburg 1983

3. ZAHOOR, A, and Paris, "A preliminary fracture analysis in the integrity of HSST intermediate test vessel", NUREG/CP 0010

4. GARWOOD, S.J., "Crack growth resistance, geometry effects ...", NUREG CP 0010

5. ERNST, H., Technique of analysis of load displacement records by J integral methods", Thesis, 1979, WASHINGTON UNIVERSITY

ACKNOWLEDGEMENTS

This work is sponsored by the M.I.R. (Ministère de l'Industrie et de la Recherche) and AEROSPATIALE

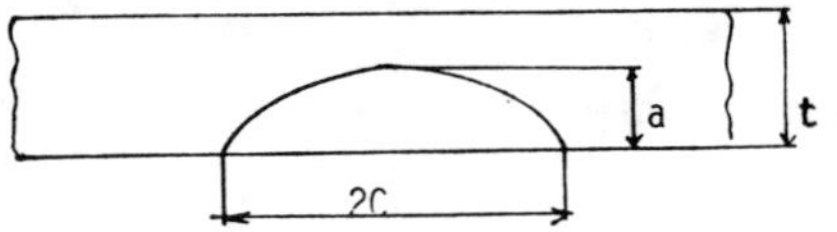

Figure 1

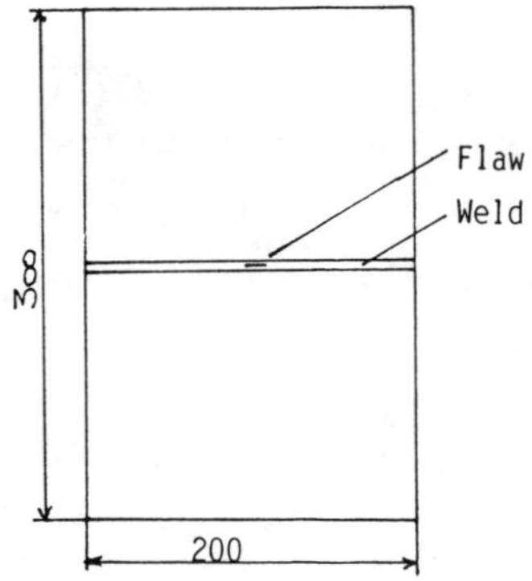

Figure 2

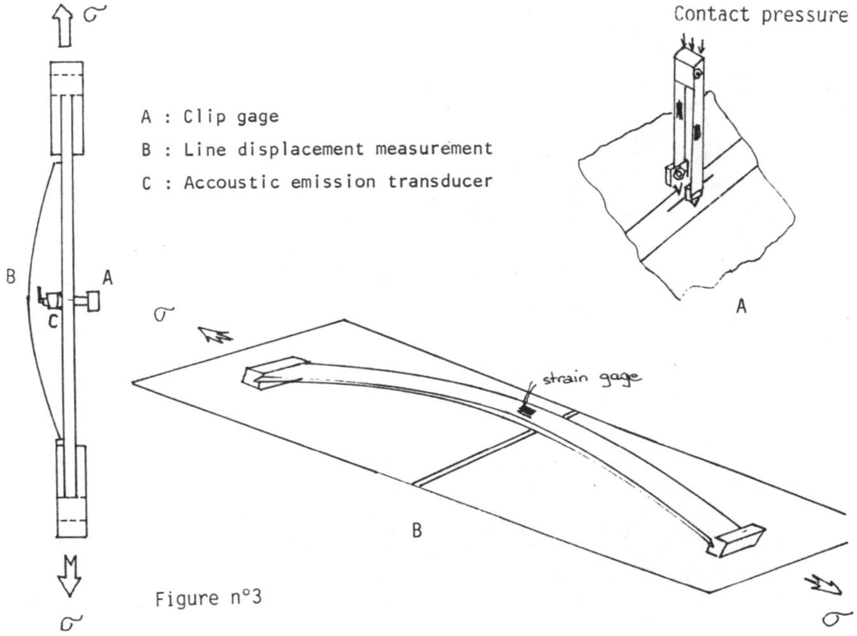

Figure n°3

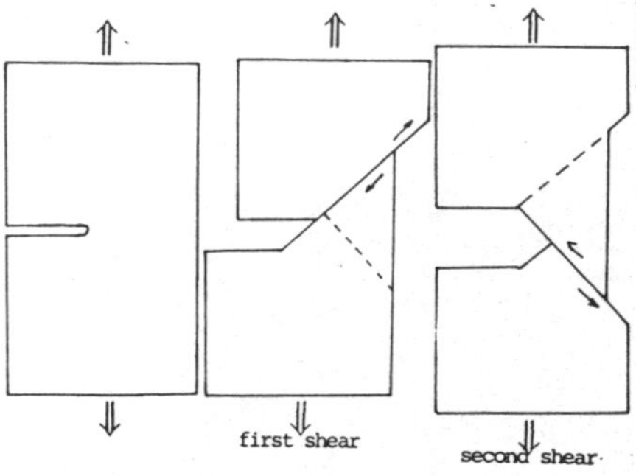

FIGURE 4

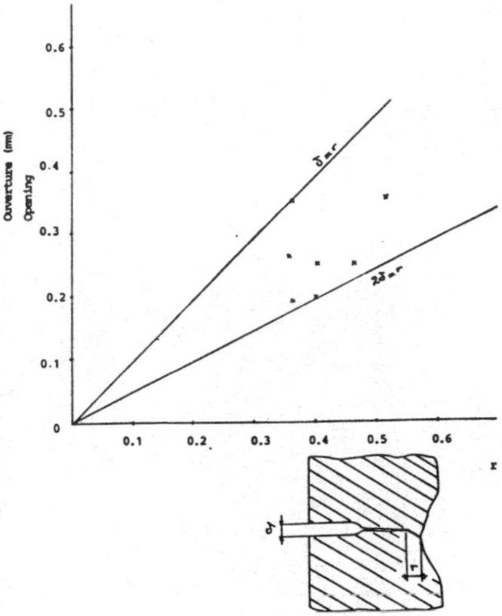

FIGURE 5

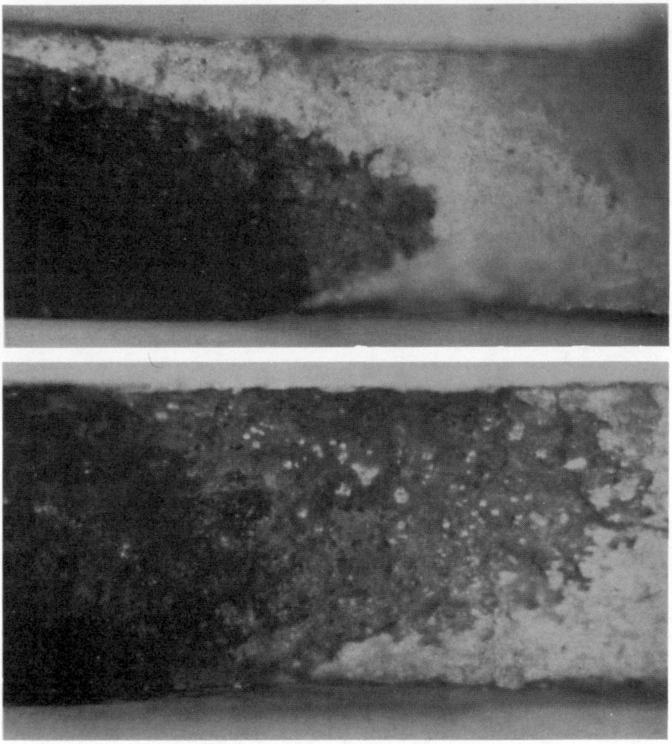

Figure 6 : Edge propagation

Figure 7 : Through the thickness propagation

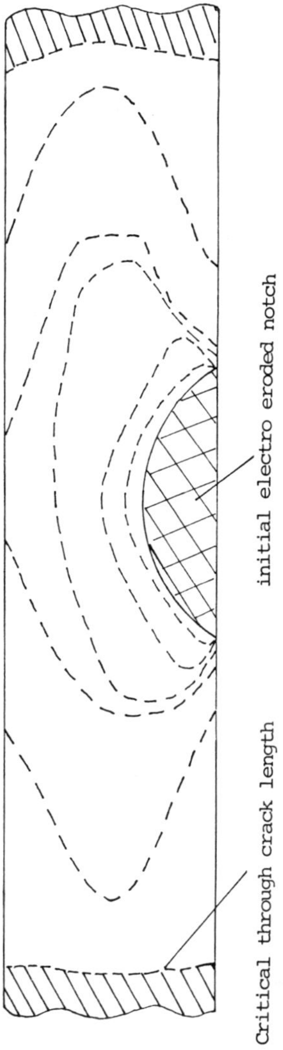

Figure 8: Crack front evolution from initiation to leak and total rupture

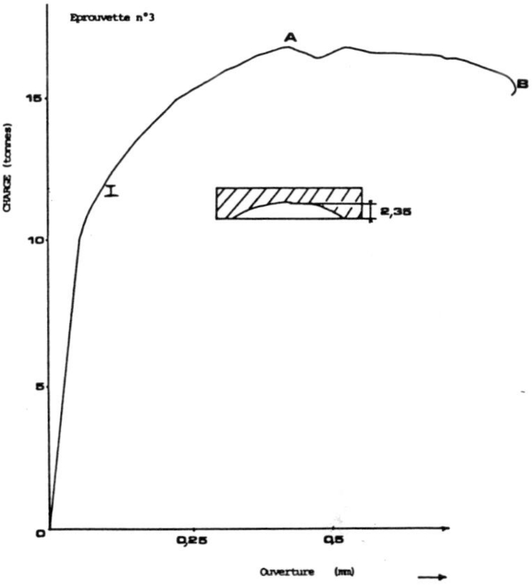

Figure 9

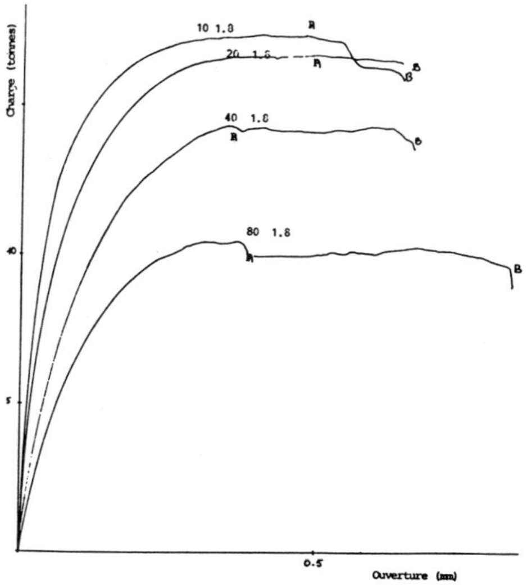

Figure 10

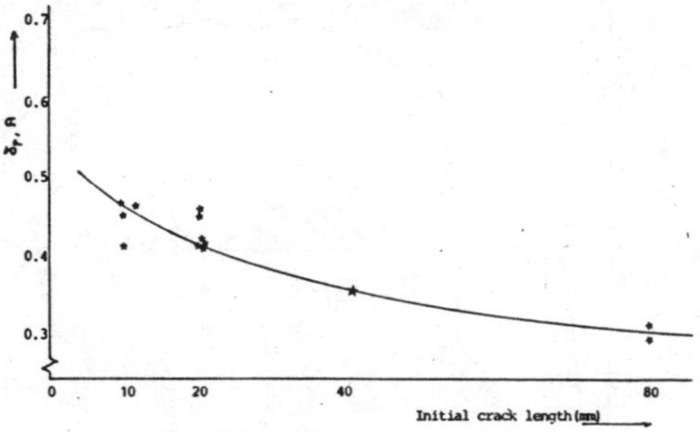

Figure 11: Leak opening versus initial crack length

Figure 12: Opening at total rupture vs initial flaw length curve

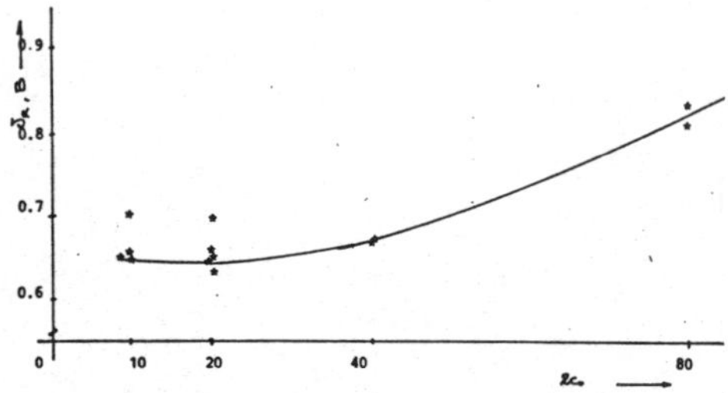

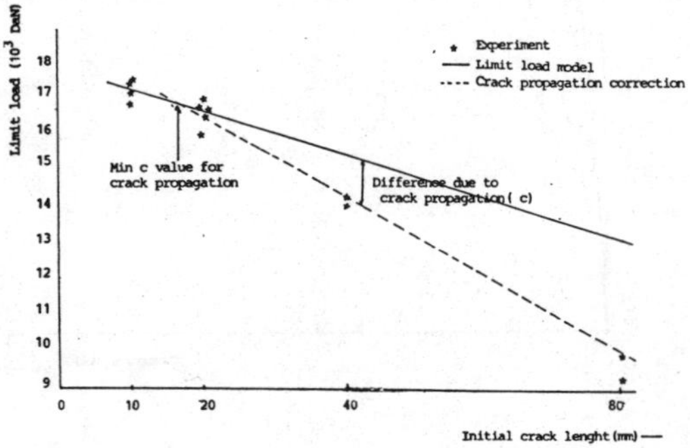

Figure 13

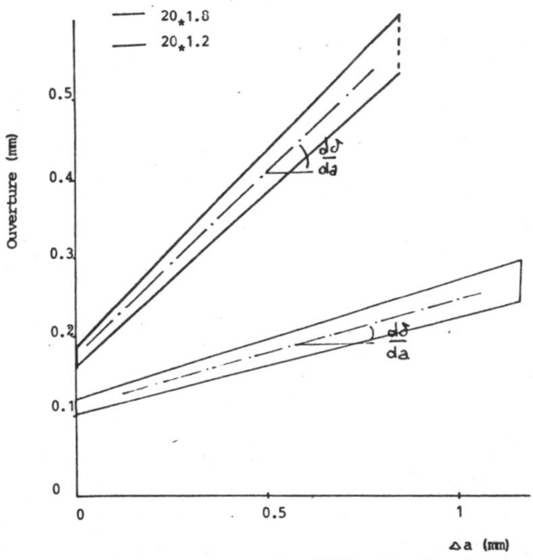

Figure 14: Opening vs crack growth (a direction) curves

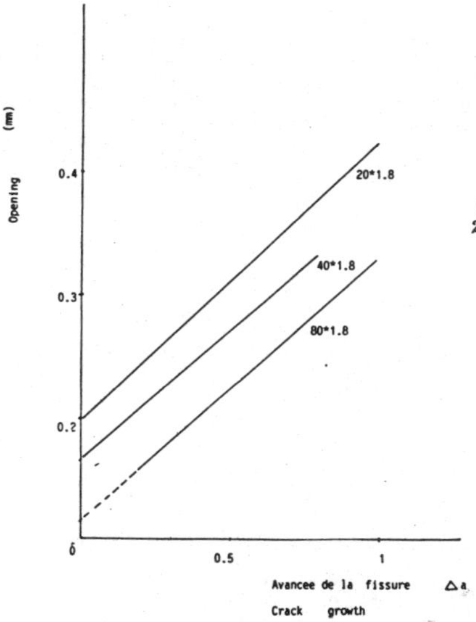

Figure 15: Influence of flaw length on opening vs crack growth

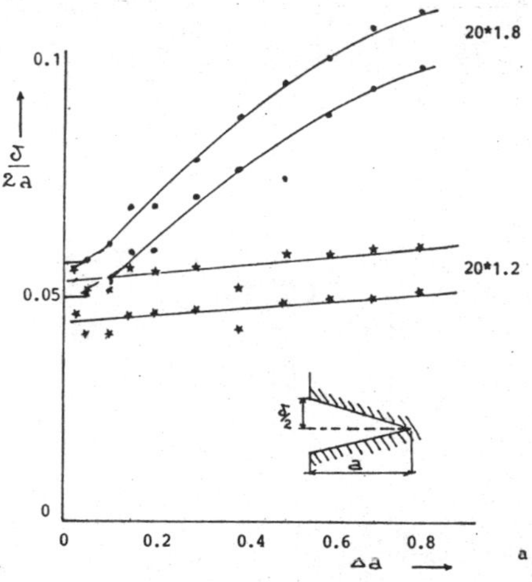

Figure 16

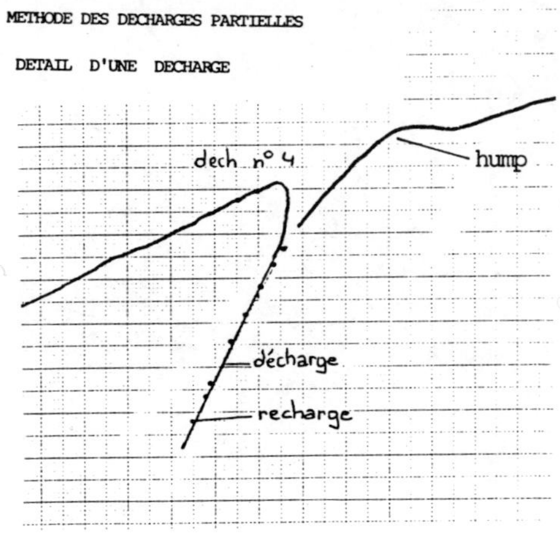

Figure 17

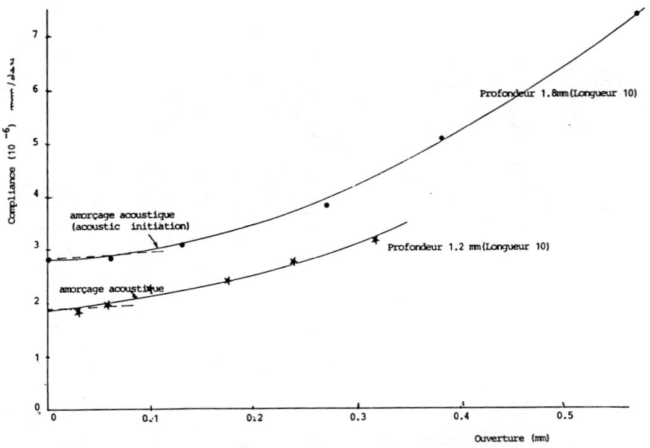

Figure 18: Influence of flaw depth on compliance vs opening curves

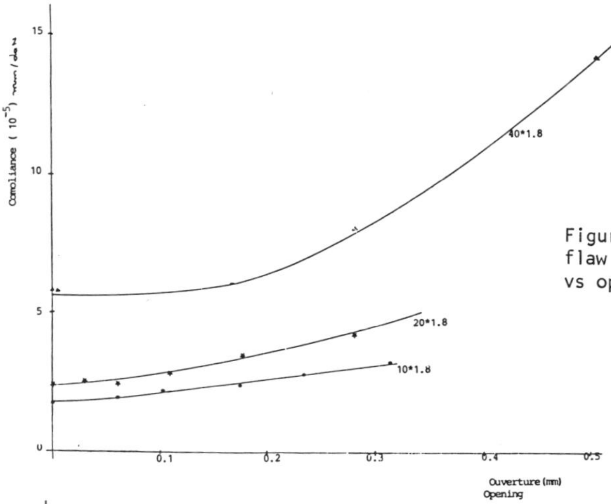

Figure 19: Influence of flaw length on compliance vs opening curves

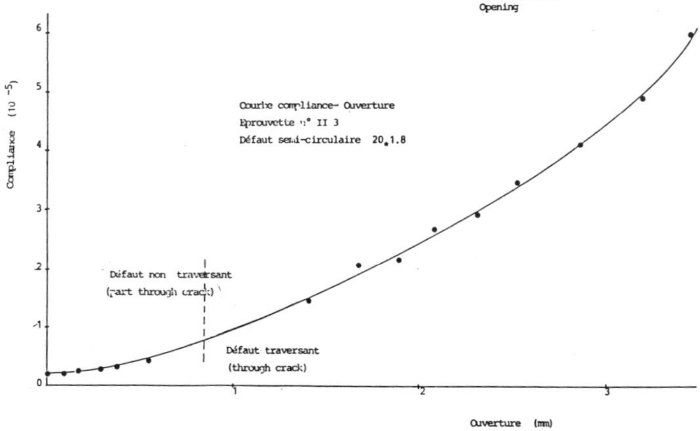

Figure 20

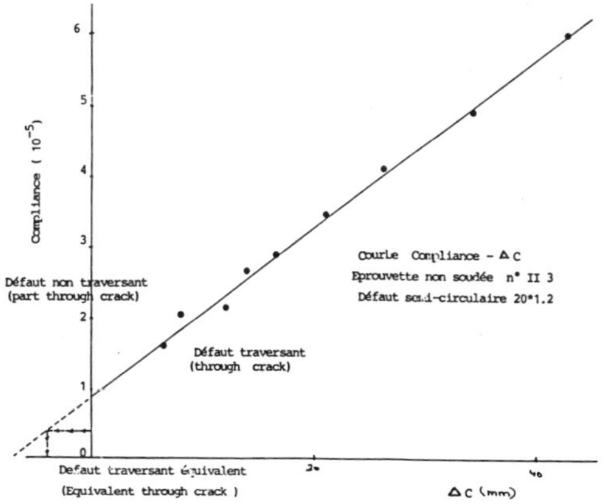

Figure 21: Compliance vs crack growth curve

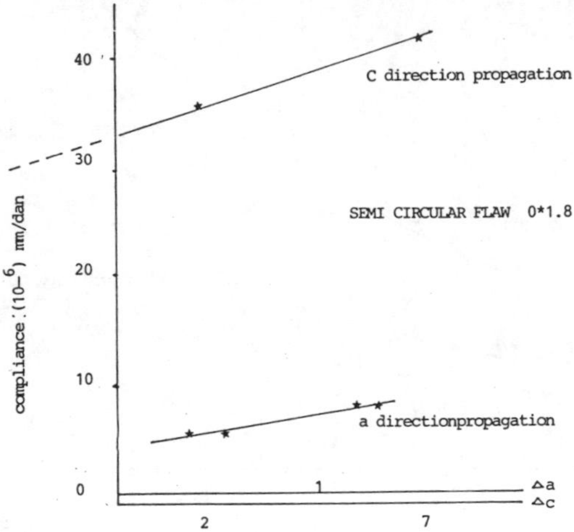

Figure 22: Compliance versus crack growth curve

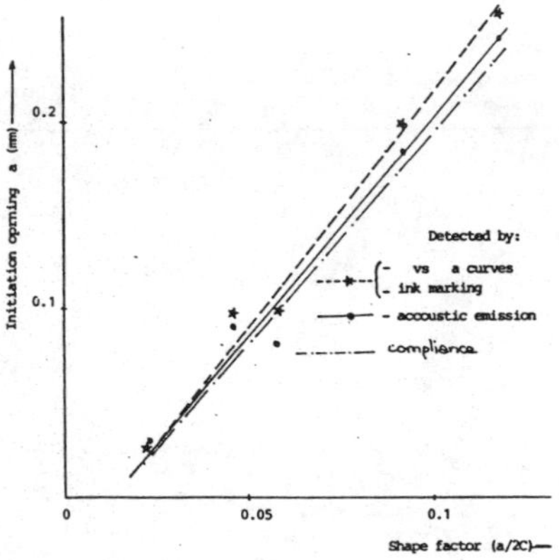

Figure 23: Initiation opening versus crack shape curve

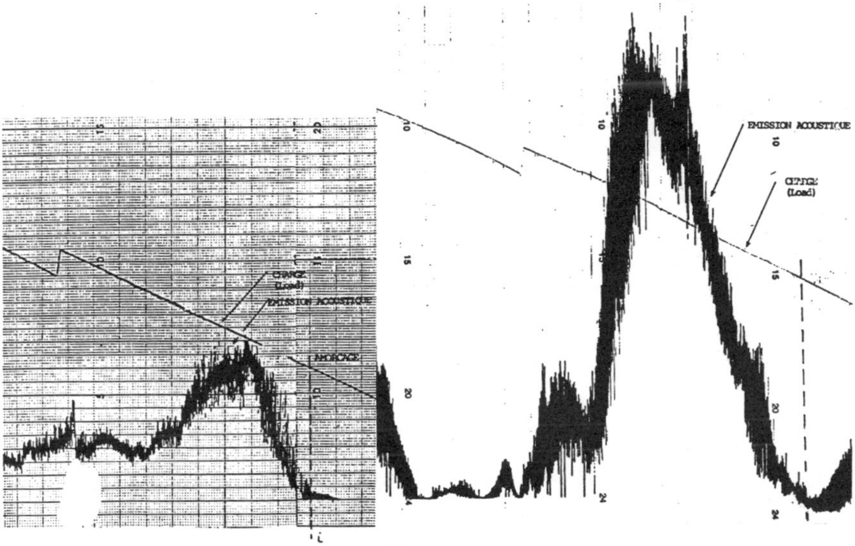

non welded plate

welded plate

Figure 24: Accoustic emission records

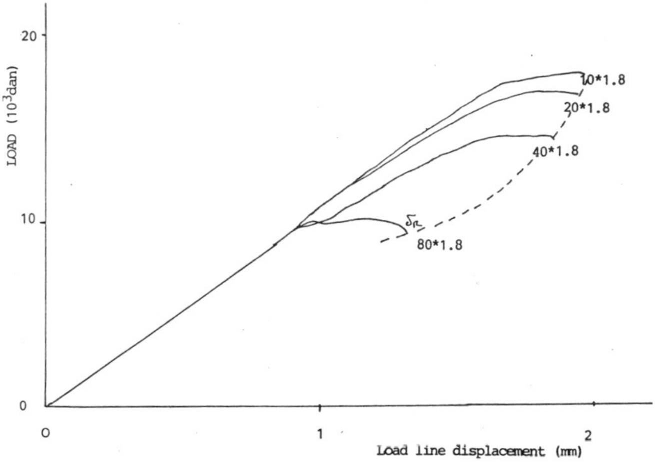

Figure 25: Load versus load line displacement curve

DEFECT ASSESSMENT BASED ON GROSS SECTION YIELDING.

Rudi M. DENYS *

A brief outline is given of the applicability of wide plate testing for the assessment of the significance of defects on failure behaviour for notch ductile materials. Wide plate test results are assessed using the Gross Section Yielding concept. This concept aims to define a maximum tolerable defect size a_{gy} for gross section yielding before fracture ensues. The examples given illustrate that this approach permits a realistic assessment of the integrity of structures serving an important safety function.

INTRODUCTION

In recent years a notable improvement in the quantitative assessment of fracture properties of engineering materials and structures has been established. However, during the past decade attention was mainly focussed on the development of single notch toughness fracture parameter testing methods, such as CTOD, J integral, R curve etc..., whilst little attention was paid to testing techniques which are closer reproducing the condition for large scale or service behaviour.

This development can perhaps be justified if we rely only on "lower bound" levels for design purposes in which an inherent unified factor of conservatism is unavoidable. However, these ideas may not always hold good when fitness for purpose concepts are introduced for the assessment of defects in expensive and high performance structures built from potentially tough materials. The main reason for this is related to limitations of the present fracture mechanics approaches in the elastic plastic deformation regime. For situations which are beyond the application field of LEFM and especially for high toughness materials it has been proved that the empirical correlations between the results of single notch toughness tests and tests on structural components (e.g. wide plates) are either conservative or may give a distorted picture of the actual safety of a structure against failure .

* Gent University - St. Pietersnieuwstraat, 41, B - 9000 GENT

This brings us to the important question : "What kind of test should be used to assess defects or to predict service performance of huge or important engineering components ? ". As far as elastic-plastic behaviour is concerned everyone will agree that the preference goes to tests on samples which simulate service behaviour. The problem consists then in selecting a testing technique representing the actual structure. Since no small scale test is known to correlate exactly with service behaviour, we have to look for a test which resembles and simulates as close as possible all service conditions. According to a survey carried out by the author (1), it has been shown that the test-sample is preferably a wide plate panel of full plate thickness.

The assessment of wide plate test results to prevent the occurrence of unexpected and sudden failures in engineering structures and components has been the subject of intensive research at the Gent University. Based upon the progress which has been achieved and the knowledge of the many factors influencing a reliable and non conservative assessment of defects, an overall assessment concept has been developed. By applying the concept of "Gross Section Yielding" (GSY) to situations in which the elastic-plastic fracture mechanics is either invalidated or over conservative by excessive yielding (i.e. yielding beyond the so called plastic collapse behaviour), it will be shown hereinafter that this approach offers an opportunity to examine and apply fitness for purpose principles in a more practical sense.

FITNESS FOR PURPOSES ASSESSMENTS.

In assessing how welds and weld defects might affect fitness for purpose, it is seen from literature that one relies either on test results obtained from small test specimens (such as Charpy-V specimens) and/or intermediate scale tests (such as the CTOD tests). However, these approaches, which are to be considered as a final goal, may pose serious problems. The range of problems to which the existing methods are applied, can be divided into two categories.

The first category includes these cases where the final decision depends upon the required impact properties. Most people feel uneasy about applying the criteria established for C and C-Mn steels (upon which most codes are based) to modern materials. Indeed, it is common practice that most requirements arbitrarily either edge up the required impact values or lower the minimum testing temperature without adequate justification from full scale behaviour.

The second category includes these cases where the application of single notch tip fracture toughness parameters such as CTOD, J.. is recommended. Again , the engineer feels unhappy about a generalisation of the defect tolerance calculation methods , which are - mainly for analytical reasons-, always the result of simplifications of the real problem. In this connection, it can be asked whether e.g. the CTOD design curve approach may be extrapolated to notch tough materials, without considering a coherent basis similar to the ones on which the original work was based.

As a consequence we believe that for modern and tough materials the engineering significance of defects with regard to fracture initiation and propagation may not always be quantified by fracture mechanics methods directly, without making reference to full scale behaviour. Especially for high performance and expensive structures a widespread adoption of fitness for purpose approaches based on fracture mechanics requires a more detailed knowledge of the safety factors. Only then unnecessarily cautious predictions and uneconomical solutions can be avoided. Therefore, we are inclined to advocate the need for tests, e.g. wide plate tests, resembling the actual structural detail and which are subjected to conditions that might be regarded as similar to those encountered in service.

Although the wide plate test does not correlate exactly with service experience, it answers at least a lot of puzzling questions with regard to the fitness for purpose philosophy. Following this line of thought, it is almost self-evident that once we are prepared to utilize the actual material properties (which differ from the idealized perfectly elastic-plastic characteristics) in ductile strain hardening materials the advantages of large scale testing with regard to fitness for purpose are indeed numerous - Denys (1). Moreover, the author realizes that the recommendation for wide plate testing applies only for important and expensive structures.

ASSESSMENT OF WIDE PLATE TEST RESULTS.

The wide plate test results are normally used to confirm the validity of defect tolerance calculations from small scale data. For this purpose, reference is frequently made to the most widely applied method in the elastic plastic regime: the CTOD design curve. The limit of applicability of the design curve is currently the onset of plastic collapse. Consequentely serious problems arise when the wide plate test exhibits fully ductile behaviour. In these cases it is suggested to assess failure prediction by plastic collapse. However, the adopted methods for dealing with plastic collapse are ill-defined with respect to tolerable defect size estimations. To overcome the limitations it is proposed to judge the wide plate behaviour in quite a different manner.

It is evidently much more realistic to look for criteria which relate to practical behaviour and which are easy to use. In the author's opinion, the estimation of safety, the significance of defects, and thus service performance, must be directly related to the overall behaviour. The assessment of overall behaviour can only be based on either gross strength or gross ductility. For convenience, it is preferable to look for strength, and if we claim a gross strength of at least yield magnitude we automatically obtain a good overall ductility. The philosophy behind this requirement is explained in Figure 1, and is based on extensive experimental work carried out at the Gent University. This method for assessing wide plate test results is referred to as the " Gross Section Yielding" approach.

GROSS SECTION YIELDING CONCEPT.

The origin of the Gross Section Yielding approach is based on the employment of full thickness wide plate specimens containing a notch. The notch is located in that area of plate where high deformations will occur and in these regions where low toughness values are to be expected. The notched wide plate specimen is subsequently subjected to a tensile load at the minimum operating temperature. The use of full thickness ensures further that the constraint in the specimen matches that in the structure.

The experience in using this testing method for various kinds of materials and defect geometries (through thickness-, surface and buried defects), revealed that three distinct deformation modes can occur. The net section stress at fracture either exceeds the material's uniaxial yield stress (0.2 % proof stress) and the flawed wide plate specimen deforms by NET or GROSS section yielding. Or the net section stress at fracture is below the uniaxial yield stress, so that only CONTAINED yielding occurs - see Figure 2. The analysis of these deformation modes in relation with decreasing crack dimensions indicates that tough materials deform either by GSY or by NSY, whilst for less tough materials the sequence of deformation modes to be considered are GSY, NSY, CY and NSY. This difference may be explained by the plate width effects (1) Apart from the apparent plate width effect, it is obvious that for both situations a shift from GSY to NSY exists.

These observations led to the consideration of a direct approach of defect tolerance, solely based upon wide plate testing . The demarcation between net to gross section yielding permits estimation of the maximum tolerable defect size for gross section yielding a_{gy}. (Fig.3). Thus, a defect smaller than a_{gy} induces gross section yielding guaranteeing a good overall elongation and a strength of at least yield magnitude. Consequently it can be construed that defects smaller than a_{gy} are acceptable. At this stage, we must emphasize that we utilize and assess the actual material properties for safety assessments in notch tough strain hardening materials, and that we do NOT allow gross yielding in the structure. We only utilize the deformation phenomenon observed in wide plate test specimens to define acceptable defect sizes. Moreover, the possibility of gross section yielding may be considered as a safeguard in case of e.g. accidental overloading.

METHOD OF APPLICATION.

Since the purpose of this paper is not to acquaint the reader with all the experimental details of wide plate testing, only the general outlines will be described hereinafter. To apply the GSY concept the following experimental data are required:

1. The uniaxial yield strength of the (parent) material at the minimum operating temperature.

2. The ultimate tensile strength of the defective region (i.e. from the material containing the defect - only necessary for the determination of a_{gy} - see also further)
3. The gross stress at fracture (i.e. the load at fracture/gross section) of the wide plate specimen.

The maximum tolerable defect size a_{gy} is that at which the plot of gross section failure stress against defect size intersects the yield stress of the plate. The plot of gross section failure stress against defect size passes through the points corresponding to the gross stress at fracture as well as through the point defined by the ultimate tensile strength of the notch containing-material and zero defect size (Fig. 3).

The method has also been developed to incorporate consideration of transverse weldments and to cover through thickness surface and buried defects - Denys (2, 3). It should be noted that for the cases of transverse welds, in which both HAZ and weld metal overmatch the parent plate in yield stress, it is in principle only necessary to exceed the yield stress of the parent material to achieve gross section yielding.

It should be emphasized that the gross section yielding concept is not always applied to define the maximum tolerable defect size a_{gy}. It is rather intended to check whether a particular defect can be safely left in a structure.

For instance, in case the notch toughness (code) requirements (such as C_v or/and CTOD) are not achieved and as soon as the material used has strain hardening properties, it can be justified to apply the GSY concept. In these circumstances, it is considered that a defect can be present, even when NDT reveals no defects, so that the evaluation will be recategorized in a fitness for purpose approach. For this purpose, a large scale or wide plate test with a defect of dectable size will be carried out in order to check wether gross section yielding can be obtained. If that is the case, it is the experience that a code relaxation can be discussed with the governmental quality control authorities.

Finally, the GSY concept, as it stands, is currently applied to assess defects in structural elements such as pipes, storage tanks, plate and nozzle intersections, etc ...

PRACTICAL APPLICATIONS

The following examples illustrate the application of the method just described.

Exemple I. Check whether buried defect of 10mm x 50mm and a continuous embedded defect 10mm x 350mm located in the HAZ of 30 mm thick welded StE 355 plates are acceptable (t= -20°C). The following general data are available - Denys, Musgen (4).

The submerged arc welding procedure, with K preparation, was used (as it was envisaged to sample the HAZ only). The heat input was 2,5 kJ/mm. No PWHT was applied.

The weld metal yield strength approximately matches that of the plate. The mechanical properties at -20°C as determined on wide plate specimens of plain material gave a yield strength of 425 N/mm^2 and a σ_u of 629 N/mm^2

The minimum CTOD values at -20 °C (specimen size 2BxB) for HAZ and plate material were 0.23 mm and 0.96 mm respectively

Results The test results, depicted in Figure 4, show that gross section yielding occurred irrespective of defect dimensions. It is remarkable to see that a buried defect with a section equalling one third of the plate section failed at 5% gross strain. In order to assist in evaluating the deformation mode, a selection of moiré pictures is given in Figures 5a and 5b. The interference patterns confirms that gross section yielding occurred. The moiré fringes in the unnotched part of the specimen are clearly visible. From the high density of moiré lines viewed from Figure 5a, the buried defect of 10mm x 50mm can be located.

Example II. An internally pressurized pipe (size 273mm x 6,3mm) containing a surface defect of 160mm x 2mm can accidentally be loaded beyond yield. The pipe material has the following minimum specified mechanical properties, yield stress 350 N/mm^2 and a σ_u of 450 N/mm^2. The minimum design temperature is +20°C. Verify if gross section yielding is possible.

Results. The pipe has been pressurized to a maximum pressure of 183 bars,which corresponds to a gross stress level of 396 N/mm^2. The maximum strain and GCOD were 1.87% and 1.05 mm respectively. The values given above correspond to the point when the test was stopped prior to failure. The moiré photograph in Figure 6 portrays clearly gross section yielding; the same can be construed also from comparing the maximum stress level and the yield stress level of the unnotched material, the former exceeding the latter.

FINAL OBSERVATIONS - CONCLUSIONS

An outline has been given of the applicability of wide plate testing for the assessment of the significance of defects on failure behaviour. The wide plate test results were assessed using the Gross Section Yielding concept. This concept aims to define a maximum tolerable defect size a_{gy} for gross section yielding before fracture ensues. These maximum tolerable dimensions enables the definition of acceptable defects. Defects smaller than a_{gy} are considered to be acceptable, since they tolerate a strength of at least yield point magnitude and a sufficient overall ductility.

The gross section yielding concept must be considered as a direct fitness for purpose approach. This concept, which gives an adequate margin of safety in terms of overall deformation, should be considered as either an alternative, or a complementary method that should be used together with defect tolerance calculation methods based on a single crack tip fracture toughness parameter. Wide plate testing is in particular recommended for expensive structures for which conservative defect tolerance levels may prove to be extremely expensive.

Furthermore, the gross section yielding concept permits a realistic assessment of the integrity of those structures that serve an important safety function and that have deliberately been designed not to fail in the elastic range of stress but only under gross overload in the plastic range. In other words, the gross section yielding concept can be considered as an important piece of the jigsaw puzzle characterized by the presently adopted procedures of analysis in fracture mechanics.

In the author's experience, larger defects can be tolerated than those predicted by the traditional fitness for purpose approaches, despite the stringent requirement of gross section yielding. This observation applies especially for notch tough materials which contain either surface or buried defects. Moreover, the size of defect used in wide plate testing giving rize to gross section yielding, are normally found to be so large that they can be reliably detected using the convensional NDT techniques.

SPECIAL SYMBOLS USED

a_{gy}= Value of a, demarcating Gross section/Net section yielding.

GCOD =Gent Crack Opening Displacement (Gauge length : 8 mm).

GSY. =Gross section yield (i.e. gross stress > yield stress).

NSY. =Net section yield (i.e. gross stress < yield stress).

REFERENCES

1 DENYS,R., 1983, Absicherung des weitersbetreibs fehlerbehaf teter Bauteile durch Grossplattenversuchen, TUV Conference proceedings - Mit Rissen Leben, Essen, W.Germany

2 DENYS,R., 1982, The wide plate test and its application to acceptable defects, WI Congress Proceedings Fracture Tough ness Testing - Methods, Interpretation and application, -June - Paper 13 - London.

3 DENYS,R., 1979, Plastische breukmechanica - Heterogeen materiaal- PT werktuigbouw 34 - 1 en 2 Den Haag.

4 DENYS,R.,and MUESGEN,B., 1982, Gross section yielding crack tolerance of St E 355 and St E 690 steels - WI Congress Proceedings Fracture Toughness Testing - Methods, Interpretation and application -June - Paper 12 - London

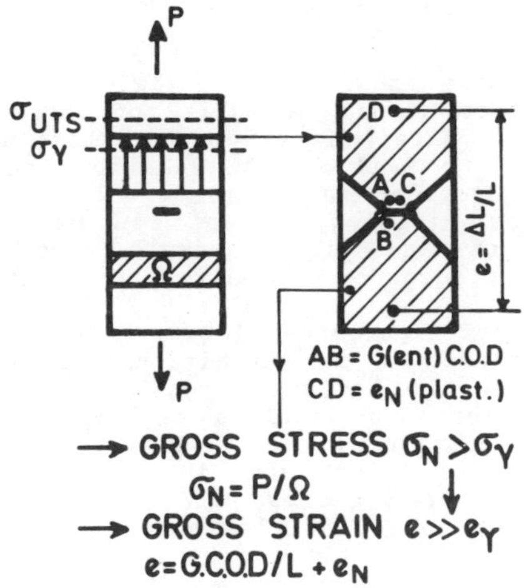

Figure 1 Schematic representation of Gross Section Yielding.

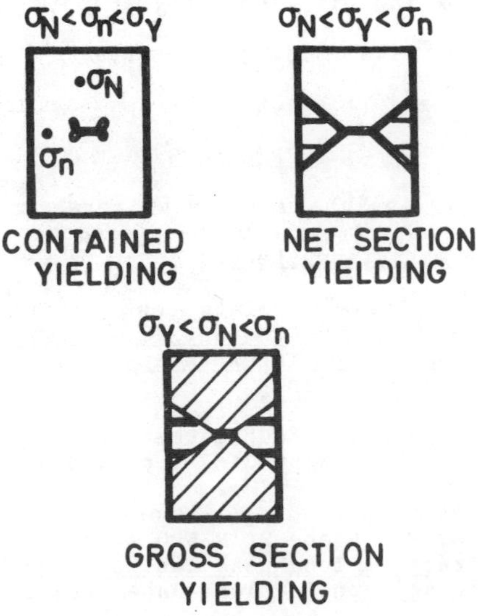

Figure 2 CONTAINED, NET and GROSS section yielding.

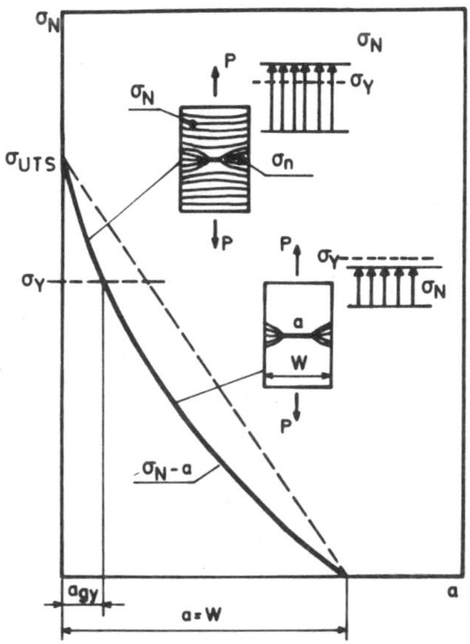

Figure 3 Gross stress dependence of crack length.

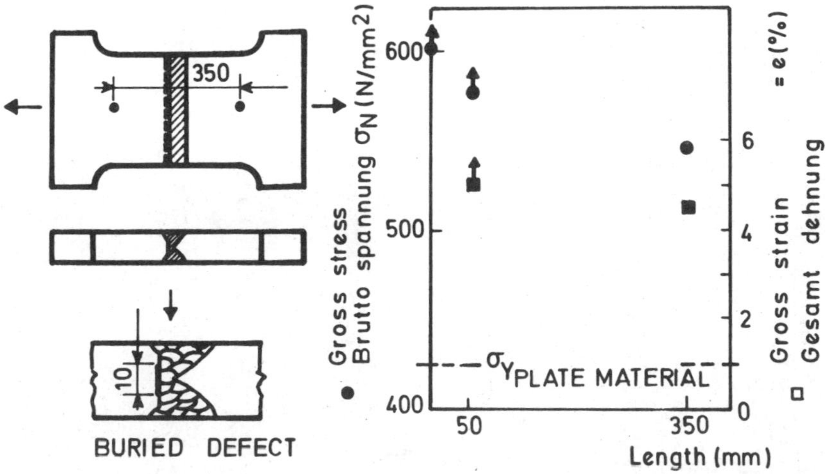

Figure 4 Measured gross stress and gross strain of weldment with an embebbed defect.

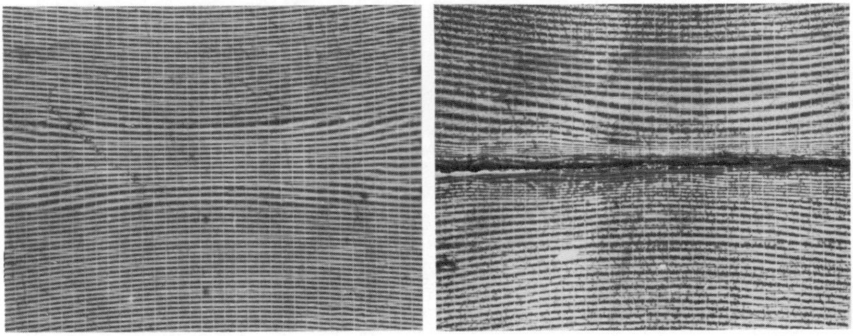

Figure 5 Moiré pictures of weldments with a buried defect.
a) 10mm x 50mm - b) 10mm x 350mm

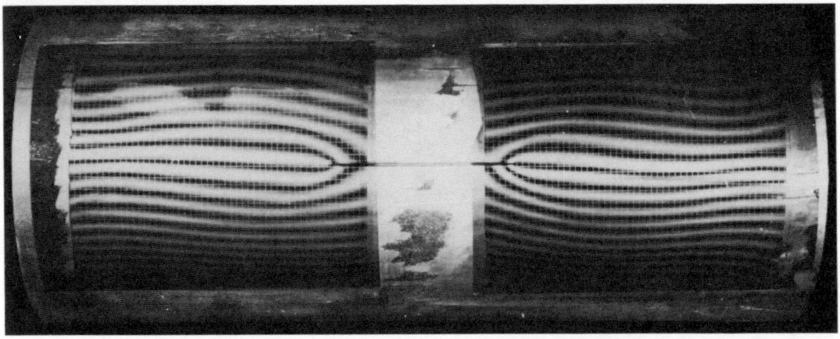

Figure 6 Moiré picture of gross section yielding in a pipe.

DYNAMIC FRACTURE BEHAVIOR OF NODULAR CAST IRON

*Walter L. Bradley and *Marjorie R. Andler

Ferritic nodular cast iron has been found to be a much tougher material than previously believed based on Charpy impact test results. As a result this material is being considered as a substitute for Stainless Steel in nuclear waste transport containers.

We have determined K_{1c} and K_{1d} values for nodular cast iron with varying values of silicon and percentage of pearlite in the matrix. Regular V-notch charpy bars and fatigue precracked charpy bars have been tested to determine the initiation and propagation energy and the effect of notch acuity on transition temperature.

INTRODUCTION

There has been a trend in recent years to replace steel components with nodular cast iron. This material has been used in many applications but is currently precluded from many more critical applications because of the concern about its fracture toughness. For example nodular cast iron is being considered as an alternative to stainless steel in nuclear waste transport containers. This substitution is being delayed until the dynamic fracture behavior is better understood.

Recent work in fracture mechanics testing of nodular cast iron by Bradley and Mead (1) and Salzbrenner et al. (2) have used the J-integral approach developed by Rice (3) to determine the quasistatic fracture toughness (K_{1c}). Bradley and Mead (1) have obtained K_{1c} values of 45 to 55 $MPa\sqrt{m}$ on materials with yield strengths of 269-352 MPa. Salzbrenner et al. (2) have reported K_{1c} values of 87 to 107 $MPa\sqrt{m}$ on the same materials. The differences in the results are due to the variations in the methods of testing. More details may be obtained elsewhere (2,4).

The results of the previous studies are surprisingly high considering the relatively low Charpy impact values typically observed in nodular cast iron (less than 20 joules). Correlations have been made between Charpy V-notch results and fracture mechanics results for steels by Rolfe and Barsom (5). Using Equation (1) and appropriate Charpy V-notch values for upper shelf, a K_{1c} of 45 $MPa\sqrt{m}$ would be expected. This is less than 50% of the value obtained experimentally. In addition these K_{1c} values give a $(K_{1c}/YS)^2$ value greater than 0.025 meters which is comparable to the $(K_{1c}/YS)^2$ values of steel alloys used in many critical applications. The larger the $(K_{1c}/YS)^2$ value, the tougher the material and the better its ability to tolerate large defects without failure.

* Department of Mechanical Engineering, Texas A&M University, College Station, TX

$$(K_{1c}/YS)^2 = [A/YS\ (CVN - (YS/20))] \tag{1}$$

The objectives of this project were to (1) determine the initiation and propagation energies for standard Charpy V-notch specimens on eleven grades of nodular iron at various temperatures; (2) to determine the dynamic fracture toughness (K_{1d}) at various temperatures for eleven grades of nodular iron; (3) to evaluate qualitatively and quantitatively, the fracture mode in each specimen using Scanning Electron Microscopy; (4) to determine the effect of notch acuity on the transition temperature and on the fraction of total energy dissipated in crack extension; (5) to determine the effect of silicon content and percentage of pearlite in the matrix on K_{1d} and the transition temperature; and (6) to correlate Charpy V-notch and fractography results with previous K_{1c} data on the eleven grades of nodular cast iron to determine the strain rate sensitivity of the fracture behavior.

This report presents a brief description of the experimental and analytical procedures and a discussion on the results. Further information may be obtained elsewhere (4).

EXPERIMENTAL AND ANALYTICAL PROCEDURES

The impact fracture behavior of ferritic and pearlitic nodular cast iron was studied using fatigue precracked Charpy V-notch specimens and regular Charpy V-notch specimens. Eleven grades of nodular cast iron were tested. The material was obtained from broken compact tension specimens from a previous study (1). These materials were used because K_{1c} values had already been obtained in the earlier studies (1,2).

The specimens were prepared as specified by ASTM E23-81 (6). They were broken at various temperatures using a Sonntag Universal, Model SI-1, Charpy impact machine which was equipped with a Dynatup Model 371 instrumentation system. The Dynatup system is used to monitor the dynamic behavior of the test piece. It contains a strain-gaged tup, a dynamic response module and a velocometer. The system allows a load time trace to be recorded. This record was stored on a digital storage oscilloscope and was subsequently transferred to a DIGITAL MINC 11 computer for data reduction and a plotter for hardcopy production.

Data Reduction

The load-time records obtained, were converted to Pd (energy) using Equation (2). By assuming that crack extension occurred at maximum load, the

$$E = V \int Pdt\ [1\ (V \int Pdt/4E_o)] \tag{2}$$

initiation and propagation on energies were also obtained. The equivalent critical stress intensity for dynamic fracture, K_{1d} was calculated using Equations (3) and (4).

$$J = [f(a/W)A_1]/Bb \tag{3}$$

$$K_{1d}{}^2 = J_{1d}E \tag{4}$$

The J value obtained in Equation (3) (J-integral) was evaluated at maximum load for the fatigue precracked specimens and was used as J_{1d}.

Scanning Electron Microscope Fractography

The specimens were examined in an SEM and representative fractographs were taken. A point count method was then used to determine quantitatively the amount of ductile and brittle fracture. These results were used to draw the curves shown in Figures 1-7.

RESULTS AND DISCUSSION

The experimental program and analysis provided a set of data which will be discussed in this section. The primary focus of the project is to evaluate to fracture toughness of nodular cast iron based on Charpy impact test results and fracture mechanics test results (K_{1c}) and (K_{1d}) from this study and previous studies. In addition the effect of silicon content and percentage of pearlite on the toughness will be discussed. A discussion on the possibility of correlating Charpy V-notch energies to K_{1d} values will also be presented.

The load-time trace of an impact test can be used to determine whether the fracture is primarily ductile or brittle. The ductile fracture has a load-time trace that shows a gradual decrease from maximum load, whereas a brittle specimen shows a sharp drop after maximum load to zero. In addition the very ductile specimen may take ten times as long to fracture as the brittle specimen. It is clear from these measurements that ductile fracture requires a continuous input of additional energy beyond maximum load to propagate a crack through the remaining ligament. By contrast, in brittle fracture the elastic energy stored prior to initial crack extension is sufficient to propagate the crack across the remaining ligament.

These results along with similar traces taken for the other alloys over a range of temperatures were analyzed to give (1) the energy input into the system leading to initial crack extension, to be called the crack initiation energy, E_i; (2) the additional energy required to subsequently propagate the crack across the ligament, to be called the crack propagation energy, E_p; (3) the initial energy absorbed per unit area of crack extension, J_{1d} (or the equivalent critical stress intensity K_{1d} which may be calculated from J_{1d}). The fracture surfaces were examined carefully using a scanning electron microscope for both a qualitative and quantitative determination of the fracture mode (i.e. ductile or brittle).

Fracture Energies From Charpy Tests

The initiation energy, propagation energy and total energy are shown as functions of temperature for both a fatigue precracked Charpy V-notch specimen and a regular Charpy V-notch specimen in Figures 1-3. The energies shown in these figures are in units of joules/mm^2. Each energy was normalized to the area of the uncracked ligament; namely, (W-a) x B, where W is the specimen width (10 mm), a is the crack or V-notch depth (approximately 5 mm for a fatigue precracked specimen and 2 mm for a regular V-notch specimen) and B is the specimen width (10 mm). The energies were normalized in order to make comparisions more direct since the cross sectional area of the fatigue precracked specimens was smaller than that of the regular Charpy V-notch specimens by about 40%.

Several general patterns emerge from a careful examination of these results. First E_i, the normalized crack initiation energy, is much greater for a blunt notch specimen then a sharp notch specimen. Second, the ductile to brittle transition for crack initiation energy occurs for V-notched specimens at a temperature 10 to 30°C lower than that observed for fatigue precracked specimens. Third, the normalized crack propagation energy E_p is similar for the blunt notched specimen and the fatigue precracked specimens, as is the ductile to brittle transition temperature. The transition temperature for crack propagation energy for both types of specimens is similar to that for crack initiation energy for the blunt notched specimens. Therefore, it is lower than that for crack initiation of fatigue precracked specimens. Fourth, the crack initiation energy ranges from approximately 25 to 40% of the total fracture energy for V-notched specimens and 15-25% of the total fracture energy for fatigue precracked Charpy specimens for temperatures corresponding to upper shelf behavior. For lower shelf behavior, the Charpy V-notched specimens use 80% of the total fracture energy to reach crack initiation; for fatigue precracked specimens, the initiation energy on the lower shelf ranges from 20 to 50% of the total.

The state of stress at the crack tip of a sharp crack is more nearly plane strain when compared to a blunt notch. The notch acuity causes a shift in the transition temperature. Thus, the sharp notch increases the transition temperature relative to the V-notch transition temperature. The greater stress concentration coupled with the greater constraint combine to account for the lower energy required to initiate crack extension for the fatigue precracked charpy specimens. Once crack initiation occurs for the fatigue precracked specimens, the crack propagation energy is not much affected by the original notch acuity. This suggests that the stress field around the crack tip of the initial crack extension must be similar for both types of specimens. This could possibly be because of considerable crack tip blunting in the fatigue precracked charpy specimen prior to initial crack extension and/or a crack tip geometry after initial crack extension that is insensitive to initial notch acuity.

Dynamic Critical Stress Intensities

The J_{1d} values calculated from the measured load-time curves were converted to equivalent K_{1d} values using Equation 4. It should be noted that these were calculated assuming initial crack extension began at maximum load. This has been found to be the point at which crack extension occurs in several studies (2,7,8). It is questionable whether the fracture parameters obtained in this study should be labelled J_{1d} and K_{1d} since J_{1c} (or J_{1d}) is stictly defined by ASTM E813-81.(9) This standard calls for a J versus a curve to obtain the moment of crack extension, whereas it was assumed that crack extension began at maximum load. Therefore, we will hereafter refer to these as K_{1d}* and J_{1d}*. Figure 4 shows the values of K_{1d}* versus temperature and value of K_{1c}* versus temperature. These are recalculated from the earlier work of Bradley and Mead (1) on the same materials, assuming crack extension began at maximum load. More information may be obtained elsewhere (4).

These results clearly indicate a significant shift in the ductile to brittle transition temperature as one goes from quasi-static to dynamic fracture. The shifts are greatest for the lower yield strength materials and seem to be similar in magnitude to the transition temperature shifts observed for steels (10) at similar values of yield strength. Values of transition temperature (TT) shift as high as 90°C are noted. The upper shelf K_{1d}* values are also larger than the K_{1c}* values, but these larger values were observed only at much higher temperatures.

Effect of Silicon and Pearlite Content

To better evaluate the effect of chemistry and microstructure on the dynamic fracture behavior as measured by K_{1d}*, the dynamic critical stress intensities have been plotted as a function of temperature for various groups of specimens where only one chemistry or microstructural variable was changed. These results, presented in Figures 5 and 6, indicate the effect of silicon content, and percentage of pearlite in the matrix. The conclusions that may be drawn from these observations are as follows: the percentage of pearlite in the matrix has a dramatic effect on both the transition temperature and the upper shelf K_{1d} values; and the silicon content has a significant effect on the transition temperature with very little effect on the upper shelf values.

Increasing the silicon content and/or the percentage of pearlite in the matrix increases the yield strength without having a proportionate effect on the cleavage stress. This would give the observed shifts in transition temperature. Pearlite also greatly reduces the strain to fracture in ductile rupture, which lowers the upper shelf K_{1d}* values. The ductile fracture strain is not a sensitive function of silicon content. Thus, silicon content does not affect the upper shelf K_{1d} values to a large degree.

Fractography

There is no conspicuous difference in the ductile fracture topography of the fatigue precracked Charpy specimen and V-notched specimens. The cleavage behavior is also essentially the same. Thus, the effect of the notch acuity seems to be principally in shifting the transition temperature, as has been previously noted, without changing in any significant way the basic mechanisms of fracture.

The trends from ductile to brittle fracture are more easily ascertained from the fractographic observations than from the fracture energies or critical stress intensities; i.e. there seems to be less scatter in these results. Thus, the fractographic data were used to help determine the shape of the curves drawn through the fracture energies and critical stress intensities presented in Figures 1-7. Finally, the fraction of ductile fracture in fatigue precracked specimens versus test temperature for one of the alloys studied is presented in Figure 7. Also included in this figure is the K_{1d}* versus temperature results previously presented in Figure 4 where they were compared to K_{1c}* values. The transition temperature for K_{1d}* correlates well with the transition from ductile to brittle fracture.

Correlating Charpy Energies to K_{1d}* Values

It is widely recognized that the Charpy impact energies for ductile iron are much lower than those for steels. Yet this study has clearly indicated that the K_{1c}* and K_{1d}* values for ductile iron are surprisingly high. Using the Equation (1)for steels given by Rolfe and Barsom A has a value of 5 for low strength steels (5). A correlation for the upper shelf values was made using this equation for nodular cast iron. Results for ferritic cast irons in this study showed A to be approximately 25. In this case the correlation coefficient for nodular iron is approximately five times the value for steel. In other words, nodular iron with 16 joules of impact energy will have a similar K_{1d} to steel with a Charpy impact energy of 80 joules. This suggests that a comparison of Charpy values for ductile iron and steel is not very useful as a predictor of relative dynamic fracture toughness.

There are two possible explanations for this discrepancy. One involves a microscopic approach and the other a macroscopic approach. The microscopic approach deals with the difference in the different characteristics of the microstructure and its effect on ductile fracture with different notch geometries. Ductile fracture requires plastic flow leading to the formation and growth of voids at inhomogeneities in the matrix such as second phase particles (graphite in cast iron). These voids, when sufficiently large, will coalesce giving a dimpled fracture surface and local crack extension. This process then requires a critical strain to cause void nucleation and growth. This strain must also occur over a some critical volume that allows several such voids to form and then coalesce. In nodular cast iron, void nucleation is relatively easy at the graphite particles. However, the relative coarseness of the microstructure makes achievement of the critical strain over some critical volume the limiting consideration in fracture. The microstructure in steels is relatively finer and the critical strain somewhat higher as the carbide particles are not as easy a nucleation site for voids. Thus the achievement of the critical strain is the limiting factor in steels, with achievement of such a value over some critical volume being less important.

In a blunt notch test, the stress concentration at the tip of the notch is much less than that in a sharp notch test (i.e., specimens with fatigue precracks). This means that achieving the critical strain will be more difficult since the stress concentration is less but exists over a greater volume of material in the region of the crack tip. Thus, in a blunt notch test, a material that is critical strain limited rather than critical strain over critical volume limited will appear to be relatively tougher. In a sharply notched specimen with the very high but very localized stresses and strains, achieving the critical strain over a critical volume is the limiting factor. Thus, materials with coarser microstructures would appear relatively tougher in such a test.

This idea is supported by recent work in steels. It has been demostrated that a very high austenitizing temperature actually gives an increase in K_{1c} by coarsening (i.e., the grain size is enlarged) the microstructural features critical to fracture, though for many years it has been common practice to avoid such austenitizing temperatures because of the reduction it gives in Charpy impact energy (10). This demonstrates that the Charpy test penalizes a coarse microstructured material.

The macroscopic approach to explaining this discrepancy is based on an observation made after examining tensile specimens, compact tension specimens, Charpy V-notch specimens, and fatigue precracked Charpy V-notch specimens. It was noticed that in all cases of 100% ductile fracture no shear lips were formed on either type of Charpy specimen or the compact tension specimen, nor did the tensile specimen exhibit a cup and cone fracture surface. This suggests that the contraint in all of the tests on ductile iron was sufficient to prevent large shear lips from forming. Steel by contrast usually forms shear lips during charpy testing except for temperatures just above the start of the ductile to brittle transition or temperatures on the lower shelf. Thus, for steels we are correlating plane strain K_{1d}* values to plane stress CVN energies whereas in cast iron we are correlating plane strain K_{1d}* values to plane strain CVN energies. Irwin (5) has estimated the plastic zone size for plane stress to be three times as large as the plastic zone size for plane strain conditions. Since energy dissipation in fracture correlates roughly with plastic zone size, this could explain why at the same K_{1d} values, a steel Charpy bar might absorb three times as much energy as a ductile iron if the steel has large shear lips (indicating plane stress) and the ductile iron has no shear lips.

CONCLUSIONS

1. Dynamic plane strain fracture toughness values (K_{1d}) have been obtained at several temperatures for eleven grades of nodular iron.

2. It has been clearly shown that Charpy impact energies alone do not give a good indication of the toughness of nodular iron.

3. Increasing the silicon content increases the transition temperature of nodular iron without having a significant effect on the upper shelf energy in the range studied.

4. Pearlite is clearly detrimental to the toughness of nodular iron in that it raises the transition temperature and lowers the upper shelf energy.

5. The initiation energy is much greater for a blunt notch than for a sharp crack.

6. The propagation energy is essentially the same for a blunt notch and a sharp crack.

7. The crack extension zone was the same for the blunt notch specimens as the sharp crack specimens.

8. Nodular iron does not form shear lips (or cup and cone features) as are normally observed in steel.

SYMBOLS USED

a = Crack depth

A = Constant of proportionality

A_1 = Area under load time curve from moment of initial impact to maximum load

b = Uncracked ligament width (W-a)

B = Specimen thickness

CVN = Charpy V-notch energy

E = Young's modulus

E_i = Energy required for crack initiation

E_o = Maximum energy obtainable by the hammer or instrumented tup assembly (before impact with the specimen)

E_p = Energy required for crack propagation

E_T = Total energy required for fracturing the sample

J = J integral

K_{1c} = Static fracture toughness

K_{1d} = Dynamic fracture toughness

V = Initial velocity of the hammer

YS = Yield strength

REFERENCES

1. Mead, H., and Bradley, W., 1980, AFS Transactions, 265.

2. Salzbrenner, R., Van den Avyle, J.A., Lutz, T.J., and Bradley, W.L., 1983, "Fracture Toughness Testing of Ductile Cast Irons," Sandia National Laboratories, Albuquerque, New Mexico, U.S.A.

3. Rice, J.R., 1968, Journal of Applied Mechanics, Vol. 35, 379.

4. Andler, M.R., 1983, Dynamic Fracture Toughness of Nodular Cast Iron, Masters Thesis, Texas A&M University, College Station, Texas, USA.

5. Rolfe, S.T. and Barsom, J.M., 1977, "Fracture and Fatigue Control in Structures," Prentice Hall, Inc., Englewood Cliffs, New Jersey, USA.

6. American Society for Testing and Materials Standards, 1981, ASTM E23-81 Philidelphia, PA., USA.

7. Luyendij, and Nieswaag, H. 1982, Report presented at the 49th International Foundry Congress, Chicago, Ill. USA.

8. Nishi, S., and Kobayshi, T., 1976, Proc. 4th ICSMA, Volume 2, 524.

9. American Society for Testing and Materials Standards, 1981, ASTM E813-81 Philidelphia, PA., USA.

10. Ritchie, R.O. and Horn R.M., 1978, Metallurgical Transactions 9A, 331.

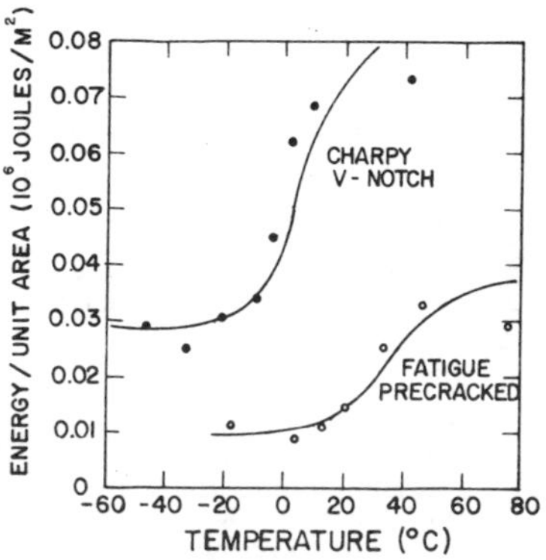

Figure 1 Initiation Energy vs. Temperature (2.5 % Silicon; <2 % Pearlite)

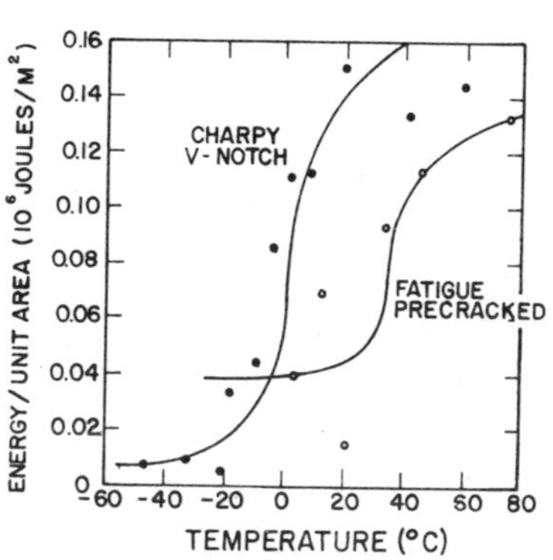

Figure 2 Propagation Energy vs. Temperature (2.5 % Silicon; <2 % Pearlite)

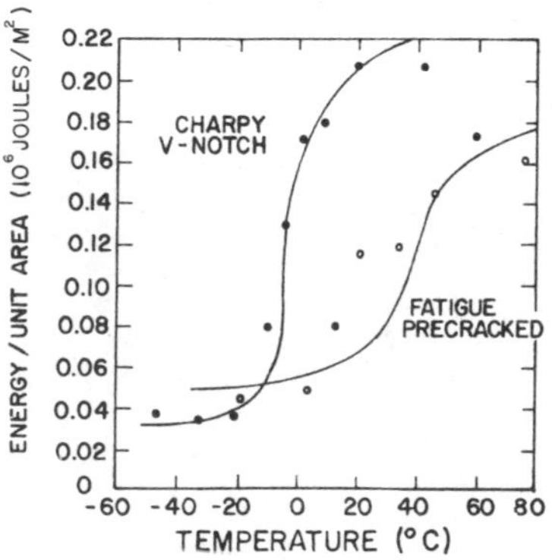

Figure 3 Total Energy vs. Temperature (2.5 % Silicon; <2 % Pearlite)

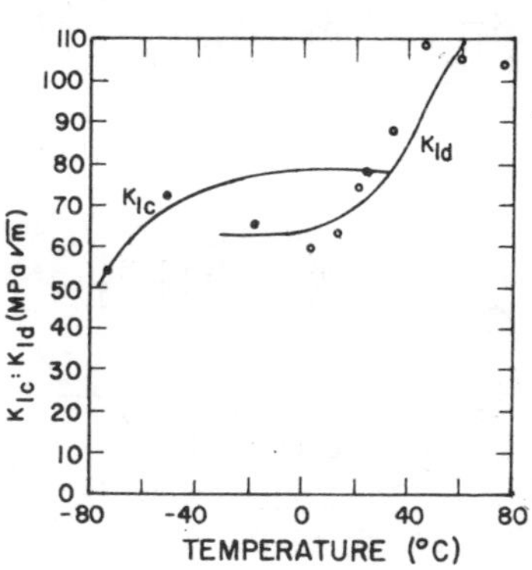

Figure 4 K_{1c} and K_{1d} vs. Temperature (2.5 % Silicon; <2 % Pearlite)

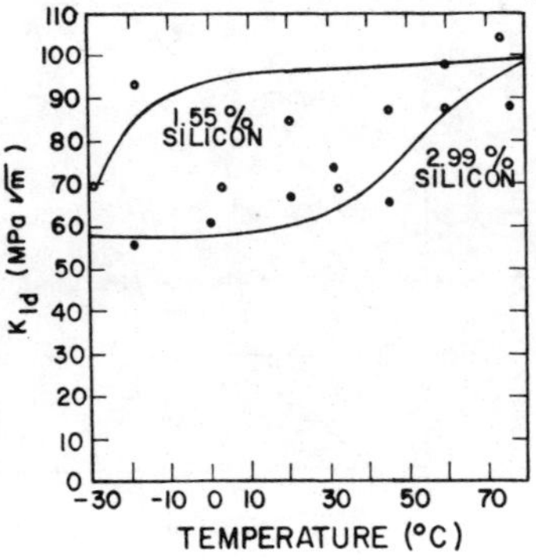

Figure 5 K_{1d} vs. Temperature (Silicon Group)

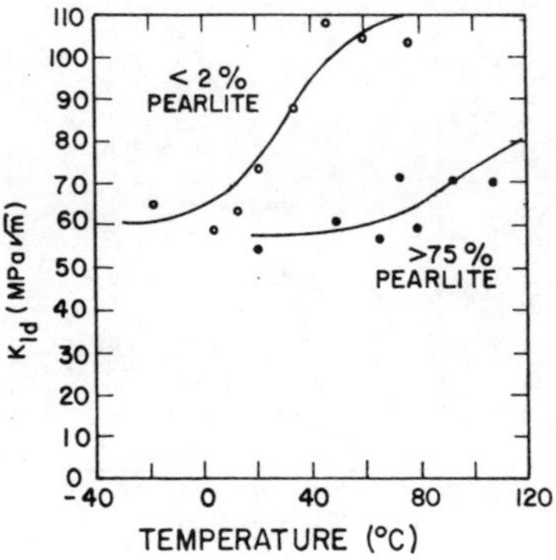

Figure 6 K_{1d} vs. Temperature (Pearlite Group)

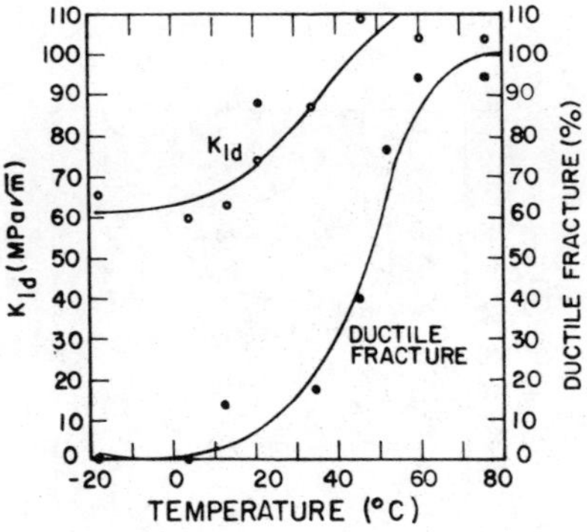

Figure 7 K_{1d} and % Ductile Fracture vs. Temperature (2.5 % Silicon; <2 % Pearlite)

INTEGRITY OF AUSTENITIC STAINLESS STEEL PIPING WELDS FOR NUCLEAR SERVICE

A. Canalini* / L.R.Lopes**

A criterion applying K_{1d} concept was developed to determine the fracture mechanics properties of austenitic stainless steel nuclear piping welds. The critical dimensions, length and depth, for crack initiation were established and plotted in a chart. This study enables the dimensions of a discontinuity detected in an in-service inspection to be compared to the critical dimensions for crack initiation, and the indication can be judged critical or non-critical for the component.

INTRODUCTION

The nuclear power industry has utilized thorough inspection and testing of components during manufacture, construction and initial start-up phase.

However, the industry also recognizes the need for a continuing in-service inspection program.

The purpose of ASME Code Section XI (1) is to assure the mechanical integrity of the pressure boundary of a plant for its expected service life. Prior to the introduction of an evaluation technique into section XI, the only possible action if non-acceptable indications were detected during service was to repair or replace the component.

In some cases, however, either repair or replacement is difficult for both economical and technical reasons. Changes and additions to section XI have been made to provide a conservative flaw evaluation procedure based on the principles of fracture mechanics.

Flaws that exceed the inspection standards can be analytically evaluated to determine if the indication detected in an in-service inspection would grow to a dangerous size during the remaining service life of the component.

* Welding and Non-destructive Testing Engineer
Angra I Nuclear Power Plant - Furnas, Brazil
** Nuclear Power Systems and Technical Support Engineer
Furnas, Brazil

Upon satisfying the flaw acceptability criteria the component may be returned to service without repair.

Although the majority of nuclear components in a nuclear power plant are built of austenitic stainless steel, the flaw analytical evaluation of section XI (1) has only been developed for ferritic materials.

The purpose of this study was to develop an evaluation criterion for discontinuities detected in austenitic stainless steel nuclear piping welds.

K_{1d} tests were performed on type 304 stainless steel piping weld metal and heat affected zone: relationships between the length and depth of discontinuities were established. The critical dimensions for flaw initiation for a given pipeline were determined and plotted in a chart.

Materials and Experimental Tests

K_{1d} Determination

Weld metal and heat affected zone specimens from coupons welded according to the same essential variables used in the production welding were impact tested according to ASTM STP 563 "Instrumented Impact Testing". The tests were performed in a Tinius Olsen equipment with an instrumented tup. The specimens were pre-cracked with crack lengths between 4,5 and 5,5 mm. All specimens presented elastic-plastic behaviour (Figures (1) and (2)). K_{1d} values were obtained by the equivalent energy method and the following equation was used:

$$K_{1d} = \frac{p * s}{B.\ W^{3/2}} \left[2{,}9\ (t/W)^{1/2} - 4{,}6\ (t/W)^{3/2} + 21{,}8\ (t/W)^{5/2} - 37{,}6\ (t/W)^{7/2} + 38{,}7\ (t/W)^{9/2} \right] \quad .....(1)$$

B - specimen thickness: 10,0 mm
W - specimen width
t - crack depth

TABLE 1 - The highest and lowest K_{1d} values obtained experimentally

	Highest $MPa\sqrt{m}$	Lowest $MPa\sqrt{m}$
Weld metal AWS ER 308 AWS E 308	153	128
Heat affected Zone AISI 304	132	115

The lowest K_{1d} values were employed in this study.

Material. The weld metal presented the following chemical analysis:

C = 0,05%;	S = 0,015%;	P = 0,021%;	SI = 0,45%;
Mn = 1,53%;	Cr = 20,6%;	Ni = 9,8%;	Mo = 0,18%;
Nb + Ta = -;	Cu = 0,18%;	W = 0,01%;	V = 0,07%;
Co = 0,24%			

Mechanical Tests. The tensile tests were performed in a 10 ton Instron machine, according to the requirements of the ASME code, section IX

K_1 Determination

For the determination of the stress intensity factor K_1, the plasticity of the material for flaw initiation was considered.

The analysis has been performed on Reactor Coolant System Piping Welds: Hot, Intermediate and Cold Leg. The longitudinal stress was considered and determined by the equation:

$$\sigma = \frac{1}{2} \left(\frac{pxr}{e} - 0,1\ p\right) \qquad (2)$$

Once the longitudinal stress had been determined, the study developed by Sih and Hagendorf (3) for K_1 determination considering a cylindrical shell subjected to a uniform extensional load was applied. For the present study, a flaw parallel to the weld bead was considered, subjected to an equal and opposite uniform extensional load due to hydrostatic pressure. The stress intensity factor at the top and bottom surface layers is given by the following equations:

$$K_1 \left(+ \frac{e}{2}\right) = F_1 \left(\frac{e}{2a}, \frac{e}{R}, \nu\right) \frac{No\sqrt{a}}{e} \qquad (3)$$

$$K_1 \left(- \frac{e}{2}\right) = F_2 \left(\frac{e}{2a}, \frac{e}{R}, \nu\right) \frac{No\sqrt{a}}{e} \qquad (3)$$

Some assumptions were made for K_1 determination:

- No values were obtained for flaw lengths equivalent to $\pi/8$, $\pi/4$, $3\pi/8$, $5\pi/16$ and $3\pi/16$.
- For each length the following depths were considered: 10%, 20%, 30%, 40%, 50%, 60%, 70%, 80%, 90% and 100% of the pipe thickness.

No values referred to equation (3) were calculated multiplying the flaw area by the longitudinal stress.

Once No values had been calculated, it was determined the ratio between the pipe thickness and flaw length. Depending on this parameter, it was used the ratio between the pipe diameter and flaw length or the ratio between the pipe thickness and pipe radius for F Factor Determination (Figure (3) and (4)). K_1 is then obtained by the equation in reference (3).

Results / Discussion

For austenitic stainless steel type 304 piping, K_{1d} values from weld and heat affected zones were obtained experimentally. In order to analyse the integrity of the pipe those values were compared to the K_1 values obtained mathematically.

Making a comparison between K_1 and K_{1d} values, when the following correlation is satisfied:

$$K_1 < K_{1d}$$

instability for flaw initiation is not expected.

The critical length and depth that satisfy the correlation

$$K_1 = K_{1d}$$

where the instability may start to occur are presented in Figures (5) to (10).

Flaws were considered in this study that show up the internal or external surface of the pipe. Internal indications that do not show up the internal and external surface of the pipe are considered less critical for the component.

Fatigue and stress corrosion cracking were not considered in this study.

The critical length and depth of indications were determined considering hydrostatic pressure and room temperature. For service conditions higher temperatures and lower pressures are expected.

K_{1d} were determined by the Equivalent Energy Method. Flaws that exceed the "critical size" are expected to present ductile-tearing rupture.

In an inservice inspection the length and depth of indications detected by a non-destructive testing volumetric method can be compared to the length and depth for flaw initiation, Figures (5) to (10) and an indication can be considered critical or non-critical for the component.

Conclusions

Considering circumferencial welds in austenitic stainless steel nuclear pipelines, hot, intermediate and cold leg:

It was possible to derive a chart relating length and depth of discontinuities to their corresponding stress intensity factor.

Following the criterion $K_1 = K_{1d}$ several critical dimensions for crack initiation could be evaluated.

REFERENCES

(1) American Society of Mechanical Engineers ASME, 1980, XI Division 1, 14

(2) Rebello, J.M.A., and Soares, G.F.W., 1982

"Weld Qualification Joints", ECEPEL Centro de Pesquisas de Energia Elétrica, Report 160, 4.

(3) Americal National Standard Institute B - 31.3., Longitudinal Stress Calculation

(4) Sih and Hagendorf, 1974, Stress Intensity Factors, 73,1-1.

SYMBOLS USED

a = one-half the total length of a surface crack (in)

B = specimen thickness: 100 mm

e = pipe thickness (in)

F = factor to be determined in the Figures (3) and (4) for K_1 calculation

K_{1d} = critical plane strain stress intensity factor (dynamic) $(MPa\sqrt{m})$

K_1 = defect stress intensity factor $(ksi\sqrt{in})$

No = uniform extensional load applied perpendicular to the crack plane (pounds)

ν = Poisson's ratis (ν = 0,3 for austenitic stainless steel)

p = hydrostatic pressure (psi)

σ = longitudinal stress (psi)

R = pipe internal radius (in)

r = pipe external radius (in)

S = distance between the supports (during the test: 40 mm)

t = crack depth (in)

W = specimen width (mm)

Conversion factor:

1 in = 25,4 mm

1 psi = 145,038 Mpa

1 $ksi\sqrt{in}$ = 0,90 $Mpa\sqrt{m}$

TABLE 2 - Example: K_1 values obtained from cold leg pipe of a typical nuclear plant

Cold leg 32,19" OD $e = 2,32"$ $p = 3107$ psi

For $\frac{\pi}{8} r$ indication length

Indication depth (t) % of thickness	K_1 value $(MPa\sqrt{m})$ + $e/2$	- $e/2$		
10	17,17	15,03		
20	33,71	29,50		
30	50,63	44,30		
40	67,01	58,63		
50	83,13	72,74		
60	99,02	86,65		
70	114,44	100,33	critical	$K_1 = K_{1d}$
80	130,09	113,33	propagation	$K_1 > K_{1d}$
90	145,15	127,00	propagation	$K_1 > K_{1d}$
100	160,07	140,06	propagation	$K_1 > K_{1d}$

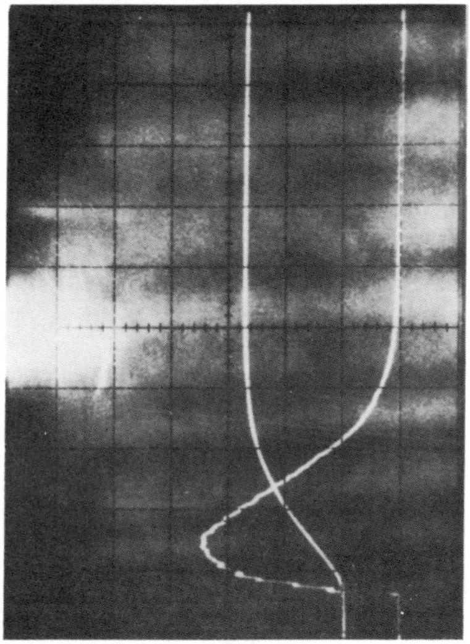

FIGURE 1 K_{1d} Determination

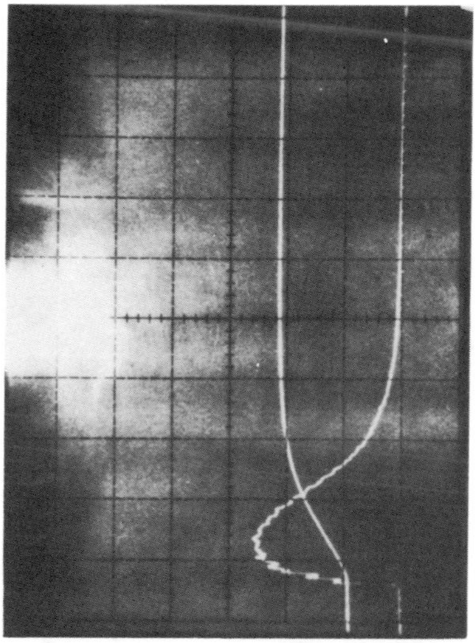

FIGURE 2 K_{1d} Determination

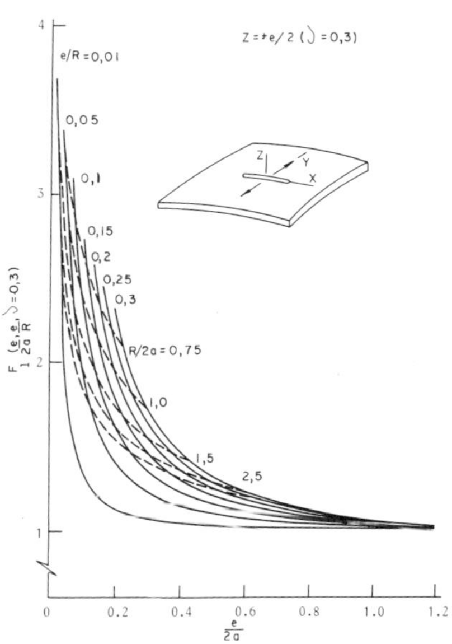

FIGURE 3 F_1 determination for K_1 calculation - Reference (3)

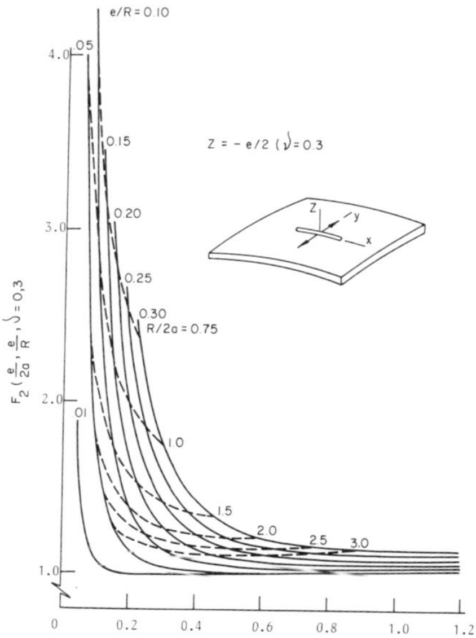

FIGURE 4 F_2 determination for K_1 calculation - Reference (3)

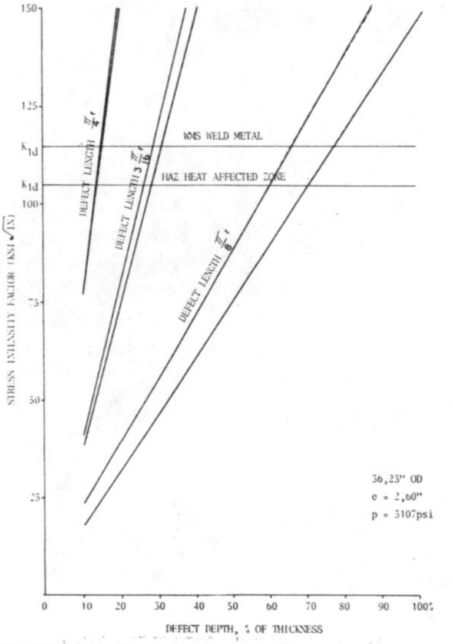

FIGURE 5 Stress intensity factors as function of the defect sizes for the intermediate leg pipe

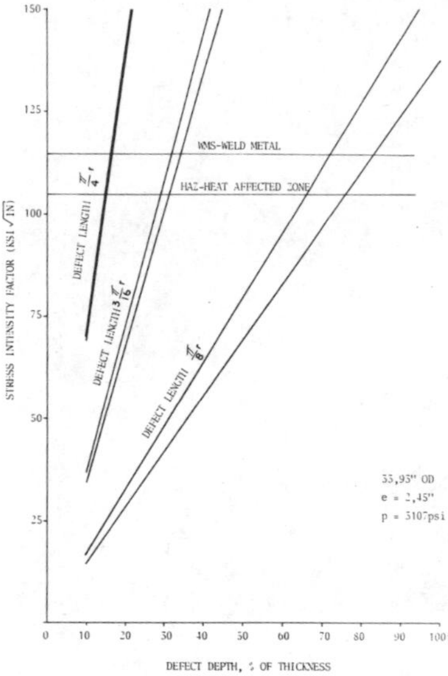

FIGURE 6 Stress intensity factors as function of the defect sizes for the hot leg pipe

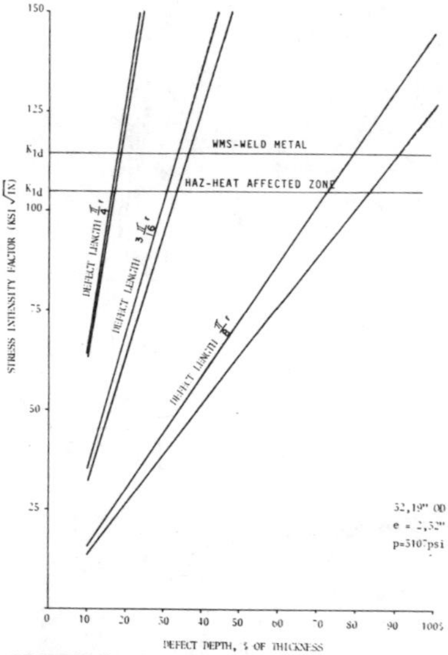

FIGURE 7 Stress intensity factors as function of the defect sizes for the cold leg pipe

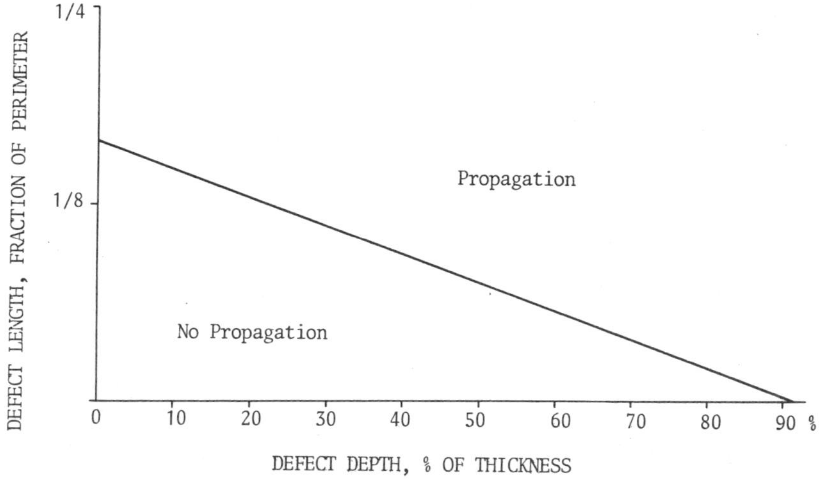

FIGURE 8 - Critical sizes for a circumferencial defect in the intermediate leg

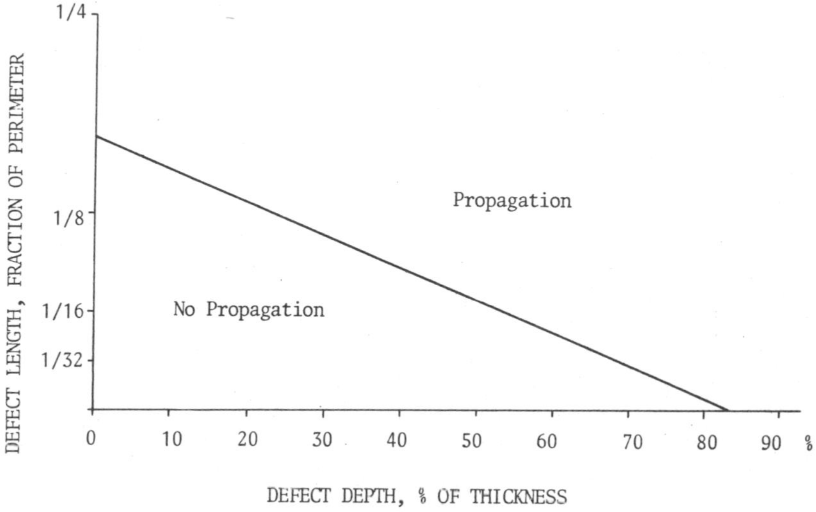

FIGURE 9 Critical sizes for a circumferencial defect in the hot leg pipe

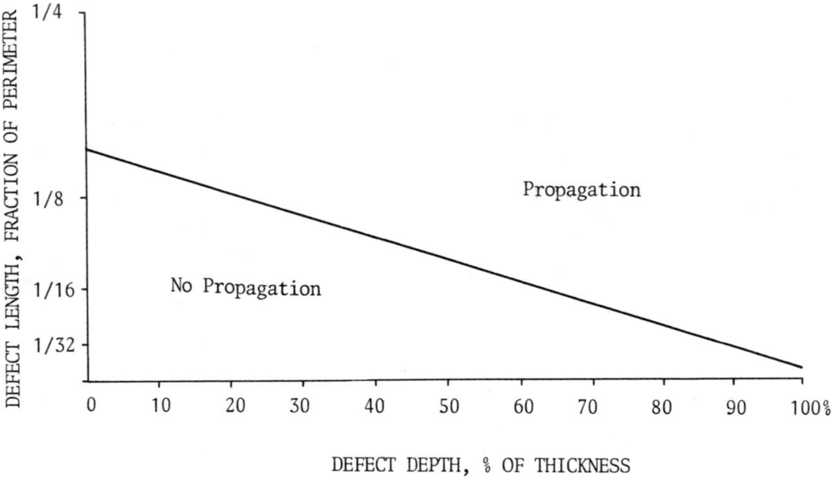

FIGURE 10 Critical Sizes for a circumferencial defect in the cold leg pipe

FATIGUE LIFE PREDICTION FOR A COLD WORKED T316 STAINLESS STEEL

M. J. Manjoine*

Permanent damage curves of initiation-life and propagation-life which predict the fatigue life of specimens of a cold-worked type 316 stainless steel under complex strain-range histories were generated by a limited test program. Analysis of the test data showed that fatigue damage is not linear throughout life and that propagation life is longer than initiation-life at high strain ranges but is shorter at low strain ranges. If permanent damage has been initiated by prior history and/or fabrication, propagation to a given life can occur at a lower strain range than that estimated from the fatigue curves for constant CSR.

INTRODUCTION

The fatigue damage process for metals can be divided into four steps: 1) generation of persistent slip bands, 2) initiation of permanent damage, 3) coalescence of micro-voids to form a crack and 4) crack propagation, as described by fracture mechanics, to fracture. Each step may follow a different accumulative law in a local volume before the next step is activated.

In a prior publication by the author, (1) other damage processes were discussed and a damage model was presented for an annealed stainless steel.

In this paper the damage process is simplified by combining steps 1 and 2 into a) initiation of permanent damage and steps 3 and 4 into b) propagation of permanent damage. Permanent fatigue damage is defined as that local fatigue damage which cannot be removed by mechanical bonding, thermal-mechanical sintering, or by heat treatment.

The purpose of the work reported here is to demonstrate that a modest low-cycle fatigue program can generate permanent damage curves for initiation and propagation, I-P damage, which can predict the fatigue lives of complex strain-range histories within an acceptable factor.

*Consultant, Westinghouse Research and Development Center, Pittsburgh, Pennsylvania.

TEST PROGRAM

The test program includes four types of low-cycle fatigue tests with different histories as described below.

Conventional Low-Cycle Fatigue Tests. The materials used in the tests of this paper were from three heats of a 20% cold-worked type 316 stainless steel which has been characterized and tested at low- and high-cycles by Manjoine and Landerman (2). The low-cycle fatigue failure curve they generated under constant strain range, CSR, was utilized to calculate the linear damages of all the tests.

Two Level Fatigue Tests. In the two level fatigue tests a prior number of cycles at a CSR was followed by cycling at a lower level of CRS to fracture. This lower level of CSR was always about 1/2%.

Block Loading Tests. In the block loading tests a prior number of cycles at a CSR is followed by a number of cycles at a lower CSR and then this "block loading" is repeated to fracture.

Three Level Tests. In a three level test a prior number of cycles at a first level of CSR and another number of cycles at a second level of CSR is followed by a third level of CSR to fracture. The level of CSR is always changed when the load passes through zero from the compression loading at the last cycle of the preceding level. The reference of the strain range is about the original zero. For one series of tests in which the CSR levels were about 2%, 1%, and 1/2%, the sequence included all six combinations of high, (H), intermediate (I), and low (L).

FATIGUE DAMAGE EVALUATION

Linear Damage Rule

The linear damage rule, dashed line of Fig. 1, assumes that fatigue damage is a linear function throughout life of life-fraction (number of cycles at a given CSR divided by the number of cycles to "failure" at that CSR, n/n_f) and failure is a "linear damage" summation of life-fractions to unity.

ASME Code Fatigue Design Method

The American Society of Mechanical Engineers by the Boiler and Pressure Vessel Code describes a fatigue damage evaluation which utilizes a "design fatigue curve" for austenitic steels (3) and the linear damage rule. The design fatigue life curve was determined from the low-cycle fatigue data of annealed austenitic steels and utilized the lower of the life divided by 20 or the CSR (for a given life) divided by 2. Failure is a linear damage summation of life-fractions to unity.

Initiation-Propagation Damage Rules

These rules shown by the solid lines of Fig. 1 assume that a) the damage is zero until initiated, b) the fraction of life for initiation is a function of the strain range and c) the damage is linear with the "remaining-life fraction". Curves of this type have a sequence effect on life prediction. For example: assume a cycling history in which the number of cycles correspond to a life-fraction of 0.2 at 2% CSR and a life-fraction of 0.32 at 0.5% CSR. For a high-low sequence the linear damage is 0.2+0.32=0.52. No failure is predicted and 48% of life is remaining. The initiation-propagation rules of Fig. 1 requires 0.03 of life for initiation at the 2% CSR so that a life fraction of 0.2-0.02=0.17 is available to produce a damage of 0.17. The damage produced at 0.5% CSR by a life-fraction of 0.32 is 0.83 and therefore the total damage is 0.17+0.83=1 which predicts failure.

For the low-high sequence the linear damage is still 0.52. The initiation requires a life fraction of 0.61 at 0.5% CSR, therefore no damage is generated although 1/3 of the initiation life is completed. At the 2% CSR the remaining 2/3 of initiation life requires only 0.02% of life and the remaining life of 0.32-0.02=0.3 produces a damage of 0.26. No failure is predicted and 74% of life is remaining.

Initiation and Propagation of Permanent Damage

The damage curves that are developed in this paper are for complex strain histories. The fatigue damage process has been reduced to steps of initiation and propagation of permanent damage, I-P Damage. The curves of "initiation life" and "propagation life" are given as functions of the strain range but considers the effect of stress history in the damage process. Thus the curves were generated in an iterative manner to represent the average of the data of the test program. The method of calculating the I-P damage is similar to that for the initiation-propagation damage rules and the damage evaluation will be made utilizing the initiation-life and propagation-life curves generated in this paper.

TEST RESULTS FOR COMPLEX LOADINGS

For all the tests of this program under strain control the tensile and compression loads of the cycles were monitored. The constant strain range (as given by the total strain range), number of cycles at the CSR and the CSR sequences are given in Table 1. Sufficient details on stress amplitude are reported as a function of cycle history so that alternate damage evaluations can be made for other damage theories.

Two-Level Tests. The stress amplitude histories for the two-level tests are shown in Fig. 2. This cold-worked material "cycle-softens" with number of cycles and in the high to low level CSR sequence, the softening continues up to fracture. The dashed horizontal line near the end of a step is the stress level, $\Delta\sigma_c/2$, calculated for a specimen at mid-life under the same CSR throughout a test (1). The "first" or H levels of CSR were about 2.5, 1.25, and 0.7% and the number of cycles were chosen to produce about 2% linear-life fraction. The second or L level of CSR was always about 0.5% and was continued to fracture.

Block Loading Tests. In the block loading the CSR sequence was H, L, H, L, etc. The high level of CSR was planned for a number of cycles which produced a linear life fraction of about 0.2%. The H levels were about 3.5, 1.2 and 0.7% for the respective tests, Table 1. The low level was always about 1/2% CSR for 2200 cycles which is a linear-life fraction of about 0.5%. The block loading was continued to fracture. A typical stress history is shown in Fig. 3 for the first four "blocks". It can be noted that the stress amplitude reduced with number of cycles during the high CSR portion. After the low CSR portion of the block and on the subsequent block the stress amplitude for the high CSR starts at a higher value than it finished in the prior high CSR.

Three-Level Tests. For the first six tests in Table 1, the highest CSR, H, was about 2%, the intermediate CSR, I, was about 1% and the lowest CSR, L, was about 1/2%. The sequences of CSR's covered all combinations. The linear-life fractions for the first and second levels of this series were about 1% for the highest CSR, 1.5% for the intermediate CSR, and 3% for the lowest CSR. The tests were carried to fracture at the third level.

In the next four tests the life fractions for the first two levels were varied to enable more general initiation and propagation curves. The strain range, number of cycles and sequence are given in Table 1 for all the tests.

Typical stress-range histories are given in Figs. 4 to 8 for different CSR sequences. For histories that were "compressed" by the logarithmic scale, the actual number of cycles is given in the inserts.

Linear Damage Evaluation

Although the prior linear-life fractions for the two level and three level tests were less than 5%, a large effect was calculated in the linear damage summations. The linear damages based on the low-cycle fatigue life under continuous CSR (extreme right curve in Fig. 9) are given in Table 1 under the linear damage evaluation as $\Sigma\, n_i/n_f$. The test data for the three-level and two level are listed in decreasing values of linear damage summation. Only one test for the sequence of increasing CSR gave a value of unity or above which indicates a prediction of failure. The lowest value was 0.1 where the specimen, with a sequence of decreasing CSR, failed at 10% of life expected. These results led to a generation of an alternate I-P damage evaluation.

FATIGUE CURVES FOR INITIATION AND PROPAGATION OF PERMANENT DAMAGE

From an analysis of the data of this test program and an iterative process to reduce the variation of the calculated I-P damage, the fatigue curves for "initiation life" (cycles to initiate permanent damage) and "propagation life" (additional cycles to propagate permanent damage to failure) were generated, Fig. 9 for this 20% cold worked T316SS at ambient temperature and for complex strain histories.

I-P Damage Evaluation. The damage rule requires that initiation-life of permanent damage must reach a summation of unity before propagation-life proceeds. The "initiation-life fraction" is calculated by dividing the number of cycle at a given CSR by the number of "cycles to initiate permanent damage" for that CSR, Fig. 9. When the summation reaches unity, the remaining cycles are applied to propagation. The "propagation-life" fraction is calculated by dividing the number of cycles at a given CSR by the number of "additional cycles to propagate permanent damage to failure", Fig. 9. The I-P damage is the summation of propagation damage only. A value of unity is required for failure. Values over unity is an earlier prediction of failure or a conservative life prediction. A value less than unity predicts a non-failure or a non-conservative life prediction since the actual specimen failed.

In the analysis of the data it was found that the cyclic stress-strain loop is influenced by any change in strain level. In Fig. 5 for the sequence of L-I-H or increasing CSR levels the stress range drops during the first two levels but demonstrates cyclic hardening followed by relatively minor softening up to fracture. Just before fracture the stress range was 5% higher than that for mid-life stress range estimate for the same continuous CSR.

In this engineering approach the initiation of permanent damage is determined by the "effect" of prior history on subsequent life and not by quantitative microscopic analysis. However, this approach will aid this microscopic analysis by estimations of the observation periods to be used in a test program. Establishment of "microscopic signatures" will enable a diagnosis of components which have been damaged or have failed by fatigue.

Characteristics. Several observations can be cited for these "life" curves: a) the sum of the cycles at a given CSR of initiation and propagation is the I-P life and is less than that for continuous cycling data at that CSR, b) the I-P life fraction for permanent damage initiation increases with decreasing CSR, and c) once permanent damage is initiated, propagation to a given life can occur at a lower strain range than that estimated from the fatigue curve for continuous CSR.

Initiation of Permanent Damage. The damage rules from the analysis of the data of this program can be presented in an initiation propagation diagram where the percent of I-P life for initiation is plotted as a function of percent strain range, Fig. 10. This diagram clearly shows that the life-fraction or percent of life for initiation increases with decreasing strain range and therefore, the remaining life or propagation life decreases with decreasing strain range. The fatigue for a two-level straining cycle will demonstrate a damage evaluation for this 20% C.W. T316SS. If the first level of CSR is 1.6% for 5% of life, permanent damage is initiated and if the second level of CSR is 0.42% for 5% of life then propagation is carried to fracture. Thus the fatigue life for this complex loading is only 10% of that for a constant strain range throughout.

It should be pointed out that Fig. 10 is based on total I-P life and can be misleading if a design is based on propagation life only. The curve of propagation life as a function of strain range, Fig. 9, illustrates that the propagation-life curve descends below the initiation-life and fatigue-life curves to a threshold strain range that could not be determined for lives greater than 10^6 cycles by this low-cycle fatigue program.

COMPARISON OF DAMAGE EVALUATIONS

The damage evaluations are listed in Table 1 for the tests of this program.

Linear Damage - $\Sigma n_i/n_f$. The linear damage rule based on the fatigue life data for this 20% C.W. T316SS predicts failure (damage $\geq$ 1) for only one test of this series of 16 tests under complex loading. A damage less than unity is a prediction of longer life than the actual failure and is, therefore, unconservative. The lowest damage was 0.1 or unconservative by a factor of 10.

Linear Damage - ASME Code. If the ASME code design curve represented this material and the linear damage rule were applicable, then the damage value margin should be 20 for the CSR's employed. Only two tests yielded a margin greater than 20 and the lowest margin was 9.7. Although failure is predicted for design for all tests, the code evaluation does not give a uniform margin over the strain range histories of these tests. However, the code design curve is similar to the initiation-life curve and therefore the code design method protects against micro-crack initiation.

I-P Damage. The initiation and propagation curves of Fig. 9 and the I-P damage rules predicted failure (Damage $\geq$ 1) for 56% of the tests, Table 1. Failure is predicted for 100% of the tests within a factor of 1.42 (Damage $\geq$ 0.7). It is proposed that the initiation and propagation life curves can be used to generate a design procedure which has a more uniform factor of safety over the possible strain ranges.

CONCLUSIONS

The analysis of the data of a low-cycle fatigue program of 16 tests under complex loading histories support the following conclusions: (1) Fatigue damage is not linear throughout life, (2) Fatigue damage can be described by permanent damage curves of initiation-life and propagation life which are functions of the strain range, (3) Propagation life is longer then initiation life at higher strain ranges but is shorter at lower strain ranges, (4) Failure was predicted for all the tests using an initiation-life summation of unity and a propagation-life summation of 0.7.

REFERENCES

1. Manjoine,M.J.,1981,"Fatigue Damage Model for An. T304 Stainless Steel Under Complex Strain Histories",6th. SMIRT Conf., L8/1,North-Holland Publishing Co.

2. Manjoine,M.J.,and Landerman,E.I.,1982,"Techniques For Fatigue Testing and Extrapolation of Fatigue Life",ASTM.JTEVA,May.

3. ASME Boiler and Pressure Vessel Code,Sec.III Div.1,Appendix I, Fig.I-9.2.1(1983).

ACKNOWLEDGMENT

This paper contains information generated in accordance with the provisions of the research and development agreement between Commissariat A L'Energie Atomique (CEA), Electricite de France (EdF), Framatome (FRAMATOME), and Westinghouse Electric Research and Engineering for Atomic Systems, Incorporated (WEREAS).

TABLE 1 - Fatigue Test Data

Spec No.	Strain Range and Cycle Sequence						Damage Evaluation		
	$\Delta\varepsilon_1$ %	n_1 Cycles	$\Delta\varepsilon_2$ %	n_2 Cycles	$\Delta\varepsilon_3$ %	n_3 Cycles	Linear Damage $\Sigma\, n_i/n_f$	Linear Damage ASME Code	I-P Damage
				Three Level Data					
36	1.07	250	0.52	12500	2.10	1752	1.01	23.2	1.57
57	2.08	25	0.48	12500	1.12	6725	0.71	16.9	1.20
110	0.44	12500	1.35	250	2.18	722	0.49	11.2	0.74
92	0.53	12500	2.14	25	1.15	3590	0.45	9.7	0.72
116	1.11	250	2.27	25	0.58	56760	0.45	14.4	1.27
18	2.56	33	1.09	250	0.42	157915	0.10	11.9	0.80
74	0.45	25000	1.21	500	2.02	1202	0.67	13.5	1.06
71	1.13	500	0.50	25000	2.17	956	0.67	15.1	1.27
73	1.10	500	2.20	50	0.52	63320	0.27	11.8	1.01
72	2.30	13	1.00	125	0.52	58447	0.22	10.0	0.89
				Two Level Data					
22	0.74	1000	0.49	186120			0.69	22.6	1.42
26	1.22	200	0.51	136300			0.43	16.5	1.09
28	2.56	25	0.48	215800			0.40	12.2	1.79
				Block Loading					
918	0.72	120/B	0.48	2200/B	(a)		0.41	22.6	0.70
52	1.21	22/B	0.45	2200/B	(b)		0.30	16.5	0.87
54	3.47	12/B	0.58	2200/B	(c)		0.38	12.2	0.94
				Constant Strain Range Data					
1-8	$\Delta\varepsilon$ = CONST						1 ± 0.2	38 ± 12	1.56 ± 0.13

(a) 68 blocks to failure.

(b) 62 blocks to failure.

(c) 11 blocks to failure.

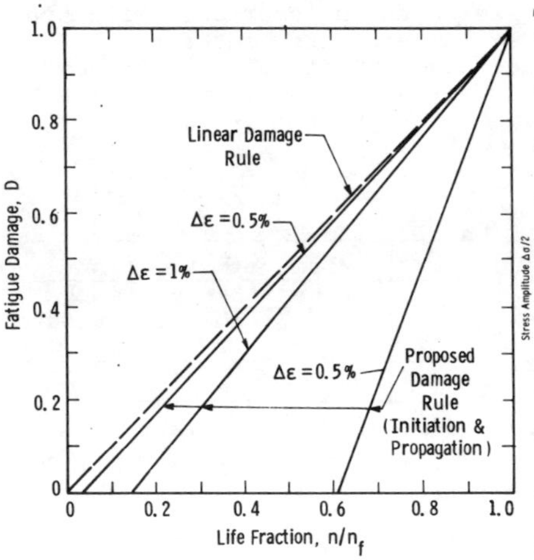

Figure 1 Fatigue damage rules

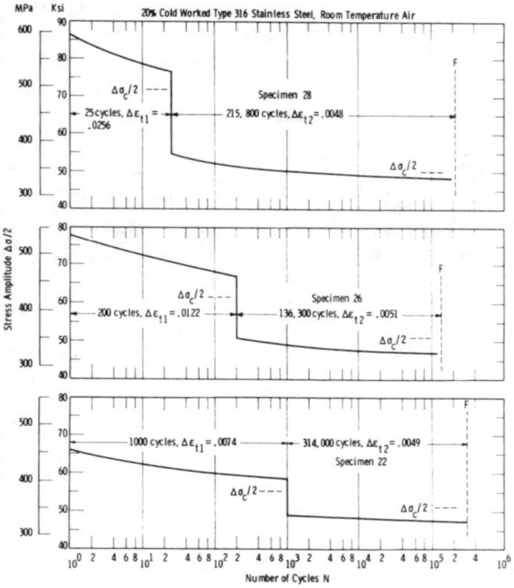

Figure 2 Stress-amplitude histories for 2-level tests

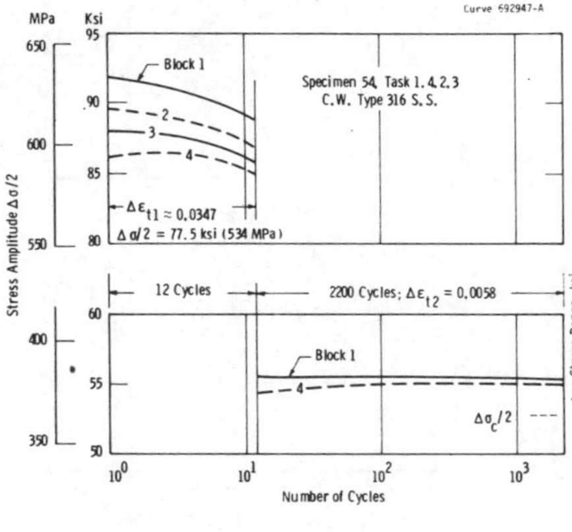

Figure 3 Stress-amplitude histories for 4 blocks, No. 54

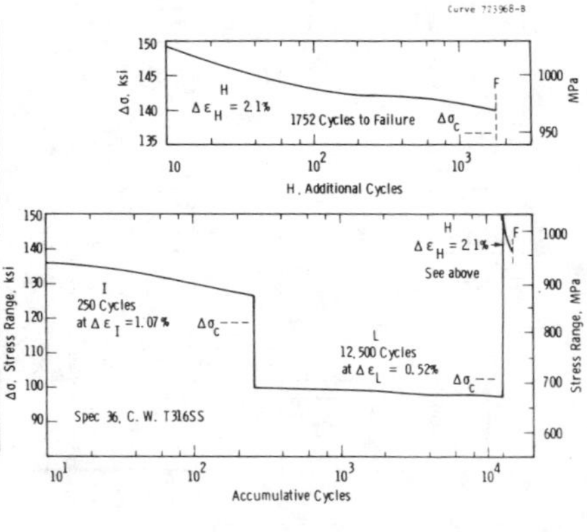

Figure 4 Stress-range history for No. 36 (I,L,H)

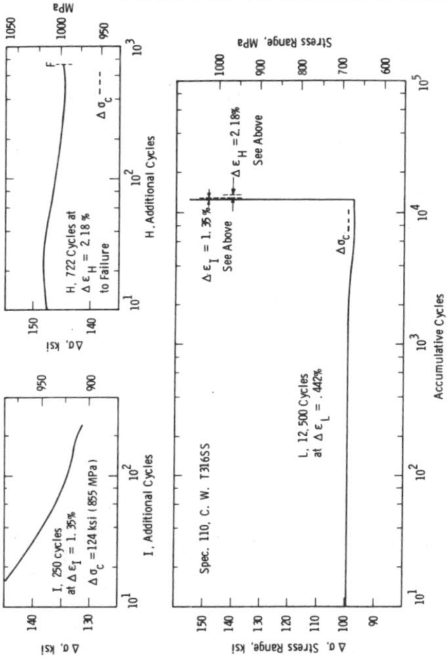

Figure 5 Stress-range history for No. 110 (L,I,H)

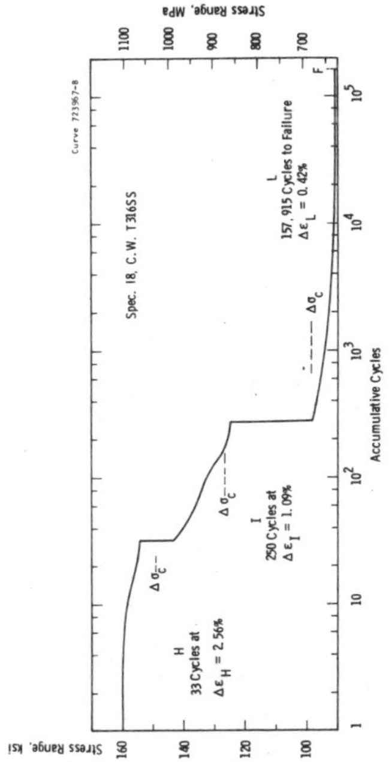

Figure 6 Stress-range history for No. 18 (H,I,L)

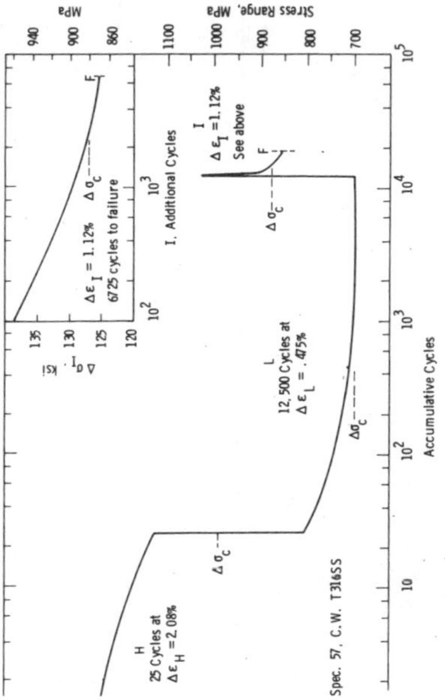

Figure 7 Stress-range history for No. 57 (H,L,I)

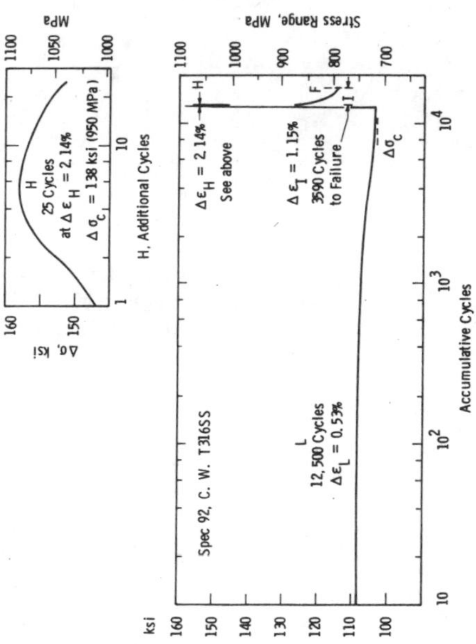

Figure 8 Stress-range history for No. 92 (L,H,I)

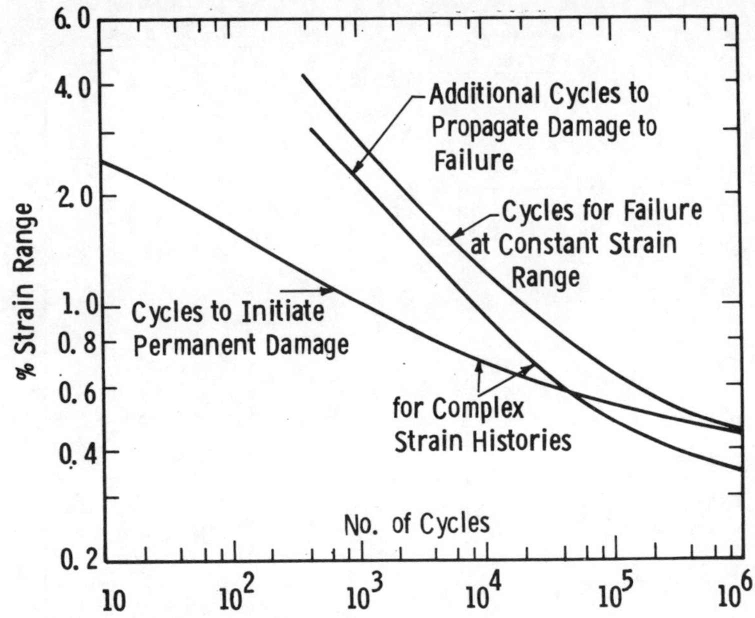

Figure 9 Fatigue damage curves

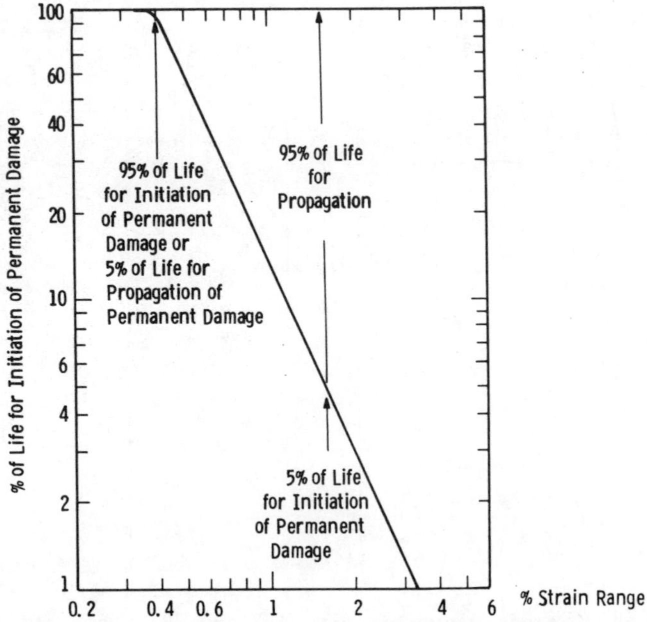

Figure 10 Percent of fatigue life for initiation of damage

THE WIDE PLATE TEST AND THE GROSS STRAIN CRITERION

W. Soete*

If a wide plate with central crack can be accepted as a good simulation of a structural element with a defect, the tensile test of the plate gives directly information about the behaviour of the real structure without requiring any mathematical interpretation. This information postulates an appreciative criterion. This so called gross strain criterion states as follows: "an acceptable defect does not initiate a crack before plastic yielding occurs in the defect free zone of the plate". Sometimes the wide plate test is rejected as being too expensive; fairly good results can be obtained on flat specimens broken in classical tensile machines; the acceptable crack lengths so obtained being conservative.

INTRODUCTION

Since welding has been introduced in metal construction, the safety concept has shifted from the design to the structural stage. Failures of metal construction due to a bad design or erroneous calculation are exceptions, although instability may be at the basis of difficulties. Most troubles find however their origin in defects which may be of geometrical, metallurgical or technical nature. Welds are a major source of all kinds of defects. Living with defects is a necessity by economic and even safety considerations. But it is obvious that the acceptance of defects is only possible if a sufficient scientific support justifies this decision. Before taking such a decision the engineer must refer to two disciplines, namely non destructive testing and fracture mechanics; both techniques are needed. If N.D.T. is actually able to characterize defects, fracture mechanics is still a subject of serious contradictions.

FRACTURE MECHANICS

Fracture mechanics is today in full expansion. If its wide appeal proves its importance, it makes it also more confusing. Although making an evaluation of the situation of fracture mechanics is extremely delicate, it can be useful to try to make such an approach.
The proposed theories can be classified in three groups:

*
Laboratory for Strength of Materials and Welding Technology
Sint Pietersnieuwstraat 41
9000 Gent - Belgium
Belgium

1. the theories which try to calculate acceptable defects: resp. L.E.F.M. and E.P.F.M.
2. the techniques which define acceptable defects on the basis of small scale technological tests and simple calculation.
3. the theories which define critical defects by doing tests on structural components.

In the first group attention is focussed on local phenomena such as first yield and crack initiation which occur at the tip of the flaw. This group embraces the physical approach (dislocation) and the mechanical approach. The last one is based on a probable correct assumption that the local phenomena are characterized by material constants, which are independent of the geometry of the specimen, in other words they are the same for test pieces and for the construction.

Such constants are for instance, the critical stress intensity factor K_{IC}, the critical crack opening displacement, the critical J integral. It is now well established that once these constants are known, fairly good results are obtained on condition the material behaves elastically and fracture initiation and fracture propagation occur simultaneously. This occurs however only with very brittle material or at very low temperatures.

But for most materials yield occurs first and crack initiation starts later. The observation of these phenomena are extremely difficult and the measurement of critical properties is practically impossible. Indeed, the measurement of a critical strain at the tip of the notch is practically excluded, because strain assumes a gauge length, which in case of a crack is non existent.

The measurement of a crack opening displacement, as proposed by Wells, seems to be more appropriate, although the questions may be raised at what scale the measurements must be done, atomic or crystal? The use of a crack opening angle solves the problem of where to measure, but the problem of recording at the correct moment of crack initiation remains. Moreover it is probable that crack initiation starts at the mid-section of the plate, this makes observation practically impossible by most used techniques which are all restricted to the surface.

These experimental difficulties are today the main reason for the large scatter of the results obtained by using the so called E.P.F.M. and the differences between all methods increases with increasing plastic deformation.

Realizing these shortcomings, the second group of techniques tries to establish an experimental relation between tests done on small specimens and the behavior of the strcture or components. As plastic deformations are in any case unavailable, results, deduced from these tests are geometry dependent, which means that a large scatter will occur. In order to decrease this scatter most small scale specimens are tested in bending in order to confine the plastic spread to a zone near the notch. In these circumstances a certain relation between the small test and the behavior of the structure or its components can be established. The large scatter of the test done on the small specimens, requires the use of a large safety factor which in essence must be based on experimental experience. This situation brings us to the old technological tests. It must however be recognised that these tests have a value for the manufacturer of steel and weld consumables, but their value as a contribution to fracture mechanics is doubtful.

Contrary to the theories which focus the attention on local phenomena, the third group, considers global phenomena. By doing so, the main objection, i.e., the difficulty of observing is eliminated. They require that the sequence of the phenomena must be as follows:

elastic deformation (global)
local plastic deformation (local)
general yield (global)
crack initiation (local)
crack propagation (global)

As general yield is the last global observation before rupture starts it is logical to use it as the safety alarm. The determination of the critical defect is simple, it suffices to do a few tests on structural components with defects, the largest flaw which still satisfies the general yield criterion is the critical defect. To define an acceptable defect one can require an overall elongation larger than n times the elongation measured with the critical defect or by accepting defects n times smaller than the critical one.

Besides its extreme simplicity the general yield or gross strain theory has the advantage to guarantee a ductile behavior and a strength at least equal to the yield strength. If good ductility can be attained by a good material choice, the strength requirements fix for certain steel the size of the critical defect.

Sizing of the critical flaw is normally done on structural components. Such components are e.g., the wide plate used specially for storage tanks, ships. But other elements can be used as pipes and profiles, ... even more complicated welded components may be used. In most cases the components will be loaded in tension, it will be necessary for these tests to build special equipment The most simple and most applied component is certainly the wide plate, many laboratories have today at their disposal machines of high capacity for pulling wide plates. As some authorities have still some doubt about the application of the gross strain theory, some advantages and some criticisms will be discussed here.

ADVANTAGES OF TESTING COMPONENTS

A. Temperature effect.

The brittle fracture appearance of most catastrophic failures is the main reason why most fracture analyses have been concentrated on temperature effect. The conclusion of these studies was the introduction of a so called transition temperature. Unfortunately this temperature transition depends on the geometry of the structure. The best known temperature transition is the one determined with the Charpy test. This concept is very usefull for manufactures of steel or weld consumables because the temperature to which these materials will be exposed in service is unknown by the manufacturer. It is the duty of the user to make a good material choice on the basis of the information given by the supplier of the material. But the user knows the lowest temperature to which his construction will be exposed. This means that tests on components must be run at this well defined temperature. The unknown factor for the constructor is the importance of the structural defects.

So it is the duty of the safety engineer to test structural components at one well defined temperature but with defects of different importance. By increasing load the defect will be transformed into a flaw, which can be characterized by its dimensions. It is actually well established that by increasing flaw dimensions the behavior of the component switches from a general yield behavior to a behavior where plastic deformation is confined to material in the immediate vicinity of the defect. The geometry transition is characterized by a sudden drop in overall elongation.

The corresponding critical crack may be considered as a material property which depends however on temperature. If the material behaves brittly the fracture initiation is well defined, but if there is a ductile crack initiation, observation is more difficult and as already mentioned this difficulty is a main objection of all techniques based on the observation of local phenomena. But the gross strain theory has the advantage to record yielding in the defect free zone of the components, observation which can easily be done e.g., by putting a strain gage in this part of the specimen. Yielding must occur in this zone before fracture initiates at the flaw. If the material behaves in a ductile manner, it is possible that a small stable crack initiates before yielding is observed in the defect free zone of the component. But if no complete fracture occurs, the existence of a ductile stable crack can be taken up by defining an acceptable defect based on the knowledge of the critical defect. This technique can be applied as well to brittle as to ductile fracture, which means that the general yield theory is applicable for all temperatures.

B. Residual stresses.

A major difficulty in E.P.F.M. concerns the role of residual stresses. The amount and the distribution of these stresses are generally unknown, so are their effects on the mechanical properties of materials. But one fact has been clearly theoretically and experimentally shown: general yield is not influenced by the existence of residual stresses, contrary to the local phenomenon where it has been established that the amount of plastic behavior is increased by the presence of residual stresses. This compels the users of L.E.F.M. to introduce in their calculation residual stresses which for the sake of safety are assumed to have a yield strength magnitude. This empirical assumption is superfluous in the gross strain theory, because the critical crack length is independent of residual stresses.

C. Biaxial state of stress.

A question often raised concerns the validity of some fracture mechanics techniques if the structure is submitted to a biaxial state of stress. As flaws have two dimensions it is obvious that the direction of loading plays a major role versus the orientation of the flaw. Practically all tests or calculations assume that the uniaxial load is directed perpendicular to the surface of the flaw, which is certainly the most critical orientation. But what happens if the loading is biaxial as e.g., in a spherical vessel with internal pressure? Some local measurements, such as the crack opening are strongly influenced by the load applied parallel to the crack and the application of E.P.F.M. is once more troubled. By avoiding the observation of local phenomena, the problem is once more simplified. It is indeed well known that the appearance of plastic deformation in the defect free zone is not influenced by the biaxiality of the loading. A theorical proof is given by the yield criterion of Huber-Hencky-Mises.

D. Triaxial state of stress.

An objection which has been made, when applying the wide plate for simulating some structures, is the absence of a third stress perpendicular to the plate. It is claimed that when such a third stress is active the critical crack defined with a plane plate could be unsafe. To clear this important objection, it is necessary to handle separately the two requirements which are at the basis of the gross strain theory, these are:

a) a strength at least equal to the yield strength;
b) a good overall ductility depending on the nature of the structure.

A wide plate with a central crack can be considered as composed of a plate I without a crack (Figure 1), a plate II with a crack and a second plate III without a crack, all being loaded by the same longitudinal load. It is clear that ductility of part II will be limited due to the presence of the flaw, so it is illusive to require a good elongation from this part of the specimen. On the other side, there is no reduction of either strength or ductility of part I and III. So the only feeble link in the plate is the lack of ductility of part II. If it is possible to avoid appealing on this ductility, the whole specimen may have a satisfactory behavior. To obtain this goal, it suffices that sufficient strength exists in part II and that the required ductility is given by parts I and III. By separating the functions strength and ductility and requiring them respectively from part II and the combination I - III, it is possible to satisfy the general yield criterion.

To increase the strength of part II, different possibilities exist, e.g.:

a) by bridging the flaw through an overlap fixed on the plate by two transverse fillet welds; this overlap should be sufficiently short so that its elongation is shorter than the critical crack opening of the flaw (Figure 2).
b) by cold deformation of the flaw tips.
c) in the case of butt welds by overmatching the weld metal.

In the same trend local increase of strength may be obtained by applying a stress perpendicular to the plate surface at the flaw tips. It is indeed well known that triaxiality increases strength but decreases the ductility. So if the triaxiality increases the strength so that the yield strength can be reached before fracture starts at the crack, general yield is guaranted. This means that, with a limited increase of strength, there is a good possibility to get better results than without the triaxiality. In order to check the effect of increasing local strength by triaxiality, tensile tests were done on specimens as indicated on Figure 3. The results of the tensile tests are given in Table I.

The specimens were fabricated from mild steel plates; they had a length of 750mm and a width of 140mm. A central notch was machined by drilling and sawing with a jeweler's saw. The original plate thickness of 24mm was reduced to 8mm in the notch free parts (zones I and III). The thickness of 24mm was maintained in the central notched area, but reduced by a saw cut to 8mm in the plane of the notch. By this machining the test plate had in fact a thickness of 8mm with a local thickness of 24mm in the zone of the central notch. At this place a very high triaxial constraint existed during the tensile test.

Two specimens were broken at room temperature (Figure 4). The first had a central through crack length of 30mm. The specimen fractured in the notch free zone after a very large overall elongation as can be seen by the contraction in both parts I and III; the tests result did not only satisfy the general yield condition but indicates that fracture strength of the zone with a through crack of 30mm was higher than the fracture strength of the notch free part of the specimen (Figure 5).

The second specimen has a central through crack of 60mm (43% of the section!), the specimen fractured brittly in the notched zone (Figure 6) but the strength at fracture in the notch free zone was $410 N/mm^2$, compared to the yield strength of the steel which was $270 N/mm^2$, indicates that the criterion of general yield was largely satisfied.

The results are summarized in Table I.

Specimen	Crack length a_{mm}	Yield strength N/mm^2	Fracture stress N/mm^2
1	30	270	540
2	60	270	410

Spec. 1 Ductile fracture in the notch free zone (Figure 5).
Spec. Brittle fracture in the notch zone (Figure 6).

They indicate that triaxiality is severe so that strength is high and no plasticity is required in the notched area, an even more stringent criterion than general yield can be satisfied, namely fracture in the notch free zone. A similar result is obtained in butt welds if the strength of the weld metal versus the strength of the parent metal is overmatched.

CRITICS ON TESTING STRUCTURAL ELEMENTS

The main critic which is often heard when discussing wide plate testing is the cost. It must be clear that these tests are only used for important structures where N.D.T. technique has revealed important defects. In such cases a clear decision concerning repair or no avoids tedious discussions and may save a lot of money if tests indicate that repair is not necessary.

But it can be useful even for steel manufacturers to know the critical defect size of their steels. In fact many have already this information.

But even for the steel user it is good to get this information before starting a construction, a first crude determination of the critical defect size is not so expensive. It is indeed possible to have an idea of these dimensions by a few tensile tests on narrow plates which can be pulled in a classical tensile machine. The critical defect size determined on narrow plates will be smaller than the one determined on wide plates as can be seen on Figure 7 the results will be on the conservative side. Even if a tensile machine of sufficient capacity is not available, the determination of critical crack depth can be estimated by doing bend tests.

If the specimen is loaded in pure bending (Figure 8) general yield can be observed if plastic deformation occurs at the tensile side of the specimen, beyond the notched area. This will be the case if the flaw is not to deep or subcritical.

STEEL CHOICE

If the gross yield criterion is accepted it could be useful when making a steel choice to take this requirement into consideration. So the question may be raised: are some steels more prone to satisfy the general yield criterion than others. The answer is affirmative. It has clearly be demonstrated that steels with a large Luders plateau have a better general yield behavior than steels without this plateau. Fortunately most structural steels have this plateau, this is also the case of most H.S.L.A. and duplex steels.

The explanation is simple. Graphs giving the applied (σ_N gross stress) as a function of the elongation Δl measured on a large gage length are represented on Figure 9. The line OABC is the $\sigma_N/\Delta l$ curve for a unnotched specimen; the line OA'B'C' represents the same curve for a specimen with a subcritical notch, and the line OA"B"C" is a curve for a specimen with a hypercritical notch. Due to the strain gradients in the notched specimens, an increase of the deformation requires an increase of the applied stress. In the specimen with the subcritical notch increase goes on till the yield stress is reached (A'B').

At this moment the local deformation at the crack is stopped and deformation switches over to the notch free part of the specimen. This situation cannot be observed on a diagram giving the load as a function of local deformation at the tip of the notch, because during further overall deformation both magnitudes are stopped.

To illustrate this situation, during a wide plate test, the applied load, the crack opening displacement and the overall elongation as a function of time have been recorded. From these diagrams it appears clearly that as soon as general yield starts, the load and the local deformation remain constant. These considerations make clear that local phenomena do not give any information concerning the general yield situation. They are applicable only during the elastic and during the ligament yielding, i.e. if fracture occurs for a gross stress under the yield stress. This happens if the defect is too large, but this situation is to be rejected because of lack of strength.

Steels without a plateau (Figure 10) find most of their overall elongation in the deformation occurring at the tip of the notch, each increase of the load consumes some plasticity at these places. So danger of crack initiation exists at any moment. Only highly alloyed steels are able to satisfy a good overall ductility without calling on general yield. This is for instance the case of 9% Ni steel, which is, notwithstanding the fact that the steel has no Luders plateau, able to guarantee at cryogenic temperatures a very good ductility. The different behavior of steels with and without Luders plateau can also be observed when looking to the C.O.D. during a tensile test. For the steels with a plateau the increase stops or slows down as soon as general yield occurs and the inclination of the curve C.O.D./ΔL decreases. This is not the case for steels without a plateau indicating clearly that a further exhaustion of ductility at the notch tip goes on (Figures 9 and 10).

CONCLUSION

We must realize that the behavior of a structure is very complicated and that during loading deformations vary not only quantitatively from one point to another but also qualitatively. Some parts will behave elastic other plastic. This ascertainement bears serious consequence; it means indeed that properties defined on materials, cannot be transferred to structures. It puts in question the possibility of the applicability of fracture mechanics when trying to apply test results obtained on small specimens to structures and illustrates the necessity to make a clear difference between tests on materials and tests on structures. The first can be done by measuring local phenomena but cannot be used to explain a global behavior, except perhaps, if this behavior is either fully elastic or plastic, this explains the limited applicability of the linear elastic fracture mechanics.

To grasp the behavior of a structure only global properties can be used, which are not restricted to the observation of a limited area, e.g., a crack but which gives also information of the occurance of other events happening at a certain distance and which have a direct influence on the behavior of the structure e.g., plasticity occuring away from a notch before a crack starts at the tip of the notch.

By doing tests on components and interpreting the results by the gross strain theory the behaviour of the structure can safely be assessed moreover, the influence of such factors as temperature, residual stresses, bi-or triaxiality are realistically taken in consideration. Finally the question may be raised if it is not time to resolve fracture mechaniscs for yielding mechanics applied on components.

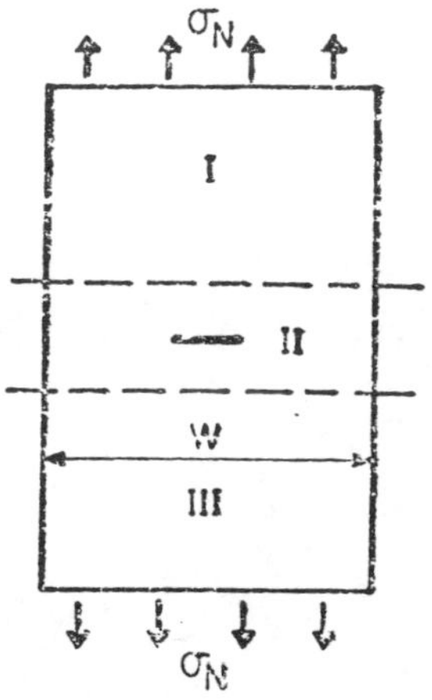

Figure 1

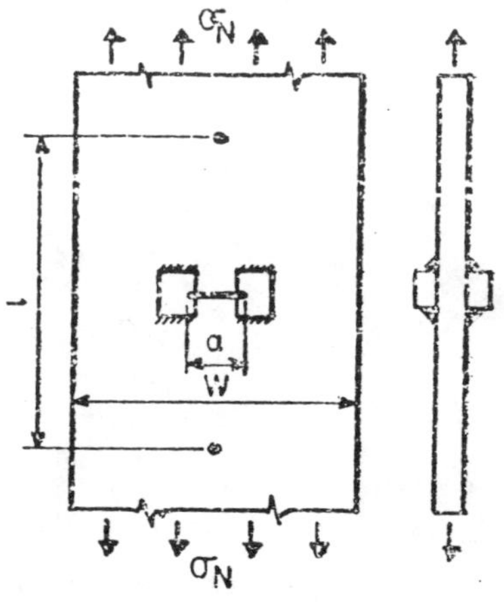

Figure 2

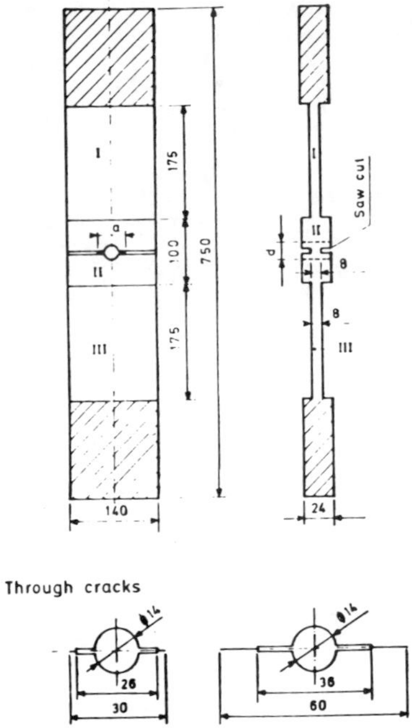

Figure 3

Figure 4

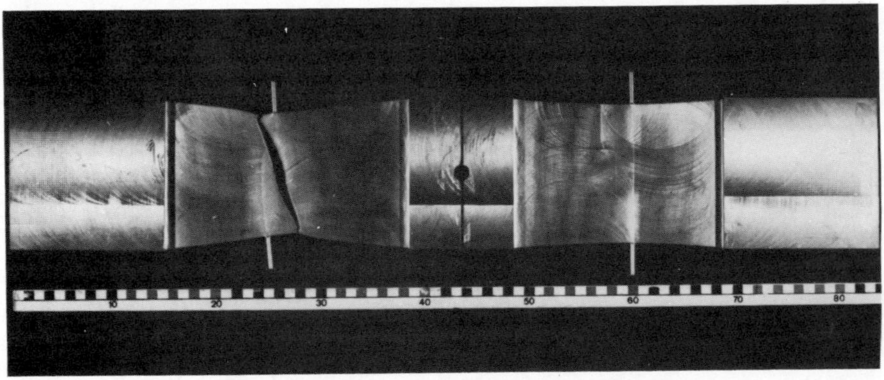

Figure 5: Crack length 30 mm

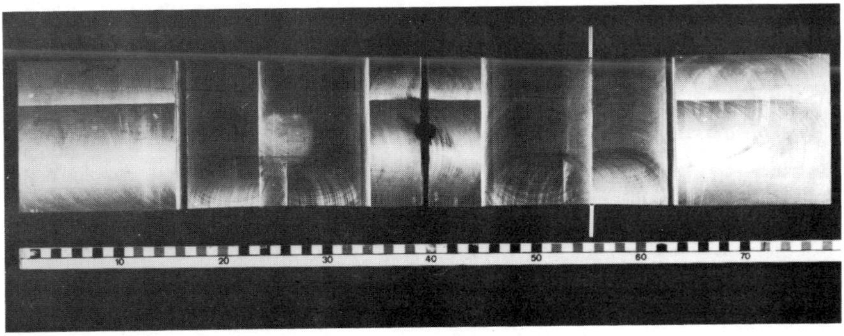

Figure 6: Crack length 60 mm

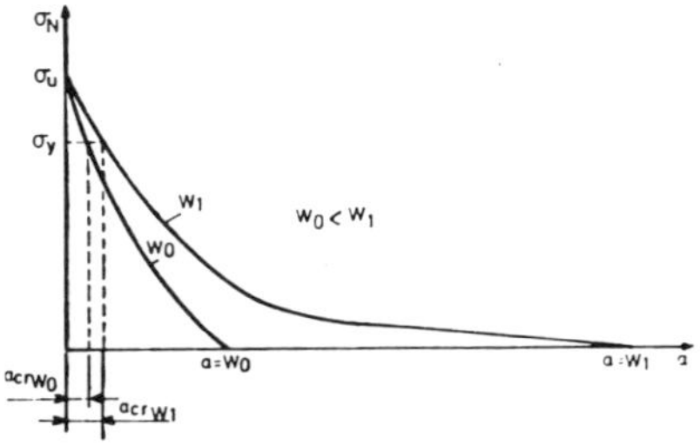

Figure 7

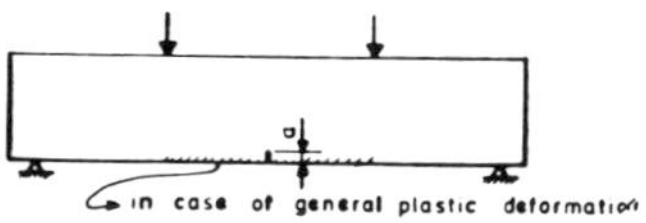

Figure 8

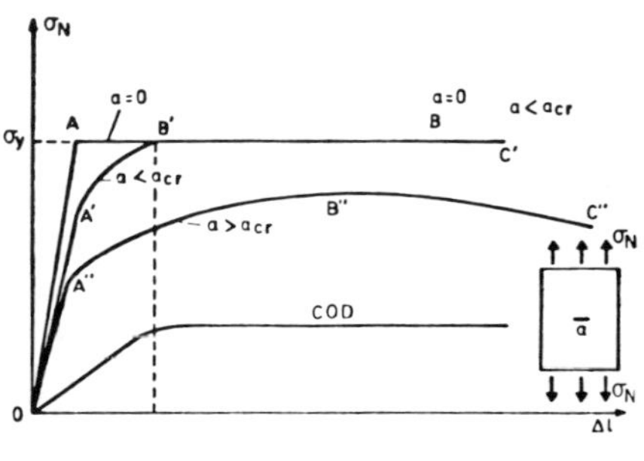

Figure 9

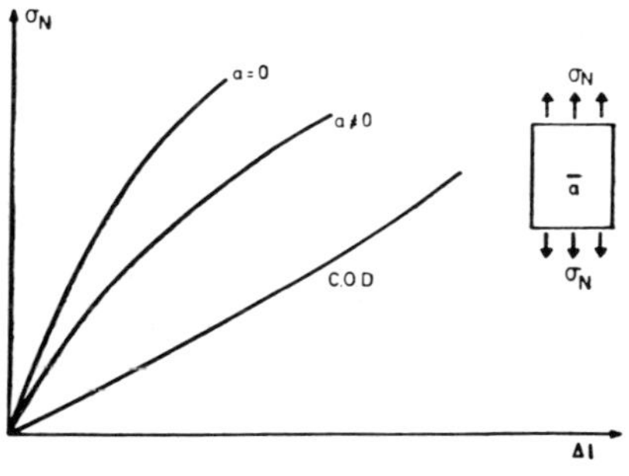

Figure 10

PIPELINES

ALLOY DESIGN FOR ABRASION-CORROSION RESISTANCE IN MINERAL TRANSPORTATION SYSTEMS

J.A. Peters*, G. Wright+, J.V. Bee* and G.G. Garrett*

Improved alloys for abrasion-corrosion resistance have been developed, using a microstructural design approach, to produce optimum combinations of properties. These materials have been evaluated in two gold-mining applications: shaker conveyors and waste-backfilling pipelines. The results show that these alloys have similar increased wear resistance in both cases. The outstanding performance in plate tests suggests that these materials will provide significant benefits in the operation of equipment subject to sliding wear in mining environments.

INTRODUCTION

Abrasive-corrosive wear constitutes a major component of the costs of plant maintenance and replacement in the minerals processing industry. Considerable effort has been made therefore by the Chamber of Mines Research Organisation in the development of new engineering materials for use underground in South African gold mines. In minerals transportation networks in particular, the prevention - or more realistically, inhibition - of failure through progressive materials degradation is a dominant factor in the implementation of new developments for the optimisation of materials handling procedures. This paper reports on two such developments and the potential for significantly improved materials utilisation through the application of principles of (microstructural) alloy design.

These two developments relate specifically to gold mining where, since the matrix for gold is quartzite, the extreme hardness of this material (900 to 1300 HV) implies that all equipment used in mining and transporting this ore is subject to severe abrasive wear. In addition, the corrosive nature of mine water combines to produce an extremely aggressive operational environment.

Conveying Systems

In recent years the need has arisen to improve the performance and efficiency of both existing and new equipment, and in the latter case considerable effort has been directed at the mechanisation of stoping operations in South African gold mines (1). In one particular application, a prototype shaker conveyor (2), Fig.1, is employed to transport rock from the face. This consists of a number of pans, each 2 m long, extending to lengths in excess of 80 m, which move the rock by the linear oscillatory movement of the pans. In this example, low-stress abrasion aggravated by corrosion has

* Department of Metallurgy. University of the Witwatersrand, Johannesburg, R.S.A.
+ Council for Mineral Technology, Randburg, R.S.A.

been identified as the specific wear mechanism (3). This equipment was selected for the initial evaluation of new materials since this would provide a guide to their performance under conditions of sliding wear, which are common in many components used in the whole mining industry.

In the search for a rapid evaluation of potential new alloys, a comprehensive, controlled experimentation programme has already been carried out to establish a reliable laboratory wear test, through the correlation of results obtained in the laboratory with *in situ* tests (3).

Pipelines

One of the major technological problems associated with mining at depths of the order of 3000 m is the occurrence of rockbursts, which can be minimised by appropriate control of the volumetric convergence of the mined-out area. Of the methods available for controlling stope closure, waste backfilling is one of the most promising. This involves the pneumatic or hydraulic transport of waste material to the mined-out area to provide a positive support medium for the rock (4). However, pipe wear represents probably the most serious problem in each of the several alternative techniques available. For example, pneumatic stowing of waste quartzite rock up to 80 mm in size, transported at velocities of 30 m/s and rates of 50 tonnes/hour (producing compaction densities of ~ 80% of the virgin rock) can cause pipe rupture in only four hours of operation. Thus, since pipeline costs account for almost half of the total project costs, the economic viability of this development is threatened.

Materials Selection vs Alloy Design

Studies of the deterioration of materials used in gold mining applications have indicated that degradation processes vary widely from predominantly dry abrasion through to essentially pure corrosion. Logistical and operational considerations have formulated the demand for a spectrum of materials utilisation, ideally centred on a single low-cost, general purpose, abrasion- and corrosion- resistant material.

In the first instance, excellent gouging wear resistance can be obtained by the use of high-chromium martensitic white irons, but their relatively high degree of brittleness, even during transportation (5), limits their potential for use in stope areas. Material hardness, of course, is of importance in determining abrasion resistance, and Richardson (6) has shown that before any significant improvement in abrasion resistance can be achieved the material should have at least half the hardness of the abrasive medium. For use with quartzitic materials, therefore, a minimum surface hardness of ~ 500 HV is a prerequisite.

Secondly, it is also generally accepted that resistance to both crack initiation and crack propagation is desirable for good abrasion resistance and, indeed, Zum Gahr has reported (7) that beyond a certain hardness level, the material toughness becomes the property which controls abrasive wear resistance. Studies of a wide range of existing steels (8) have indicated that a Charpy impact energy of at least 30 Joules is a minimum requirement for appropriate abrasion resistance. This level of toughness is also considered to be the minimum acceptable in mining applications where rugged demands for transportation and day-to-day service preclude the use of more brittle materials.

Thirdly, the high corrosivity of the stoping environment is anathema for many structural alloys, and it is frequently observed that corrosion processes are accelerated by abrasion. For this reason, in metallic materials, adequate corrosion resistance dictates a minimum chromium content of around 10% (consistent with acceptable material and production costs).

Finally, of course, desirable fabrication characteristics and realistic financial considerations contribute to an unenviable exercise in materials selection!

A wide range of materials are obviously readily available for use in abrasion-corrosion applications, including polymerics, ceramics, surface treated steels, coatings, high chromium cast irons or transformable austenitic stainless steels. However, none of these materials have yet proved adequate in meeting the combination of requirements, as defined above, for more general purpose use in gold mining environments. In consequence, an alternative approach through microstructural design has been developed, in which new alloy compositions are formulated to provide the necessary operational (and economic) benefits.

ALLOY DESIGN

A wide range of materials, including stainless, transformable and martensitic steels, has been studied extensively by the Chamber of Mines Research Laboratories in the search for improved resistance to abrasion and cavitation erosion. This work identified important desirable microstructural features. In existing commercial steels these are rarely found, and in the present study developments were based on the high strength, high toughness martensitic steels formulated by Thomas et al. (10,11).

Microstructure

In these dual-phase alloys, the desired microstructure is essentially a fine-grained austenite, which has transformed to dislocated lath martensite surrounded by continuous films of retained austenite. A fine grain size promotes both strength and toughness.

The toughness of the lath martensite is also important and appears to be influenced by two factors: the presence of internal twinning (11 - 13) and the martensite packet size (14, 15). The extent of twinning in martensite is significantly influenced by composition and through the effect of alloying elements in lowering the martensite transformation temperature (M_s). The corresponding loss in toughness at lower M_s values appears to be associated with a restriction of slip during deformation. A fine martensite packet size is desirable since the average fracture direction must change on crossing a packet boundary. Control of twin density and lath structure can be achieved through appropriate manipulation of chemical composition and processing procedures, as will become apparent.

The importance of maintaining thin, continuous inter-lath films (~ 5 - 10 nm thick) of retained austenite for improved toughness in high-strength martensitic steels has been noted by a number of authors (for example 9, 13 - 16). It has been suggested (16) that the presence of this phase along the martensite lath boundaries serves to interrupt the crystallographic alignment of laths within a packet, thus preventing trans-packet cleavage. Best combinations of strength and toughness in medium-carbon martensitic steels seem to result from ~ 5% volume fractions of retained austenite.

Carbide size and distribution are also important. A fine, intra-lath dispersion of carbides has been shown to be beneficial to strength, toughness and abrasion resistance (e.g. 9 - 11). Coarse, inter-lath carbides, however, can be most detrimental to mechanical properties, as exemplified in the phenomenon of tempered martensite embrittlement (17).

Another desirable microstructural feature is, if possible, the absence of inclusions. While the precise relationship of cleanness to steel quality is still not fully understood, cleaner steels generally result in improved properties, providing benefits both in fabrication and in service (18).

Chemical Composition

The first step toward improved martensitic steels was an increase in the chromium content to provide improved corrosion resistance. Additional benefits of this alloying addition are solid solution strengthening of the martensitic matrix and the inhibition of coarsening of the Fe_3C precipitates.

The potential deleterious effect of chromium on toughness, through the promotion of substructural twinning in the martensite, was obviated by reducing the carbon content. This carbon level provided adequate hardness, and had the further benefit of maintaining a relatively high M_s temperature. This latter effect facilitated carbon partitioning during transformation, which chemically stabilised the retained austenite.

Nickel additions were also employed to provide further austenite stabilisation, as well as improved corrosion resistance and fracture toughness (in Cr-containing steels).

Experimental

Two Fe-Ni-Cr-C alloys (A and B), containing different chromium contents, were prepared by vacuum melting and casting, then hot-rolled to plate.

Mechanical property determinations and wear testing were performed on material in the quenched and tempered condition.

In this preliminary study, both alloys were given the same heat treatment, which produced satisfactory combinations of hardness and toughness. Alloy A gave a room temperature Charpy impact value of 67 Joules (minimum) with a bulk hardness (HV30) of 530; while alloy B had a minimum impact toughness of 30 Joules at a bulk hardness of 560.

Conventional light microscopy, SEM and CTEM were used to characterise the microstructures obtained (Figs. 2 - 5) in terms of the requirements indicated in the previous section. In both alloys a fine grain size was produced, with alloy A showing the finer prior austenite grain size (approximately 30 μm in comparison to 40 μm).

CTEM (Figs. 4 and 5) showed clearly that the desired lath martensite microstructure was obtained (lath width ~ 150 nm), with limited substructural twinning (occurring more frequently in alloy B). Inter-lath films of retained austenite were also thinner in alloy B. In both alloys an extremely fine (~ 100 nm) cementite precipitate dispersion was observed, and no coarse carbides were evident.

WEAR TESTING

(a) Shaker Conveyor System

As indicated in the Introduction, a meaningful and reproducible laboratory testing procedure has been developed for evaluating material performance in abrasion-corrosion environments (3). Here, using synthetic mine water of pH 6,5 at 30°C, controlled-abraded surfaces are exposed to corrosion for timed periods. These laboratory tests have been correlated with a programme on a prototype shaker operating underground in a stope in the Doornfontein Gold Mine (3). In this rig, sections approximately 500 mm by 300 mm were cut from the bases of several shaker pans and replaced with similar-sized panels of high-density polyethylene mounted on a backing plate. Samples of materials under test were fitted to present a surface 75 mm x 50 mm flush with the sliding quartzitic rock. (Polyethylene was chosen to ensure a constant exposed sample surface, because of its slightly higher wear rate, and to eliminate any galvanic corrosion effects between test samples)(3).

Fig.6 presents results (after 19) indicating the excellent agreement between laboratory and site tests. Laboratory test data for alloys A and B are added for comparative purposes. All indications are, therefore, that alloy B in particular will provide an exciting new material for general application in all forms of mining subject to sliding wear.

(b) Pipelines

For experimental convenience, the preliminary field evaluation of materials for pipelines in wear applications has been carried out on a surface system designed to transport fused coal ash (VHN ~ 1000). The ash, normally in clinker form up to 20 mm in diameter, is transported as a slurry along a 230 mm diameter pipeline at a velocity of 3 m/s. Severe wear problems have been experienced in service. Based on the preliminary trials, a corresponding test programme has been established at the West Driefontein Gold Mine.

A test section has been introduced into the 500 m long pipeline by milling out a 1 m long, 0,08 m wide slot in standard cast iron pipe sections (1,2 m in length). Test samples of various materials were placed in pairs along the length of the milled out section, and located by means of an H-bar arrangement bolted on to the outside of the pipe. The bottom of the pipe was therefore effectively flat, but appropriate attention was paid to reducing turbulence effects near the start of the test sections.

The pipe-samples were removed and monitored on a weekly basis and the surfaces were examined to gain an understanding of the wear mechanisms operative in the pipeline. In addition mass loss measurements were made.

The results are presented in Fig.7, which summarises the behaviour of a range of metallic, polymeric and ceramic materials. It is clear that in this situation, a different wear mechanism is operative, and the performance of alloys A and B is less impressive. However, further microstructural manipulation can be employed to optimise the properties required in this application.

DISCUSSION

For mine transportation of hard quartzite ores in a hostile environment, it is evident that materials must have both abrasion and corrosion resistance.

In the shaker conveyor, corrosion-resistant materials (3CR12, 430, 316, and 314) exhibited superior performance than commercial abrasion-resistant steels (Abrasalloy and Roqlast AH 400) [Fig.6]. On the basis of laboratory tests, alloy B appears even more superior.

The new alloys (A and B) were designed primarily to produce the desired microstructure which would optimise hardness and toughness properties for abrasion resistance. Alloy B which combines abrasion- and corrosion-resistance does provide a potentially superior material for this application. However, high Cr concentrations do have disadvantages and lower Cr contents such as in Alloy A, could be preferable. Although its performance appears to be inferior on the basis of the current tests, this can be improved by further alloy development to increase its corrosion resistance (for example, by alloying with Cu, Mo or more Ni).

In pipeline use, the best wear resistance is provided by alumina and high chromium white irons (Fig. 7). Ceramics and polymerics, although attractive, may be limited in application through high material and pipe-manufacture costs. Cast irons also have limitations since they generally exhibit poor performance in underground applications due to their tendency to brittle fracture, even during transportation and installation. Thus, materials are required which exhibit better fracture toughness. In this respect, alloys A and B provide significant gains compared with mild steel and cast iron. It should also be noted that the larger abrasive sizes and increased abrasive velocities encountered in actual backfilling operations should also increase the wear resistance of the new tough alloys relative to white iron. However, further manipulation of composition, microstructure and fabrication routes to develop the optimum properties for wear resistance in this application could well lead to viable superior materials.

CONCLUSIONS

1. The solutions to minerals transportation problems in gold mining applications require the optimisation of complex combinations of desired features, including abrasion- and corrosion-resistance, ease of fabrication and economy.

2. Microstructural design for the development of optimum combinations of properties shows considerable promise for the future provision of viable improved materials for use in the mining industry.

3. Indications are that the most satisfactory combinations of properties for abrasion and corrosion resistance in engineering applications can be achieved by the appropriate manipulation of chemical composition and fabrication procedures. To this end, a microstructural design concept has been employed to develop a series of alloys with hardness in excess of 530 VPN, together with an impact toughness greater than 30J.

4. For pipeline applications, further development is required to optimise properties with respect to the operative wear mechanism.

5. The outstanding results of alloys A and B in shaker conveyor tests do prove that these steels have potential widespread applications in skips, chutes and other conveying systems in many general mining operations which are subject to sliding wear and/or corrosion.

ACKNOWLEDGEMENTS

The alloy development work described in this paper was performed in terms of a collaborative agreement forming part of the research programme of the Chamber of Mines of South Africa. Pipeline testing was carried out with the cooperation of the Council for Mineral Technology. The assistance of Mr K Pieterse is also gratefully acknowledged.

REFERENCES

1. Joughin, N.C., 1976, J.S. Afr. Inst. Min. Metall. 76, 285.
2. Joughin, N.C., 1978, J.S. Afr. Inst. Min. Metall. 78, 207.
3. Allen, C., Protheroe, B.E., and Ball, A., 1981, J.S. Afr. Inst. Min. Metall. 81, 289.
4. Marcus, R.D., Fritella, A., Verkerk, C.G., and Macur, M., 1982 "Research into the backfilling of stopes in gold mines conducted by the Materials Handling Research Group", Proceedings 12th CMMI Congress, H.W. Glen (editor), Johannesburg, S. Afr. Inst. Min. Metall.
5. Protheroe, B.E., 1979, "The Causes of Metallic Wear in Hard Rock Mining Conditions with Some Solutions". Paper presented at the 1st National Conference on Fracture, University of the Witwatersrand, South Africa.
6. Richardson, R.C.D., 1968, Wear 11, 245.
7. Zum Gahr, K.H., 1978, Z. Metallkunde 69, 643.
8. Peters, J.A., 1983, "A Microstructural Approach to Alloy Design for Superior Corrosive-Abrasive Wear Resistance", University of the Witwatersrand, South Africa, MSc thesis.
9. Narasimha Rao, B.V., and Thomas, G., 1980, Met. Trans. 11A, 441.
10. Salesky, W.J., and Thomas, G., 1981, "Sliding Wear, Toughness and Microstructural Relationships in High Strength Fe/Cr/C Experimental Steels," University of California, Berkeley, M.S. thesis.
11. McMahon, J.A., and Thomas, G. 1973, "Development of Economical, Tough, Ultra-High-Strength Fe-Cr-C Steels", 3rd Int. Conference Proceedings "Strength of Metals and Alloys", London, England.
12. Lai, G.Y., Wood, W.E., Clark, R.A., Zackay, V.F., and Parker, E.R., 1974, Met. Trans. 5, 1663.
13. Thomas, G., 1978, Met. Trans. 9A, 439.
14. Naylor, J.P., and Krahe, P.R., 1974, Met. Trans. 5, 1699.
15. Naylor, J.P., and Blondeau, R., 1976, Met. Trans. 7A, 891.
16. Thomas, G., Sarikaya, M., Smith, G.D.W., Barnard, S.J., 1981, "Microstructural Basis of Alloy Design for High Strength, Tough Structural Steels", Conference Proceedings "Advances in Physical Metallurgy and Applications of Steels", Liverpool, United Kingdom.
17. Horn, R.M., and Ritchie, R.O., 1978, Met. Trans. 9A, 1039.
18. Chandler, H.E., 1981, Metal Progress 120, 52.
19. Noel, R.E.J., 1981, "The Abrasive-Corrosive Wear Behaviour of Metals", University of Cape Town, South Africa, MSc thesis.

Figure 1 A prototype shaker conveyor operating in a dip gully

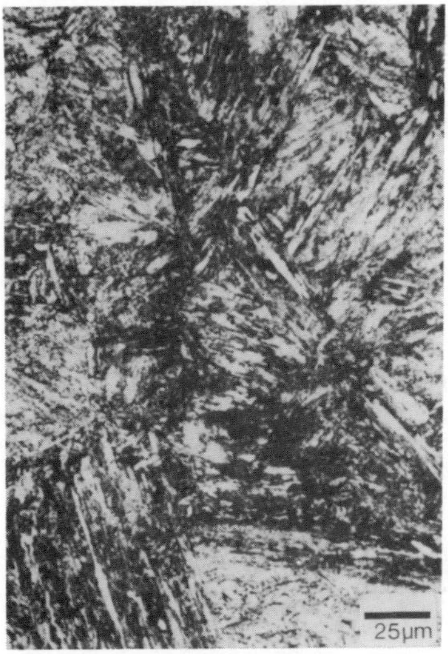

Figure 2 General structure of alloy A (Optical)

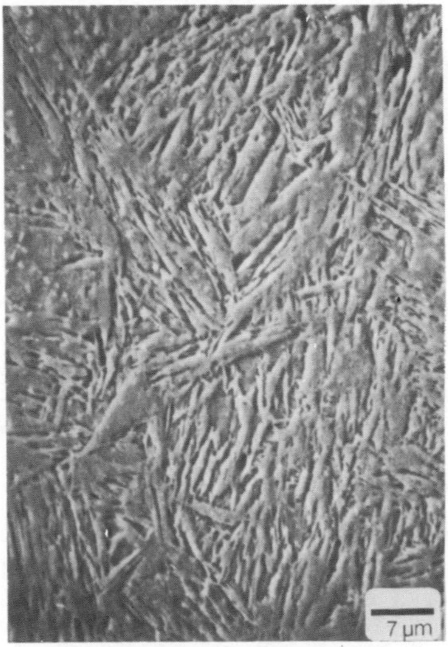

Figure 3 Martensite morphology of alloy B (SEM)

Figure 4 Desired microstructural features of alloy A (CTEM)

Figure 5 Regions of lath martensite in alloy B (CTEM)

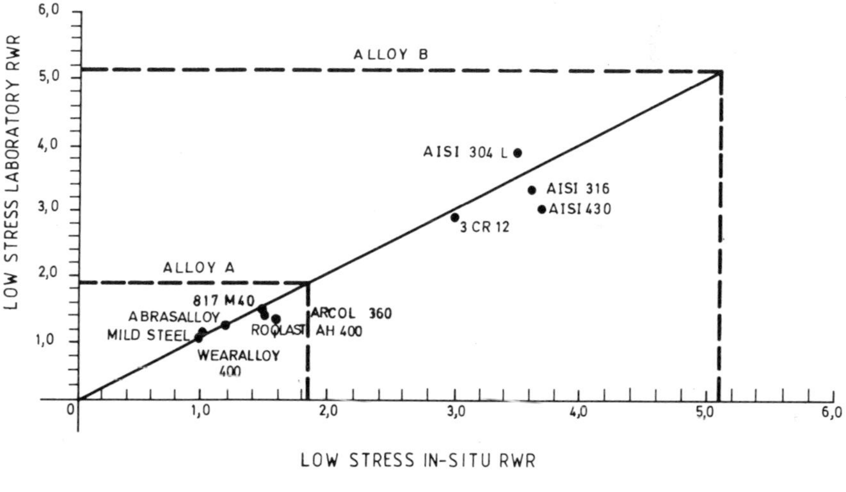

Figure 6 Correlation between laboratory and *in situ* relative abrasion and corrosion resistance (RWR)

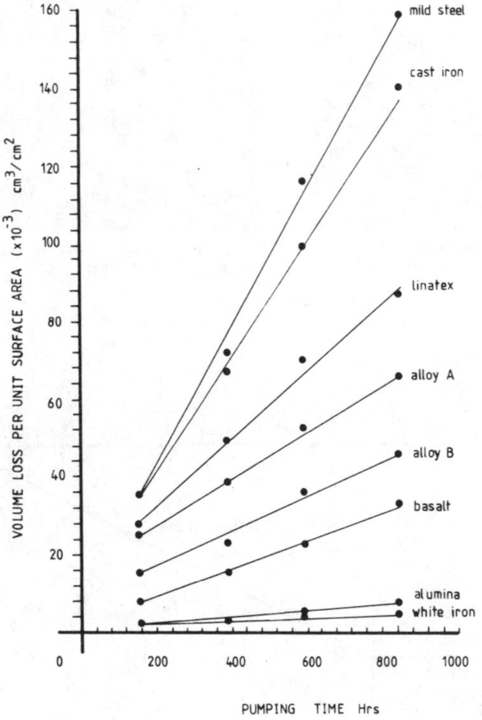

Figure 7 Cumulative volume loss of a range of metallic, ceramic and polymeric materials as a function of time.

HYDROGEN EMBRITTLEMENT IN PIPELINE STEEL.

F. Gutierrez-Solana*, M. Elices*

A fuel transmission system has been analyzed to be used as a hydrogen transmission system. The pipeline material as well as the real structures have been tested with and without hydrogen, and fracture criteria designs have been established for both conditions.

INTRODUCTION

The use of hydrogen as an energy vector has been a source of concern in the last ten years. The reviews by Gregory (1) and Cox and Williams (2), as editors, are an example of such interest.

The hydrogen can be considered as a substitute of natural gas in all its applications, but an economic study of this problem points out several limitations for it. The heat of combustion of hydrogen, 0.32 that of methane, implies higher pressures in the transmission systems for hydrogen to achieve an equivalent energy. In consequence, the use of existing gas systems, at pressures over 14 MPa, have been proposed as an economic limit to hydrogen transmission Gregory (1), Konopka and Worm (3). Under these conditions the structural components of these systems, pipelines of low to medium strength steel, can be more easily affected by fracture problems, due to hydrogen embrittlement fenomena.

These concerns led to an analysis over a system candidate to be used as a hydrogen transmission system and actually in use with other fuels. The final objetive of this analysis is to determine a criterion of design for the pipelines of the system, with and without hydrogen, able to predict the safety level under the conditions chosen, and provide more data on hydrogen embrittlement of pipelines steels. The research program comprises two parts:

Material testing. Small samples were extracted from pipes to provide mechanical characterization of the steel. Standard tensile tests as well as fracture tests, were performed in air and in hydrogen at different pressures.

Structural element testing. Full scale burst tests were also performed to realize the real behaviour of the pipelines with and without hydrogen. The correlation of the results in both kind of tests, material and structure, will show out the critical parameters to be analyzed in each case for a fracture design.

*Departamento de Física y Física de Materiales.E.T.S.Ing.Caminos.Madrid.Spain

This research program, whose preliminary results are presented here, is aimed to:

a.- Correlate laboratory tests to the performance of pressure piping for hydrogen.
b.- Attempting to provide a rational basis for designing, or rating, hydrogen pressure piping.

MATERIAL TESTING

The material of the pipelines, a ferritic-pearlitic steel with a composition and mechanical properties (Table I) similar to those of X-24 steel, was found to be susceptible to hydrogen embrittlement, Christensen et al (4). In this report the changes in its mechanical properties, specially the fracture toughness, in presence of hydrogen gas have been ascertained.

TABLE 1. Composition and Mechanical Properties of linepipe steel

Chemical Composition (% Wt)

C	Mn	Si	Co	Cr	P	S
0.10	0.70	0.26	0.17	0.15	0.033	0.022

Mechanical Properties

Yield Strength	280 MPa
Ultimate tensile strength	435 MPa
Reduction of area	58%
Elongation	32%

The first steps on this research program determined a high susceptibility of this steel to hydrogen embrittlement (4). Both IHE (internal hydrogen embrittlement) and HEE (hydrogen environment embrittlement) methods were used. For the first, losses in reduction area over 70% were found for 1 mA/cm^2 of current density. For the second, losses over 50% were shown for 7 MPa of hydrogen pressure. As the Figure 1 shows, these losses are still increasing for higher pressures.

In these tests no significant effect of hydrogen in the materials strength levels was observed. In consequence in a classical design, based on yield strength, no changes will be observed in the safety coefficients when the pipelines are used with hydrogen instead of other fuels as natural gas. But pipeline failures often result from the mechanical deformation of the pipe and the toughness of the steel becomes critical.

To ascertain the role of the presence of cracks in an aggressive environment, the fracture toughness of the material was determined. As a consequence of the elastic-plastic behaviour with strain hardening observed in all the tensile tests previously performed, a J_{IC} determination was done for this steel in air and in hydrogen gas environment at variable pressures.

The test were performed according with the method proposed by Begley, Landes and Clarke (5), (6) and adopted as an ASTM standard. Charpy specimens 5 mm. thick, due to the pipe thickness, were fatigue pre-cracked to an initial relative crack length between 0.3 and 0.7 and then tested by three-point bending. All the tests were done in a 25 T dynamic testing machine equiped with a COD clip gauge, to correlate compliance measurements with crack length in each specimen tested.

Some of the specimens were tested in air at normal conditions to determine the fracture toughness of this steel in a non-aggressive conditions.

The other specimens were tested inside an instrumented pressure -chamber adjusted to the testing machine. The chamber, built from a block of AISI-316 stainless steel to avoid welding problems, was designed for high vacuum (10^{-5} Torr) and high-pressure (7 MPa) conditions. Ultra-high purity hydrogen was used, being introduced in the chamber after passing through impurities trapps. Figure 2 shows a sketch of the facilities for one of these tests.

The displacement rate was considered very important in this tests due to the strain rate dependence of hydrogen embrittlement processes (Hofman and Rouls (7)). Accordingly, previous tests were performed to determine the speed where the hydrogen embrittlement was most effective. As an example, table II shows the changes in J_{IC} values for different displacement rates in an hydrogen environment at 4 MPa.

TABLE II. Variation of J_{IC} values with displacement rate in 4 MPa pressure hydrogen tests

Displacement rate	$\mu m\ s^{-1}$	3.30	0.33	0.33	0.03
J_{IC} values	(KJ/m^2)	56	31	34	35

Table III shows a summary of the results based on the obtained J_{IC} values and other parameters related with the fracture toughness. The K_{IC} values were obtained from the J_{IC} according with the expression:

$$J_{IC} = \frac{1 - \nu^2}{E} K_{JC}^2 \qquad (1)$$

and the critical values of crack tip opening displacement, δ_c, were obtained after a finite element study (Gutiérrez-Solana (8)) over the tests performed. This study also showed the plain strain conditions existing in all the tests performed in hydrogen gas, but not in air. This is in good agreement with the validity conditions of the J determination due to the thickness specimen limitation (Table III).

TABLE III. Results from J_{IC} tests, at 0.33 μm s^{-1}

Test conditions	J_{IC} (KJ/m^2)	K_{JC} ($MPa.m^{1/2}$)	δ_c (mm)
Air*	99.8±3.8	147	0.134
H_2 2.0 MPa	76	128	-
H_2 2.0 MPa	48	101	-
H_2 4.0 MPa	33.3±2.1	85	0.035
H_2 6.5 MPa	22.3±2.1	69	0.029

* *Insufficient thickness. Displacement rate 3,30* μm s^{-1}

Figure 3 shows a plot of the different R-curves obtained in these J_{IC} determination tests. As can be seen the values of the slope dJ/da are quite similar in all teh specimens tested in hydrogen and considerably smaller that the corresponding ones in air tests. It means that the energy spent in crack propagation is smaller in hydrogen presence and almost independent on the pressure. These changes in enegy correlate very well with the changes in fracture mode reported as microvoid coalescence in air with quasi-cleavage regions in specimen tested in hydrogen (4, 8).

An analysis of the data shows losses in fracture toughness due to hydrogen up to 53% for 6.5 MPa, when measured by K_{JC}. A linear correlation between this parameter and the square root of the pressure appears to exist, as found elsewhere, for the dependence of fracture toughness on hydrogen concentration. The expression obtained has a correlation coefficient of 0.93.

$$K_{JC} = 151.7 - 31\ P^{1/2} \qquad \text{(c.c. 0.93)} \qquad (2)$$

Despite the relevance of these results for the system analyzed, it was necessary to confirm that a critical value of the stress intensity factor may be used as a fracture parameter for pipelines. To check this hypotesis, burst tests of pipelines were performed to provide empirical comparison data.

The role of microstructure in pipeline embrittlement, to take into account welding problems (9), has been briefly explored testing two different heat treatments. These heat treatments have been done with the steel in order to transform it into more brittle microstructure, martensite, to simulate the heat affected zones (HAZ) close to weldments or hard spots.

Mechanical caracterization was done by tensile tests, showing higher strength and less ductility. The effect of hydrogen was also studied determining the J_{IC} values of these microstructures in air and in hydrogen at 6.5 MPa of pressure. As the table IV summarizes, the J_{IC} values obtained are very close to those obtained under the same conditions for the material as received. From these results one should infer that the presence of areas like HAZ or hard spots do not affect the toughness of the pipeline material.

TABLE IV. Simulated HAZ Mechanical porperties and toughness results

Heat treatment	Mechanical Properties			Toughness J_{IC} (KJ/m²)	
	Yield S.	U.T.S.	Elongation	Air	H_2 (6.5 MPa)
915°C (15m)+water Quench Microstructure partially transformed to martensite	450 MPa	660 MPa	16%	106	21
920°C (1h.)+water quench Microstructure: Martensite	435 MPa	620 MPa	16%	103	15

STRUCTURAL ELEMENT TESTING

The experimental work of this analysis has been completed performing burst tests on full scale samples. Pipe sections, 140 cm. in length, were cut from the pipelines of the transmission system, 5.6 mm. thick in average, and with an external radius of 80 mm. In all of them an internal longitudinal flaw was machined with variable geometry. The flaws have a traingular cross section and a root radius of less than 0.075 mm. to simulate a crack. Plane strain conditions are presented at the tip of this simulated cracks (Kassir and Sih (10)) due to their geometric condition. Figure 4 shows a sketch of the samples to be tested. Some of the samples were tested with water simulating a non aggresive fuel and the others with hydrogen.

Water tests were performed following a conventional method. From the burst pressure, P_b, the stress intensity factor was obtained. Two parameters have been used in this process, one h(o) considering the effect of geometry and pipeline curvature, studied in a similar case by Helliot et al (11) and the other, the plastic correction factor M_p, obtained from the value of plastic zone size ahead of the crack. Table V summarizes the results obtained in the eigth different samples tests. From these results a high scattering is found in the critical value of the stress intensity factor K_I. The value, 51±16 MPa $m^{1/2}$ is also very low compared with the K_{IC}, 147 MPa $m^{1/2}$, obtained for this material from the J_{IC} tests in air.

In order to have a more realistic fracture criterion, according with the amount of plasticity observed in all the samples tested, an analysis of a critical "flow stress" value defined by the burst values of the product σ_θ h(o) derived from an original analysis of Burdekin and Stone (12) has been done. As can be seen in Table V the value obtained for this parameter, 420 MPa, has less scattering than K_{IC}, and for pipelines design in fracture without agressive fuels a critical value of flow stress of 420 MPa can be considered. This criterion can be transformed to another similar for these pipelines considering the pressure instead of the stress. A critical value of P_bh(o) of 29 MPa has been obtained. Figure 5 presents a plot with this criterion jointly with the results obtained in the tests mentioned above.

TABLE V. Summary of results of burst tests with water

Deffect Geometry			Burst values		Critical values	
a/c	a/B	h(o)	P_b	(MPa) σ_θ	K_I (MPa.m$^{1/2}$)	$\sigma_\theta h_{(o)}$ (MPa)
0.27	0.23	1.10	24.5	366	33	403
0.28	0.39	1.20	21.6	322	40	387
0.10	0.34	1.30	19.8	296	36	385
0.05	0.36	1.41	19.6	293	42	411
0.03	0.36	1.50	20.0	299	48	448
0.23	0.80	1.65	16.8	251	63	413
0.10	0.71	1.95	16.4	245	81	477
0.07	0.71	2.45	11.9	177	64	434
					51	420

Difficulties were found in testing in hydrogen environment (8). An internal spacer was used to reduce the internal volume to fill with hydrogen. High-purity hydrogen was achieved inside the samples without a previous vacuum using a serie of pressurization and despressurization processes, with nitrogen first and then hydrogen. Also safety conditions were extremely considered. Figure 6 shows a sketch of test facilities and ancillary equipments.

During the test the pipes were pressurized with high-purity hydrogen to a pressure, P, simulating the conditions of the pipelines carrying hydrogen. This pressure was sustained time enough to achieve a maximum embrittlement of the material of the pipeline. Then more pressure was given to the burst point P_b. All the samples tested in this way showed a small plastic zone area contained near the crack tip. In consequence a K_{IC} criterion obtained from the plastic corrected stress intensity values should be considered. Table VI shows the results obtained and the analysis done with them.

TABLE VI. Summary of results of burst tests with hydrogen

Deffect Geometry			Hydrogen Pressure	Burst values		Critical values	
a/c	a/B	h(o)	P (MPa)	P_b (MPa)	σ_θ	K_I (MPa$^{1/2}$)	$\sigma_\theta h_{(o)}$ (MPa)
0.21	0.64	1.55	16.0	16.8	238	46	369
0.10	0.64	1.90	12.2	15.8	226	57	429
0.06	0.65	2.50	10.0	11.1	162	53	405
0.04	0.72	3.50	8.0	8.4	121	59	423
0.03	0.69	3.60	7.0	9.4	133	73	478

Good agreement is observed between these results considering the critical K_{IC} values and the expression (2) obtained for the J_{IC} tests over the material, mainly for hydrogen pressures under 10 MPa where the stability of K_I values is almost achieved, due probably to saturation problems. Figure 7 shows this event. This agreement suggest an analysis of all the points K_I-P obtained in both tests; J_{IC} and pipe burst. Two expressions were obtained one parabolic and another logarithmic, to consider the saturation phenomena (Figura 8).

$$K_{IC} = 146.4\ P^{-1/2} \quad \text{(c.c.: 0.958)} \quad (3)$$

$$K_{IC} = 152.6\ P^{-0.428} \quad \text{(c.c.: 0.962)} \quad (4)$$

It seems, from table VI, that a "flow stress" criterion may be useful, showing a decrease in the critical value as the hydrogen pressure increases. More tests will be needed to better determine this correlation and the corresponding values of flow stress in each condition.

However, in presence of hydrogen, also a K_{IC} criterion may be chosen given by one of the expressions relating K_{IC} with hydrogen pressure. Nevertheless, considerable stable crack growth resistance remains in hydrogen and from test results it seems that the fracture process is driven by plasticity.

DESIGN APPLICATION

As an example, a "leak before break" analysis has been applied for a pipeline to be used with hydrogen at 14 MPa of pressure. The prossible through the thickness crack that can be formed would have a length twice the thickness of the pipeline. For these conditions a K_I value of 29 MPa $m^{1/2}$ would be obtained. The critical K_I value obtained from the expression (4) is 49 MPa.$m^{1/2}$ so a safe leak condition is achieved with a safety coefficient of 1.7. The pipeline transporting a non-agressive fuel, as natural gas at the same pressure would have a safety coefficient of 2.0 (15% higher) but considering the same energy efficiency for the system, pressure about 5 MPa, the safety coefficient would be 5.5, 70% higher that the one for hydrogen.

CONCLUSIONS

1.- J-integral measurements and burst tests give similar results for the calculated equivalent K_{IC}. This techniques are less cumbersome and less expensive than burst test methods.

2.- The presence of hydrogen can originate a change in the critical parameter associated to fracture process. Pipelines with non--agressive fuels should be designed using a flow-stress criterion but when used with hydrogen a K_{IC} criterion should be considered. Although the system appears to be safe with hydrogen, a reduction of 70% in safety coefficient has been determined refered to natural gas.

AKNOWLEDGEMENTS

The authors are very grateful to Butano, S.A. (Spain) for the financial support and encouragement.

REFERENCES

1. Gregory D.P., 1972"A Hydrogen-Energy System"AGA Catalog L-21173

2. Cox,K.E. and Williams K.D.,1975-79 "Hydrogen:Its technology and Implications". CRC Press, Inc. USA.

3. Konopka A. and Worm J. 1974. 9th.Intersociety Energy Conversion Engeneering Conference. San Francisco U.S.A.

4. Christensen, D.J., Bernstein I.M., Thompson A.W. Danielson E.J. Elices, M. Gutierrez-Solana, F., 1981, in Hydrogen Effects in Metals. TMS-AIME Warrendale. pp. 997.

5. Begley J.A. and Landes J.D., 1972. ASTM STP 514 pp. 1

6. Clarke G.A., Landes J.D.,Begley,J.A. 1980.J.Test. Eval., 8 n°5, p221.

7. Hofman W. and Rauls W.1965. Welding Journ.,Welding Research Sup. 44, p 225.

8. Gutierrez-Solana,F. 1981. Tesis Doctoral.Universidad Politécnica de Madrid.

9. Thompson,A.W., 1977 ibid. ref. 2, vol. 2, pp. 85.

10. Kassir,M.K. and Sih G.C., 1966, Journ. of Appl. Mech. 6

11. Helliot S., Labbens R. and Pellisier-Tanon A. 1980. 2nd. Int. Conf. on Numerical Methods in Fract. Mech. Swansea. U.K.

12. Burdekin F.M. and Stone D.W. 1966, Journal of Strain Analysis, 1.

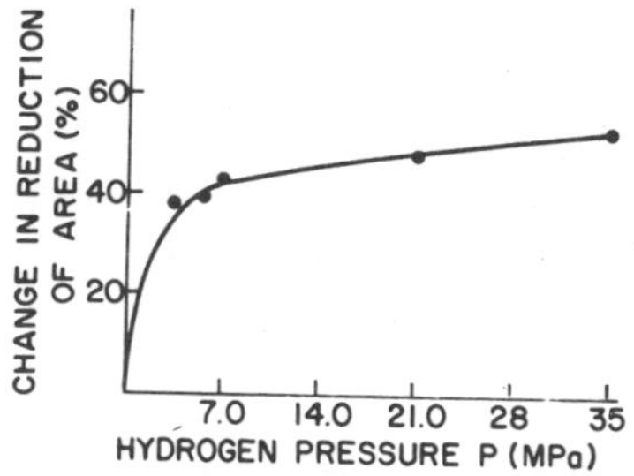

Figure 1. Susceptibility to hydrogen embrittlement.

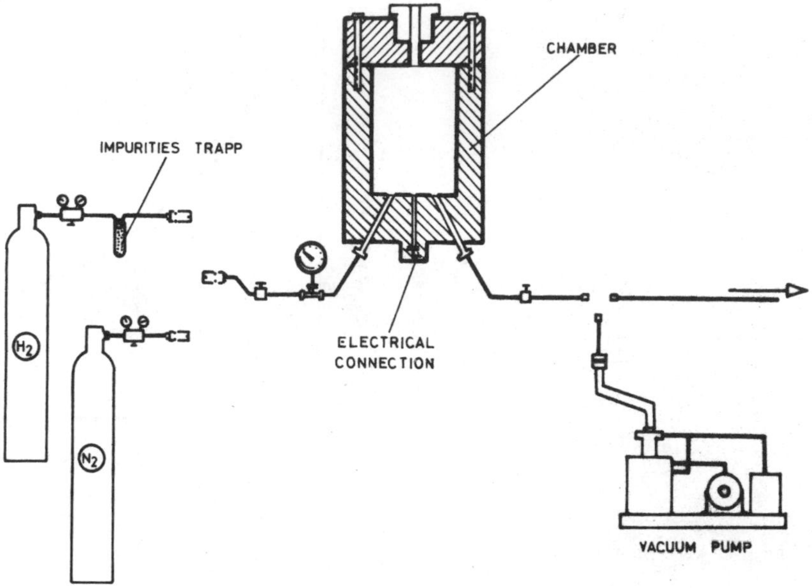

Figure 2. Pressure chamber facilities for hydrogen tests.

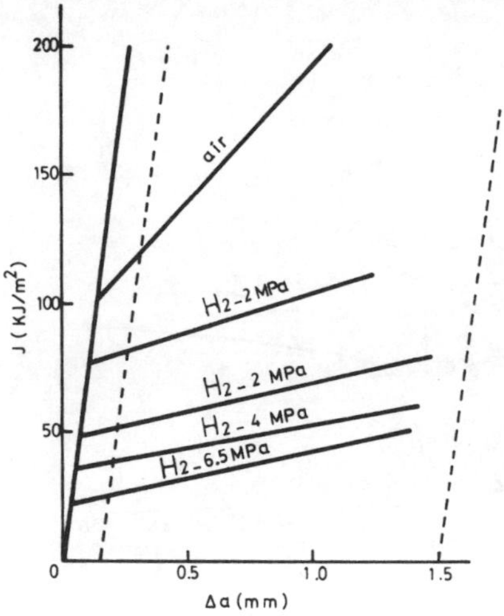

Figure 3. R curves in J_{IC} tests.

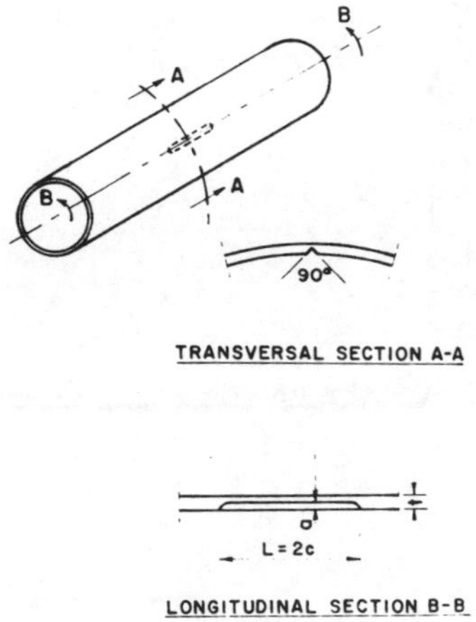

Figure 4. Pipe sample for burst tests

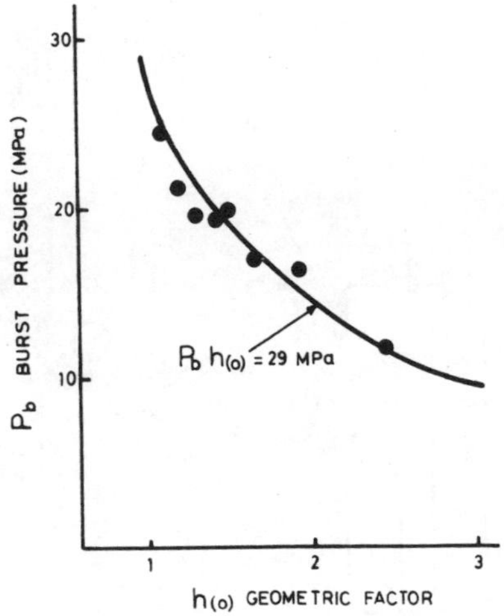

Figure 5. Flow stress criterion for pipe burst with water.

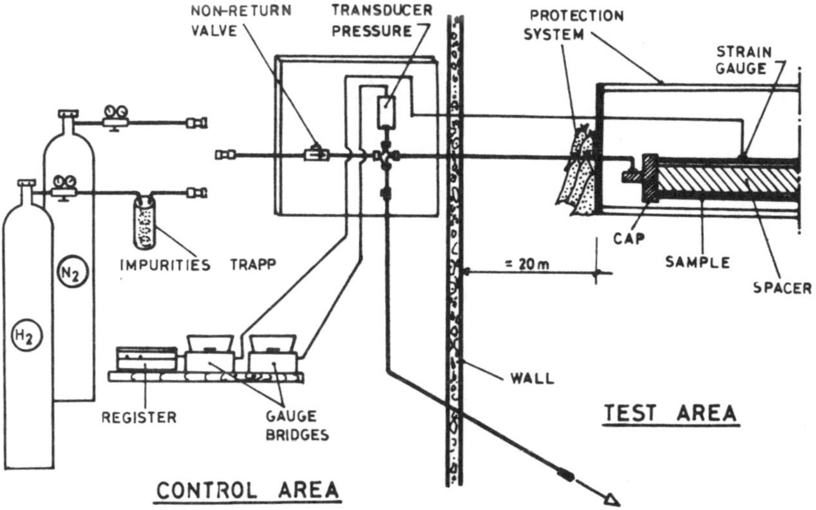

Figure 6. Equipment for hydrogen burst tests

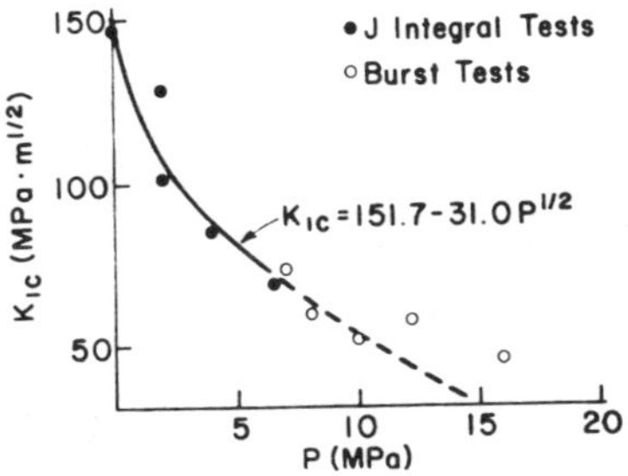

Figure 7. K_{IC}-P dependence from J_{IC} tests.

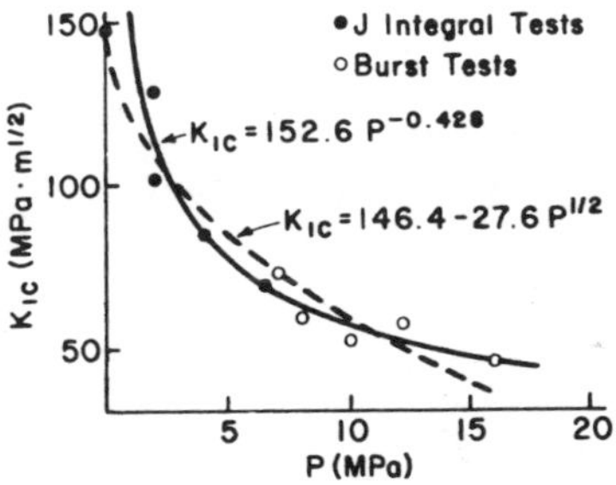

Figure 8. K_{IC}-P dependence from J_{IC} and burst tests.

THE PHENOMENON OF SEPARATIONS IN MICROALLOYED CONTROL-ROLLED PIPELINE STEELS

K. K. Chawla*

A review is made of our current understanding of the phenomenon of separations observed on the tensile and Charpy fracture surfaces of heavily control-rolled microalloyed steels. We examine two main metallurgical factors that may contribute to the phenomenon of separations, viz.; i) crystallographic anisotropy (texture), ii) mechanical anisotropy; and the effect of steel processing parameters, e.g., On Line Accelerated Cooling (OLAC) on the phenomenon of separations. The reliability of Charpy test in predicting an adequate level of toughness has increasingly become a polemical issue. In this regard the recent results obtained by Japanese High Pressure Linepipe Committee in their full scale burst tests and the Britsh Gas view point are discussed.

INTRODUCTION

A great expansion in the construction of large diameter pipelines, mainly for gas transmission, has occurred since the decade of sixties. Due to the energy crisis, gas and oil resources are being explored in all parts of the world and ever larger amounts are being transported or will require transportation through ever larger distances to consumption points. A current example is that of transportation of gas from the arctic regions (1).

Transportation of oil and gas over large distances in large quanties and under cold,hard weather conditions has resulted in rather stringent demands on pipeline materials. Use of large diameter (over one meter) and thick-walled pipes has increasingly become common. The economics also dictates operation of these large diameter pipelines at high pressures to maximize the through put and lower operating costs over the lifetime of the pipe. This has resulted in the usage of steels of higher yield and ultimate tensile strength and also greater pipe line wall thickness. This becomes readily clear if we remind ourselves that the maximum hoop stress in a pipe is given by

$$\sigma_H = Pd/2t$$

where P is the internal pressure, d is the outside diameter and t is the wall thickness. One of the problems in this respect has to do with obtaining both high strength and high toughness in thick plates.

*Instituto Militar de Engenharia, Pr. Gen. Tiburcio, 80, Urca 22290 Rio de Janeiro, RJ, BRASIL

Toward this end mainly, if not exclusively, were developed in the decades of 60's and 70's the microalloyed steels containing elements such as Nb, V, and Ti and the control-rolling technology to process these steels to obtain an optimum combination of mechanical properties in rather thick sections. It has been, however, verified that microalloyed steels submitted to control-rolling practice, in particular those with very low finishing temperatures, exhibit the phenomenon of separations, parallel to the rolling plane, on the fracture surface (2-7). This type of failure can occur as "splittings" in Charpy samples or "delaminations" parallel to the stress axis in uniaxial tensile tests or in full scale tests of the pipes. In order to distinguish this phenomenon from another similar and well known one observed in weld materials, viz., lamellar tearing, in microalloyed control-rolled steels this phenomenon has been given the name of "separations".

The problem of adequate toughness of steel is more critical in the case of gas transmission inasmuch as crack propagation velocity may be greater than the decompression rate of gas and the crack front will ramain in a high pressure region, thereby, leading to catastrophic failures. The fracture control philosophy in the case of pipeline steels can be summarized as follows (8):

i) prevent brittle failures by operating pipeline above the ductile-brittle transition temperature of the steel.

ii) prevent ductile crack initiation by specifying a high minimum toughness for a pipe operating at a specific stress level.

iii) in the case of remotely located pipelines, control ductile crack propagation by specifying some average toughness that will ensure self-arrest of the crack within an acceptable length.

Conventionally, this average toughness of the linepipe steel has been specified in terms Charpy impact test values (50% FATT* or CV100§). Control-rolled steels finished in the $\alpha+\gamma$ two phase region show higher yield and ultimate tensile strengths together with a lower DBTT and lower upper shelf energies. This lowering of DBTT may partly be due to the recrystallized ferrite but is primarily due to the occurence of separations (9). There is a good deal of criticism of the use of Charpy test for ensuring adequate toughness against ductile fracture in linepipe steel. More on this later on .

THE PHENOMENON OF SEPARATIONS

Various authors (2-7) have observed that control-rolled steels finished at low temperatures show microstructural variations through the thickness. These microstructural gradients are complex and include through the thickness variations in grain size, contents of non ferritic microconstituents, and texture (7,10,11).

---

*FATT = Fracture Appearance Transition Temperature

§CV100 = energy absorbed at lowest temperature at which the fracture is 100% shear.

Practically all authors admit the existence of planes of weakness parallel to the rolling plane. What is still rather controversial is the origin of these planes of weakness. It may reside in crystallographic or mechanical anisotropy. Hawkins (6) observed cleavage separations in Charpy samples and atributed the phenomenon to (110) component of crystallographic texture. Miyoshi et al. (12) also suggested that the separations on the fracture surface were due to cleavage failure in the material that had a strong (100) texture component. Matsuda and Kawashima (13) associated, among other things, the development of (100) and (111) texture to separations. The texture can have origin in the transformation of an already textured austenite or during the hot rolling of the transformed ferrite (14-15). According to Tanaka el al. (16), the separations initiate at inclusions and propagate along the (100) texture developed during control-rolling. According to these authors for sulfur contents less than 0,01% and with the use of inclusion control techniques, control-rolled plates show a Charpy energy in the transverse direction more than 100 J. This value is better than that shown by conventionally rolled plates.

The mechanical anisotropy is associated with the discontinuities in the matrix that become aligned during the processing. Among the common discontinuities are included the various types of inclusions, e.g., sulfides, oxides, silicates, segregated impurities, and non-ferritic transformation products. Herø al. (4) showed that in experimental steels containing very little inclusions the failure occurred along the ferritic boundaries. This was attributed to a banded microstructure or the presence of carbonates at the ferrite boundaries. The decohesion at the ferrite/carbonate interfaces and at the ferrite boundaries resulted in a linear array of voids at large strains such as in the necked region of a tensile specimen.

Bramfitt and Marder (3) studied the influence of finishing temperature on texture in microalloyed steels. Although they determined that the crystallographic texture developed during the deformation did contribute to an improvement in strength and in the fracture toughness, it was not responsible for the separations. Bramfitt and Marder, like many other researchers, observed separations oriented parallel to the rolling plane in microalloyed steels finished at temperatures below 750°C. In tensile tests, they observed that the transverse section of the bars changed from a square to a rectangular form indicating the anisotropy of the properties. According to these authors, the mechanism responsible for the appearance of separations is connected with the rather large quantity of ferrite present in the structure. These ferrite grains are elongated and flattened (pancake form) due to the control-rolling practice. These authors used a high purity Fe-1% Mn alloy. Thus, the planes of weakness could not be attributed to banding etc. The sulfur content was 0.004%, i.e., the effect of manganese sulfide on fracture would be negligible. Observations of fracture surfaces in SEM showed that the separations did not have the classical cleavage fracture appearance. The parallel cracks appeared as a phenomenon of tearing associated with a considerable necking and ductility. Thus, these authors attributed the phenomenon of separations to the special pancake form of the ferrite grains obtained during the low temperature finishing of control-rolled steels. These flattened grains enabled a large grain boundary area to be parallel to the rolling plane which contributed to a plane of weakness.

According to Baldi and Buzzichelli (7), the separations occur at a critical tensile stress. An important source of these separations, as per these authors, is the dimensional anisotropy of the microstructural unit controlling the fracture, viz., the ferrite grain or the prior austenite grain.

CHARPY IMPACT TEST vs. SEPARATIONS

Correlating the data obtained from laboratory tests to full scale application is not straightforward. Charpy impact values have been conventionally used as a means of specifying the toughness requirements for running shear fractures in pipelines. This followed from an empirical relation that exists between the shear fracture velocity and the Charpy impact upper-shelf value of pipeline steel (17). The appeal of Charpy test is quite obvious. The use of conventional Charpy test, however, is not completely justifiable. For one, the amount of material deformed in a Charpy test is much smaller than that in an actual linepipe fracture. Secondly, according to British Gas, improvements in Charpy energy do not necessarily correspond to improvements in ductile fracture resistance in the field. Jones (18) has emphasized this British Gas viewpoint in no uncertain terms. It is true, indeed, that if a material shows high absorbed energies in a Charpy test it means that the material has good toughness under conditions of that test (size, strain rate, etc.). Use of Charpy upper shelf energy as a parameter for the propagation shear fractures in pipes, according to Jones, is not valid for materials showing separations. The energy absorbed in a Charpy test will have any value for specifications against shear fracture propagation only if the material does not show separations.

According to the British Gas view point (19) the primary cause of separations is the finishing at low temperatures (in $\alpha + \gamma$ region) during control-rolling which promotes the formation of textures and carbonates at the grain boundaries. These characteristics in their turn produce the anisotropy in cleavage such that the stress necessary for cleavage in the plane parallel to the rolling direction is less than the stress required for general yield. According to British Gas (19) the appearance of separations on Charpy fracture surfaces invalidates the relation between the Charpy energy and the resistance against ductile fracture propagation. Thus, there is a clear need for a better test than the Charpy to evaluate the resistance against ductile fracture. Priest and Holmes (20) have outlined a fracture mechanics approach involving determination of total energy to fracture for different test piece sizes and relating this to the ligament length of the test piece.

Another problem possibly related to the phenomenon of separations is that of lamellar tearing, a form of cracking that occurs under the welds in rolled plates. According to some authors, a plate that shows separations in fracture will also be susceptible to lamellar tearing on welding (21). Without entering into the merits of this affirmation, it should be recognized that the problem of lamellar tearing is also connected to through thickness property gradients, more perhaps due to the presence of elongated and flattened inclusions on planes parallel to the rolling plane (22,23).

Although the phenomenon of separations continues to be an area of concern and interest, the effect of this type of failure (i.e. showing separations) on general resistance against fracture in full scale pipe burst test is not clear. The Iron and Steel Institute of Japan organized a High Strength Line Pipe Research Committee (HLP) in 1978. HLP has carried out five full scale burst tests in the Kamaishi region of Japan (24). The HLP used air as the pressurizing gas and the test pipes were manufactured by controlled rolling and quenching and tempering. One of the objectives of the full scale burst tests was to clarify the effect of separations in the control-rolled pipe on the notch ductility required to arrest ductile crack propagation. The relevant conclusion of the HLP is that ductile crack propagation and arrest can be analyzed by specifying Charpy energy values irrespective of the presence or absence of separations on the fracture surface. According to the HLP Kamaishi test, tha Charpy energy value is the best measure of crack propagation and arrest. This is sharply in contrast to the British Gas viewpoint (18,19,25). The fundamental problem, according to Rothwell et al. (26), is in the use of conventional tests such as Charpy or Drop Weight Tear, which measure energy spent in both initiation and propagation of a crack, to predict crack propagation resistance alone in full-scale tests where exists an extremely complicated strain distribution running ahead of a ductile crack. Thus, it is quite unlikely that a practical, laboratory test can be devised to "adequately simulate the precise deformation history experienced, prior to separation, in a fracturing pipe" (26). Rothwell et al. (26) also describe an instrumented drop weight tear test, together with high speed photographic analysis, to correlate with full-scale burst tests.

Thus, the opinion as regards the significance of separations on the overall engineering performance of microalloyed control--rolled steels is steel divided. As per the HLP, the separations are of no consequence in linepipe steels. In situations involving stresses perpendicular to the plate surface, there exists the possibility of lamellar tearing and the separations should not be regarded as mere 'cosmetic blemishes' (27). This implies that rolling in the two phase $\alpha + \gamma$ region, known to promote separations, should be avoided. Nippon Kokan's OLAC process is one answer to that. For a given finishing temperature (say, 800°C), accelerated cooling tends to reduce the tendency for separations. The On Line Accelerated Cooling process, OLAC as it is commonly known, is in operation at Nippon Kokan's Fukuyama works plate mill. The OLAC process (28-30) involves direct cooling of the plate at a controlled rate between 10 and 15°C/s from about 800°C to about 600°C and then air cooling to room temperature. The accelerated cooling is achieved by water spray on the run-out table after finish rolling (at about 800°C). The exact cooling rate depends on the steel composition and the plate thickness. The OLAC process results in a suppression of the phenomenon of separations in the control--rolled plate through microstructural improvement. As crystallographic texture and pearlite banding seem to be the major metallurgical factors contributing to the phenomenon of separations, one could, of course, finish control-rolling above Ar_3 and thus reduce the incidence of separations but this would result in lower strength. The OLAC process, on the other hand, produces a weak texture and uniform microstructure (ferrite + fine bainite) which results in improved properties in the thickness direction and reduced separations without deteriorating strength and toughness. Another similar way around this problem of separations and limited through thickness ductility (i.e. eliminating excessive controlled rolling) is to use a "chemistry-processing balance" (31). Specifically, in this case (31) a critical Nb/Ti content together with relatively high finishing temperatures produced a homogeneous, equiaxed microstructure.

ACKNOWLEDGMENTS

This work was supported by Companhia Brasileira de Matalurgia e Mineração (CBMM), Financiadora de Estudos e Projetos (FINEP), and Ministério do Exército through the Materials Research Center of Instituto Militar de Engenharia.

REFERENCES

1. Business Week, 1983, January 24, 70.
2. Baird, J.D., and Preston, R.R., 1973, Processing and Properties of Low Carbon Steels, J.M. Gray (ed.), TMS-AIME, New York, 1. See also discussion of this paper by Fegredo, D.M., 43.
3. Bramfitt, B.L., and Marder, A.R., 1973, Processing and Properties of Low Carbon Steels, J.M. Gray (ed.,) TMS-AIME, New York, 223.
4. Herø, H., Evensen, J.D., and Embury, J.D, 1975, Can Met. Quart., 14, 117.
5. Embury, J.D., Evensen, J.D., and Filipovic, A., 1977, Fundamental Aspects of Structural Alloy Design, R.J.Jaffe and B.A. Wilcox (eds.), Plenum Press, New York, 67.
6. Hawkins, D.N., 1976, Metals Tech., 3, 417.
7. Baldi, G., and Buzzichelli, G., 1978, Metals Sci., 12, 459.
8. McConnell, P., 1981, J. Materials for Energy Systems, 3, 28.
9. Kim, N.J., 1983, J. of Metals, 35 (4), 21.
10. Thompson, T., and Baker, J.M., 1969, Aust. J. Metallurgy, 14, 84, as cited in ref. 5.
11. McCutcheon, D.B., Trumper, T.W., and Embury,J.D.,1974, Proc.J. International de Siderurgie, Paris, 143.
12. Miyoshi, E., Fukuda, M., Iwanaga, H.,and Okazawa, T., 1974, Proc. Inst. Gas Eng. Conf. on Crack Propagation on Pipelines, Newcastle upon Tyne.
13. Matsuda, S., and Y. Kawashina, 1981, Proc. 6º Intl. Conf. on Texture of Materials, Tokyo, 659.
14. Whiteley, R., and Wise, J., 1962, Flat Rolled Products, III, TMS-AIME, New York, as cited in ref. 5.
15. Richards, P.N., 1969, J. Iron Steel Inst., 207, 133.
16. Tanaka, T., Tabata, N., Hatomura, T., and Shiga, C.,1977, Microlloying'75, Union Carbide, New York, 119.
17. Maxey, W.A., Kiefner, J.F., Eiber, R.J., and Duffy, A.R., 1972, Fract. Toughness Proc. of 1971 Nat. Sym. Fract. Mec. Part II, ASTM STP 514, ASTM, 70.
18. Jones, B.L., 1977, ref. 16, 397.
19. Jones, C.L., 1982, British Gas Corporation, personal communication,January 22, 1982.

20. Priest, A.H., and Holmes, B., 1981, Int. J. Fracture, 17, 277.

21. See the discussion of the article "Super-fine-grain microalloyed steel" by H. Gondoh, S. Yamamoto, M. Nakayama, H. Nakasugi and H. Matsuda, in ref 16, 441.

22. Stout, R.D., and Pense, A.W., 1981, Causes and Prevention of Lamellar Tearing, Amer. Iron & Steel Inst. report (AISI), New York.

23. Wold, G., and Kristoffersen, T., 1973, Development of Method for measuring susceptibility of steel plate to lamellar tearing, Det Norske Veritas, Oslo, Pub. nº 83.

24. Sugie, E., Matsuoka, M., Akiyama, T., Mimura, H., and Kawaguchi, Y., 1982, J. Pressure Vessel Tech., Trans. ASME, Senei J., 104, 338-343.

25. Fearnehough, G.D., and Jones, D.G., 1980, "Toughness specification for shear fracture arrest in pipelines", Intl. Conf. Fract. Mech., Rome.

26. Rothwell, A.B., Urednicek, M., and Gilroy-Scott, A., 1980, J. Materials for Energy Systems, 2, 30.

27. Korchynsky, M., Union Carbide Corp., personal communication, January 18, 1983.

28. Ouchi, C., Tanaka, J., Kogasu, I., and Tsukada, K., 1979, Micon 78 - Optimization of Processing, Properties and Service Performance Through Microstructural Control, ASTM STP 672, ASTM, Philadelphia, 105-125.

29. Ouchi, C., Okita, T., and Yamamoto, S., 1982, Trans. Iron Steel Inst. Japan, 22, 608.

30. Tsukada, K., Ohkita, T., Ouchi, C., Nagamine, T., Hirabe, K., and Yako, K., 1982, Nippon Kokan Technical Rep. Overseas, 35, 24.

31. Heisterkamp, F., Bergmann, B., Stuart, H., and Chaussy, L., 1982, "Developments in Niobium Steels for Linepipe Applications", Niobium Technical Report, NbTR-02/82.

PROCESS AND MECHANISM OF FRACTURE IN A PIPELINE MATERIAL

A.N. Kumar and R.K. Pandey*

The kinetics and mechanism of subcritical cracking in a hot rolled microalloyed steel has been investigated in presence of 3.5% NaCl and H_2S impregnated acetic acid solutions. The J-integral parameter is used to determine the threshold J_{Iscc} and terminal J_{If} values analogous to K_{Iscc} and K_{If}. H_2S environment appears to be more aggressive than the NaCl medium where considerable amount of energy dissipation occurs during the cracking process. Joining of fine cracks resulting from blistering of pits/voids is responsible for subcritical cracking under H_2S medium, while the process of environmental cracking under NaCl medium occurs mainly by the growth of pits to link up in the direction of stressing.

INTRODUCTION

In recent years, the High Strength Low Alloy (HSLA) and the microalloyed steels tend to replace the conventional plain carbon structural steels. The superior combination of strength and fracture toughness of these steels provides saving in weight as well as better safety and reliability of structures. Some of the fields where these steels find applications include oil and gas pipe lines, off-shore structures and platforms, storage tanks, and other structural components. Premature failures do occur in these components under various circumstances (like low temperature, high strain rate, residual stresses, welded joints, hostile environment etc.) out of which the presence of aggressive environment (like sulphide, chloride etc.) is a potential source of failure. The fracture invariably initiates from a preexisting defect (1,2) and takes place due to its subsequent growth under the environment.

The present investigation is concerned with studying the process and mechanism of fracture in a microalloyed steel which is a typical pipe line material. The study has been made in the ambient condition as well as in presence of two hydrogen bearing environments, namely 3.5% aqueous sodium chloride solution and H_2S saturated acetic acid solution. An attempt has been made to use J-integral approach to characterize the cracking behaviour under the environments as the K-approach is invalidated because of low strength and high toughness of the steel. A comparison of ambient fracture mechanism to the environmental cracking mechanism has been outlined to substantiate the role of environments on the fracture behaviour in this alloy.

* Department of Applied Mechanics, Indian Institute of Technology, New Delhi-110016, INDIA.

EXPERIMENTAL WORK

Material

The chemical composition of the alloy is given in Table 1. The alloy was available in the form of plates of 10 mm thickness in the hot rolled condition (with ferrite grain dia. 8-10 μm. The thermal history of the alloy is illustrated in Fig. 1.

TABLE 1 Chemical Composition (Wt. %).

C	Mn	P	S	Si	Nb	V
0.12	0.99	0.022	0.027	0.025	0.044	0.043

Tensile and Fracture Toughness Tests

The tensile properties were obtained by testing round specimens of dia. 4.1 mm and gauge length 27.0 mm in an Instron m/c. SEN rectangular bend specimens of dimensions, 10 mm x 25 mm x 200 mm were employed for the evaluation of fracture toughness. Both the tensile and the SEN specimens were machined with their longitudinal axis parallel to the rolling direction of the plate. The pre-cracked SEN specimens were loaded in three point bend to determine the J-integral, J_c (J_{cr}) toughness values using standard method (3,4). The tensile and the fracture toughness values are reported in Table 2.

TABLE 2 - Tensile and Fracture Toughness Test Results

Yield Strength MPa (σ_{ys})	Tensile Strength MPa	% El	% RA	True Fracture Strain, ϵ_f	J_c kJm^{-2}
404	516	24.5	72.6	1.257	46
	K_c (as estimated from J_c) = 102.5 MPa $\sqrt{m}$				

Environmental Test. A test set up similar to Brown's apparatus was constructed for environmental testing. Precracked SEN specimens were subjected to a fixed sustained cantilever loading in presence of the environment. The environments consisted of 3.5% NaCl solution (pH = 5.5) and H_2S saturated acetic acid solution (pH = 3.0). The concentration of H_2S in the sulphide solution was measured by a back titration method (5) and maintained constant in the range of 1400 to 1500 ppm. The freshly prepared aqueous environments were allowed to flow through the cracked region of the specimen continuously. Fig. 1 depicts schematically the load cycle and environmental testing procedure used. The test set up equipped with necessary attachments facilitates monitoring of the following:

i) subcritical crack growth measurement using a travelling microscope

ii) load point displacement (LPD) using a LVDT

iii) recording of failure time by a battery operated clock

iv) Crack mouth opening displacement (CMOD) using a displacement gauge.

KINETICS OF ENVIRONMENTAL CRACKING

J-Integral Approach and J_{Iscc}

In high strength materials the LEFM parameter, K has been successfully used to describe the kinetics of subcritical cracking under hostile environments. Since a large size of plastic enclave preceding the onset of subcritical cracking invalidates the K_I- approach in the microalloyed steel, the J-integral approach was used to characterize the environmental cracking behaviour. This was done in the following steps:

I. Obtaining the load (P) -LPD diagram in ambient condition (air environment) to compute J_I values in cantilever bending loading.

II. Measurement of LPD as a function of time during subcritical crack growth in the environment.

III. P-LPD diagram during loading under the environmental condition.

IV. Computation of J_I values from the above diagram at various stages using Begley-Landes approach (3).

Fig. 2 shows a typical P-LPD diagram (air environment) used to get the J-level for initiation of subcritical crack growth in air environment. The J_I values at various load levels were computed using Begley-Landes method (3) and reported in the figure. Fig.3 shows a typical LPD-time (t) plot under the sulphide and the chloride environments. The subcritical crack growth was followed by catastrophic fracture under the sulphide environment. The P-LPD diagrams under the chloride and the sulphide environments are shown in Figs. 4 and 5. The J-values during the various stages of sub-critical crack growth are shown in the figure. At each J_I level, the test was continued for 100 hrs. to check if there was any change in crack size or LPD. The process was repeated successively with higher J_I value till a J-level was achieved where a change in crack length or LPD could be noticed within a period of 100 hrs. The limiting value of J_I is termed as the threshold J, J_{Iscc} and reported in Table 3. As may be seen from Figs. 4 and 5, the load had to be raised intermittently for the continuation of subcritical crack growth giving rise to a stepped nature of P-LPD diagram. This is especially true under the chloride environment. By a step loading method used to determine the J_{Iscc} value in the present work, it was difficult to obtain a definite J_{Iscc} value, therefore J_{Iscc} has been expressed as a range in Table 3.

TABLE 3 - J_{Iscc} and J_{If} Values for the NaCl and the H_2S Environment

Environments	J_{Iscc} kJm^{-2}	J_{Iscc}/J_{Ic} (Av.)	J_{If} kJm^{-2}	J_{If}/J_{Ic}
Chloride	39.5-45.0	0.92	191.7	4.2
Sulphide	20.8-24.8	0.50	86.2	1.9

Terminal J-Value. The terminal J-value, J_{If} was calculated at the final fracture (after 84 hours) under the sulphide environment. Since the specimen did not meet unstable crack propagation under the chloride environment, the test was interrupted after an exposure for 200 hrs., the specimen was unloaded and broken open in liquid nitrogen to measure the crack extension on the mid-thickness plane (Fig. 4). It may be noted from Table 3 that the ratios J_{Iscc}/J_{Ic} and J_{If}/J_{Ic} are smaller for the sulphide environment as compared to the chloride environment. In other words lesser energy is dissipated during the initiation and propagation of cracking under the sulphide environment as compared to the chloride solution.

Crack Growth Rate (da/dt)

As the amount of crack extension over the surface was very small the extent of subcritical crack growth (Δa) under both the environments were measured from the fracture surfaces. The macroscopic crack front profile is illustrated in Fig. 6. As expected, the Δa values were found to be maximum at the midthickness plane for both the environments. The Δa and the average da/dt values are reported in Table 4.

TABLE 4 - Crack Growth Rate Data

Environments	Δa (max.) mm	da/dt (av.) mm/hr	Range of J_I (ΔJ_I) kJm^{-2}
NaCl	1.25	6.3×10^{-3}	39.5 - 191.7
H_2S	3.00	3.6×10^{-2}	20.9 - 86.2

The average da/dt value under the sulphide environment is around 5 times larger than the same under the NaCl solution, in spite of the fact that the J_I range is at lower level in the former case.

MECHANISM OF ENVIRONMENTAL CRACKING

Influence of Environment

From the preceding sections, it is evident that the environmental susceptibility for the microalloyed steel is more severe under the sulphide environment than the sodium chloride solution. It is now believed that the hydrogen is the most damaging species from the environment. The threshold K_{Iscc}/J_{Iscc} value for the hydrogen cracking may be written as (6,7),

$$J_{Iscc} = m \ln (C_{cr}/C_o)$$

where

$$m = 3RT \sqrt{2\pi r} / 2(1+\nu) \bar{V}_H$$

R-Gas constant, T-temperature, ν-Poisson's ratio, $\bar{V}_H$-partial molal volume of hydrogen in iron, and r-distance of triaxial region from the crack tip. C_{cr} and C_o are the critical hydrogen concentration for crack growth and the initial hydrogen concentration in the lattice respectively. Since m appears to be a constant, the value of J_{Iscc} will depend on the C_{cr}/C_o ratio. It appears from this investigation that the source of hydrogen also affects the C_{cr}/C_o ratio, the sulphide environment thus necessitating a lower C_{cr}/C_o ratio for cracking to take place. Also more hydrogen is available in the atomic form in the H_2S environment because of inhibition of recombination reaction. This helps in building up the critical hydrogen concentration in the stressed region resulting in faster propagation of crack in the sulphide environment. Similar observation has been made in a low alloy steel also (8,9).

Energy Dissipation During Subcritical Cracking

From the stepped nature of P-LPD diagram (Figs. 4 and 5) and high J_{If}/J_{Ic} ratio, it is evident that the energy dissipation during subcritical cracking under both the environments is significantly high. It may be noted that for many other steels, the J_{If}/J_{Ic} ratio is less than one (6,7). Also, contrary to the observations made in the micro-alloyed steel, once the subcritical crack propagation starts in high strength alloys, it leads to unstable fracture. The high energy dissipation in microalloyed steel may be attributed to a number of factors (10,11):

i) Substructural changes at the crack tip due to extensive plastic deformation. This gives rise to an increased number of hydrogen trap sites such as lattice imperfections, dislocation tangles, immobile dislocations etc.

ii) Considerable blunting and rounding-off of the crack tip reducing the effective stress intensity due to plasticity.

iii) Change of stress distribution due to relaxation of stress in the vicinity of crack tip.

iv) Higher value of C_{cr}/C_o ratio in the microalloyed steel (6,7) as $C_{cr} \propto 1/\sigma_{ys}$ and $C_o \propto \sigma_{ys}$ and the σ_{ys} of the microalloyed steel is relatively lower.

The first three factors are more effective under the chloride solution as the ΔJ for sub-critical crack growth is higher under the chloride environment. This results in higher energy dissipation under the chloride environment as compared to the sulphide environment.

Mechanism of Ambient vs Environmental Fracture

The microfractographic investigations of fracture surfaces were carried out on S4-10 SEM. In the ambient condition, fully dimpled fracture resulting from the microvoid coalescence mode was observed. This consisted of the initiation of voids on the effective inclusions and their link-up by growth over the process zone in the plastic enclave (8).

Chloride environment. The microfractographic study of the specimen tested in NaCl solution revealed deep elongated pits formed by joining of small cavities. It is evident (Fig. 7) that the pits or voids are formed by a process of decohesion at the inclusion-matrix interface, rather than by cracking of inclusions. The chlorideions are believed to be segregated at the interface regions and facilitate decohesion reducing the interfacial bond strength.

Relatively higher stress concentration at the large size inclusions coupled with the action of chloride ions enable the voids to form after a prolonged exposure to the NaCl solution. The pits appear to be more elongated and joined together at the midthickness plane, rather than near the surface (Figs. 6 and 7). As the stresses are maximum at the midthickness plane, this observation justifies the role of the mechanical force for the initiation and propagation of cracking under NaCl solution.

Sulphide Environment. The samples tested under H_2S environment reveal large number of spherical equiaxed pits of considerable depth (Fig. 8). Large number of fine cracks are also present along the ferrite-pearlite interface region. The pits formed over the inclusions are joined more by the sharp intermediate cracks, rather than by growth of voids unlike the case for the NaCl environment. Thus, the process of crack extension under the H_2S environment consists of formation of pits and cavities at the inclusions and their joining by fine cracks.

The hydrogen atoms diffuse to the trapping sites like the interfaces between the matrix and inclusions in the microalloyed steel. Some of the hydrogen atoms may precipitate as H_2 gas molecules in the microvoids around inclusions. It is believed that when the internal pressure due to hydrogen exceeds some limiting value, blistering occurs with the cracking of the voids (12,13). It has been observed in the present work that some voids are associated with a number of cracks indicating the bursting nature of cracking. The sharp cracks are found to be present in various directions on the fracture plane and stable cracking occurs by joining of these cracks till final unstable fracture takes over. It is believed in the present investigation that the failure of the microalloyed steel under H_2S environment is mainly by hydrogen induced cracking.

CONCLUSIONS

In summarizing the present work on the microalloyed steel, the following conclusions can be made:

1. In presence of large plastic enclave, the J_{Iscc} and J_{If} values may describe the onset of stable and unstable cracking under the hostile environments as analogous to K_{Iscc} and K_{If} respectively.
2. The sulphide environment is found to be far more aggressive ($J_{Iscc}/J_{Ic} = 0.50$) than the chloride solution ($J_{Iscc}/J_{Ic} = 0.92$). The average subcritical crack growth rate is roughly five times large under the sulphide than the chloride environment.
3. Considerable amount of energy dissipation occurs during the process of subcritical cracking under the chloride solution ($J_{If}/J_{Ic} = 4.2$). Presence of large plastic zone, the effect of blunting and relaxation of stresses lead to the large energy dissipation. For the sulphide environment much less energy dissipation during cracking ($J_{If}/J_{Ic} \approx 1.9$) is observed. The final fracture is catastrophic in nature for the sulphide environment unlike the chloride environment.

4. The subcritical cracking in presence of sulphide environment occurs by joining of fine cracks emanating from pits (voids) as a result of blistering. Under chloride environment the formation of pits on the inclusions and their link up by growing in the direction of stressing cause cracking.

ACKNOWLEDGEMENT

The authors wish to record their appreciation to Prof. V. Raghavan for his keen interest in the present work.

REFERENCES

1. Thompson, A.W., 1977, Proc. TMS-AIME, 379
2. Thompson, A.W., 1980, Mat. Sci. Engg. 43, 41
3. Begley, J.A., and Landes, J.D., 1972, ASTM STP 514, 1
4. Landes, J.D., and Begley, J.A., 1974, ASTM STP 560, 170
5. Fisher, R.B., and Peters, D.C., 1968, Basic Theory and Practice of Quantitative Chemical Analysis, 585
6. Gerberich, W.W., 1974, Hydrogen in Metals, ASM Proc., 115
7. Gerberich, W.W., and Chen, Y.T., 1975, Met.Trans.,6A, 271
8. Kumar, A.N., 1982,"Ambient Fracture Behaviour and Environmental Crack Growth Kinetics in a Low Alloy and a Micro-alloyed Steel", Ph.D. Thesis, Indian Institute of Tech.,Delhi
9. Kumar, A.N., and Pandey, R.K.,1983,Kinetics of Subcritical Cracking under the Chloride and Sulphide Environments in a Low Alloy Steel, Communicated to Engg. Frac. Mech.
10. Nakasa, K., and Takei, H., 1979, Engg. Frac.Mech.,11, 739
11. Nakasa, K., Takei, H., and Yoshida, M.,1980, Engg. Frac. Mech., 13, 667
12. Taira, T., Tsukada, K., Kobayshi, Y., Inagaki, H., and Watanabe, T., 1981, Corrosion, 37, 5
13. Wilde, B.E., Kim, C.D., and Phelps, E.H., 1980, Corrosion,36, 625.

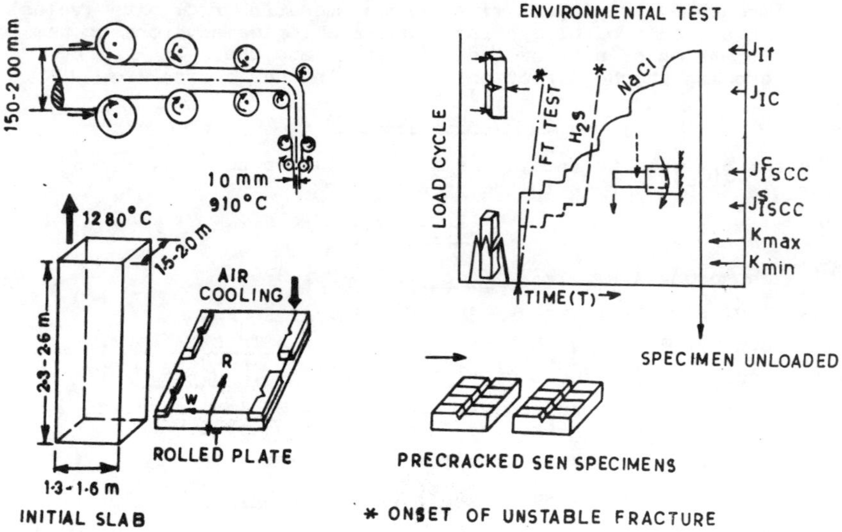

Figure 1 Thermal and load cycles for fracture toughness and environmental cracking studies

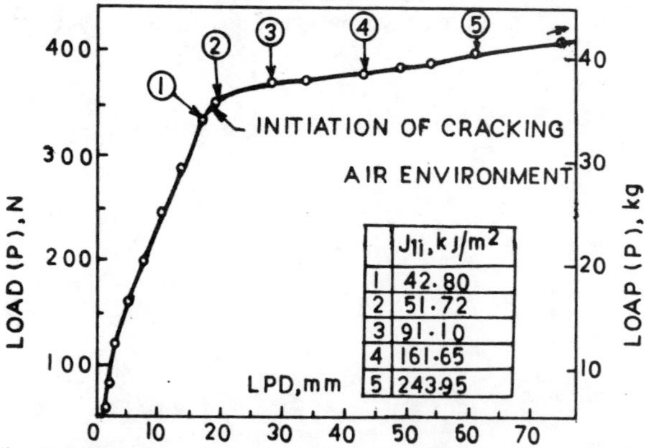

Figure 2 P-LPD plot for specimen loaded in air environment

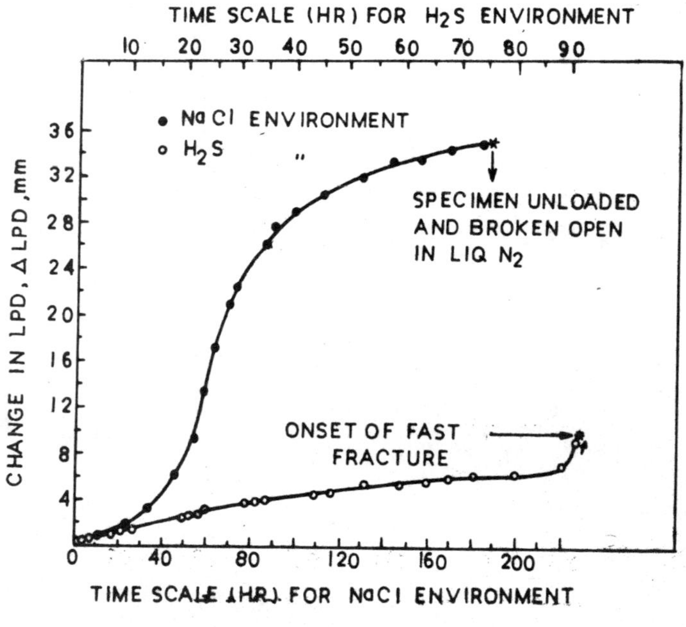

Figure 3 LPD as a function of time (t)

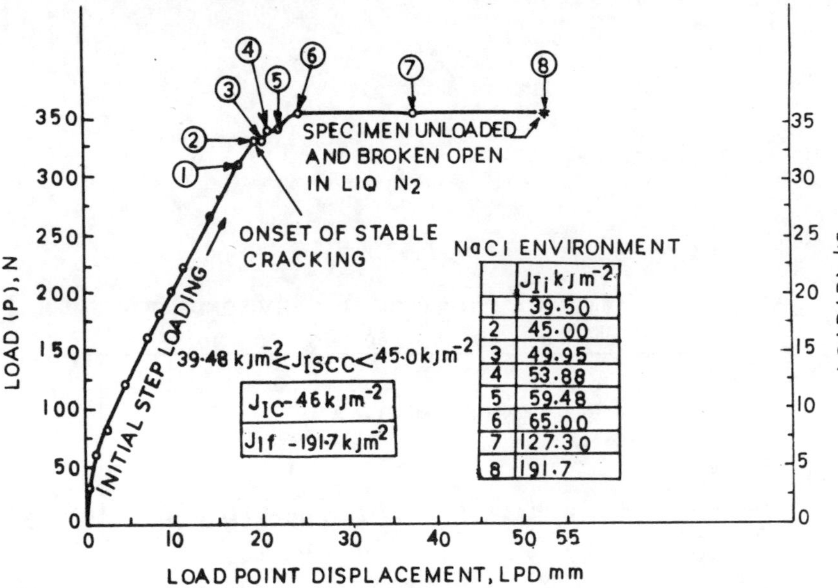

Figure 4 P-LPD plot for specimen loaded in NaCl environment

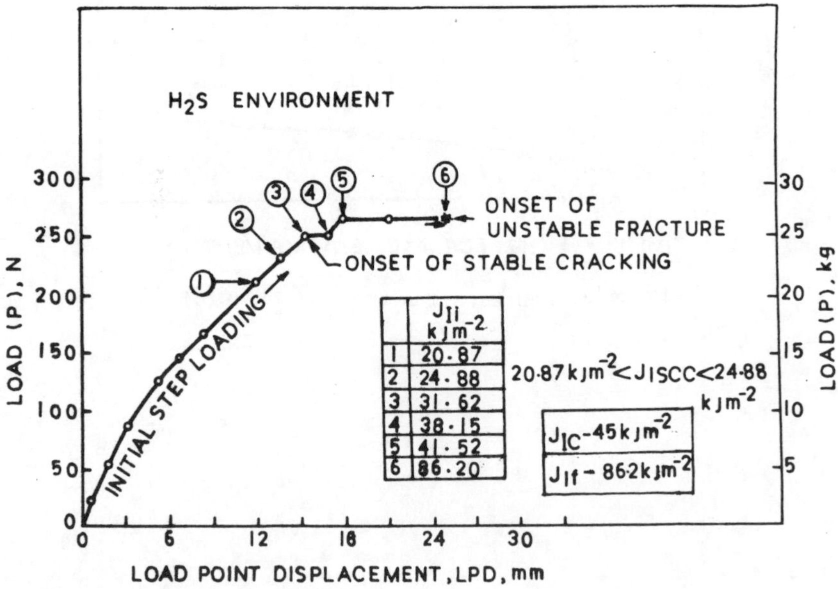

Figure 5 P-LPD plot for specimen loaded in H_2S environment

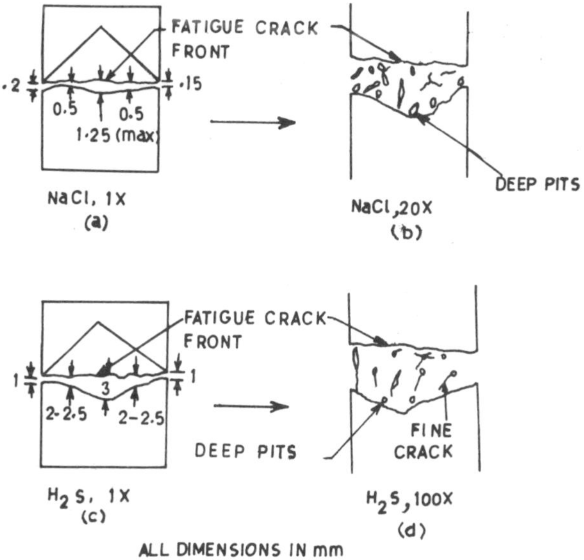

Fig. 6 Macroscopic observation of fracture plane

Figure 7 Microfractograph (NaCl environment, 25 X)

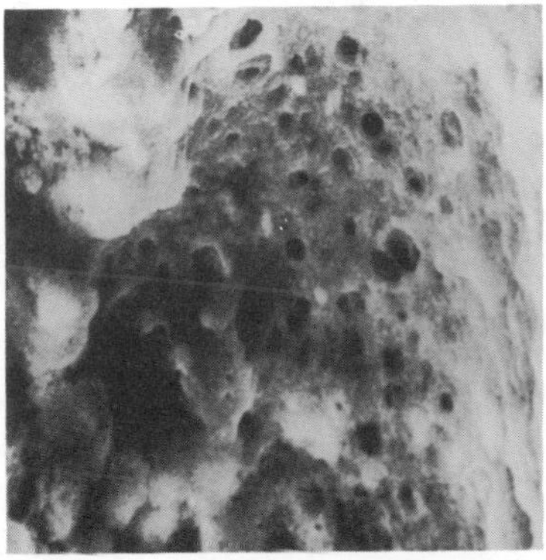

Figure 8 Microfractograph (H_2S environment, 500 X)

PIPELINE RUPTURE AND COLLAPSE: PREVENTION METHODS

A.R.D. Thorley*

The principal design features of pipeline transportation systems are normally based on expected or specified steady flows and pressures. Dimensions and materials for pipes, flanges, fittings, etc., will initially be decided on these criteria. During a subsequent stage of the design process the prudent engineer will speculate on what abnormal or fault conditions might occur and against which the pipe system must be protected. Strengthening the system is one option, but is usually not the most economical. This paper describes some of the others and offers comment on where they may be usefully employed.

INTRODUCTION

It is a well documented fact that changes in fluid flow rate are accompanied by variations in pressure. If the change is too rapid and proper account of this has not been taken a failure can occur.

The failure that is perhaps most widely known is the bursting of pipes or damage to components such as valve casings, joints and seals. This type of failure is obviously due to an excess pressure which may be encountered on the upstream side of a closing valve or pump running down, and following the collapse of a vapour cavity.

The converse case, of a low pressure on the downstream side of a closing valve or pump running down can lead to a variety of problems. If the pressure difference between the outside and inside of the pipe is great enough the pipeline is liable to collapse. This is most likely to occur with non-metallic pipes (uPVC), submarine pipelines and pipelines having a low safety factor (e.g. in aero-space applications) though it is not unknown in ordinary steel pipelines.

Bursting and collapsing of pipelines are perhaps the most general and spectacular failures that can occur, but there are other types of failure which in particular systems or applications can be just as important. For example, even if a pipeline does not collapse when the internal pressure falls below that on the outside contamination of the fluid will occur if leakage into the line is possible through faulty joints or wrongly positioned vacuum breaking devices. For this reason potable water supplies should always be

* Department of Mechanical Engineering, The City University, London, England.

maintained at a positive gauge pressure.

All of these 'failures' are the result of transient pressure waves following a single event such as a pump trip or valve movement. Repetitive or cyclic events can give rise to the phenomenon of resonance of which the most well-known occurrences are in the hydro-power industry (worn valve seals and governor hunting) and the oil industry (reciprocating pumps).

In addition to oil and water lines other examples include the fuel systems on interplanetory rockets, military and civilian aircraft, hydraulic control systems on aircraft, ships and mining equipment, pressurised die-casting of liquified plastics and metals, and fuel-coolant reactions in liquid metal cooled fast breeder reactors.

Another example with which the writer has been concerned was a slurry system in which a characteristic of the solid particles was that if the flow velocity dropped below a certain minimum value the solids fell rapidly to the floor of the pipeline and formed a compact deposit which could not be re-suspended. A 'failure' in this system was any event that allowed the flow velocity to fall to this critical value before all solids had been washed through.

'Failure', therefore, is not necessarily simply a pipe burst or collapse. It can also include contamination of the working fluid, interference with the proper functioning of system components or indeed of the system as a whole. The purpose of designing surge suppression methods or devices is to avoid such failures, and just as the nature of a failure is defined in relation to a particular system, so the most appropriate surge suppression device(s) must also be selected with that system in mind.

PREVENTATIVE MEASURES

The general principle upon which most devices or procedures operate is to reduce the rate at which changes to the flow occur since this is what governs the pressure changes to which the system will be subjected.

For a given system two or three methods of surge control may be suitable theoretically, but the final choice would normally be made after consideration of reliability, convenience, amount of maintenance required and cost.

Of the methods being discussed the first two represent 'direct action' on the primary cause of flow changes whereas the other methods may be classed as 'diversionary tactics'.

Rate of Valve Closure

If the closure time T_c of a valve in a pipeline of length L in which the propagation speed c of pressure waves is shorter than (2L/c) the full surge pressure of $\rho c V_o$ may be developed in the liquid of density ρ and having an initial flow velocity V_o.

To keep the pressure change within acceptable limits it is not enough to ensure that the closure time is slightly longer than (2L/c). A considerable proportion of the pressure change may still occur since most valves are highly non-linear in behaviour.

The only satisfactory method of determining a suitable valve closure time is to use the relationship between the valve head loss coefficient and percentage of opening as data for a computer program incorporating a valve closing in a time, T_c. The variation of maximum pressure with T_c can then be determined and a suitable closure time decided upon. Charts for various valves have been developed to aid this choice (1). They enable an estimated pressure rise to be obtained, though a computer solution is generally recommended.

It may sometimes happen that the closure time chosen in relation to surge suppression is unacceptably long from some other point of view. For instance, it may lead to too much liquid being drained from the system. If this is so, it may be possible to reduce the closure time by using two closure rates - a very rapid one for the first 75-80% of spindle movement followed by a much slower movement for the remainder.

Although not often used, it is possible to design valve operating systems using cams, or pressure sensing devices. This is known as 'valve stroking'(2).

Unfortunately, valve closure times are frequently influenced by conflicting requirements. For example, with controlled closure pump discharge valves, too fast a closure will lead to column separation and possibly pipe failure and too slow a valve closure, in the absence of a check valve, will lead to high reverse flows and reverse pump rotation. When this happens it may be desirable to use an additional suppression device, the choice being dictated by the particular system.

Increased Pump Inertia

The object of increasing the inertia of the rotating parts of a motor-pump unit is to reduce the rate at which the speed decreases after a power failure to the driving motor. If the deceleration is slow enough a 'beneficial' wave reflection from the downstream end of the pipeline will arrive back at the pump discharge in time to prevent the pressure at that point from falling too low.

As there are practical limits to the size of flywheel that can be fitted this remedy is usually restricted to pipelines that are not very long, and where the motor and associated electrical gear will withstand the additional starting current. A simple rule proposed by Stephenson (3) is that increased pump inertia will probably be beneficial in reducing surge effects if

$$\frac{IN^2}{\rho A L H_o^2} > 0.01\ (\text{rev/min})^2 \qquad (1)$$

In this expression I is the inertia of the rotating parts in kg.m^2, N the speed in rev/min, and ρ the liquid density in kg/m^3. The pipe cross-sectional area A is in m^2 and the length L and head rise H_o across the pump are in m.

A full analysis of the system will be needed to evaluate the reduction in the pressure head fluctuations downstream of the pump discharge.

Surge Shafts

The most common 'diversionary' method of surge control, particularly in hydro-power applications, is the surge shaft. Instead of converting the kinetic energy of the moving liquid totally into a very high pressure within the system, which would be enormously expensive to contain, flow is diverted into a shaft, vessel or tank. The flow is then gradually brought to rest over a long period of time, with surplus energy being dissipated through pipe friction and throttles in the entrance to and exit from the surge shaft.

Detailed theory is beyond the scope of this paper, but the interested reader may usefully consult references (2), (4) - (8). Briefly, having diverted the flow into a surge shaft and closed off the downstream end of the line the liquid column in the system will oscillate, possibly over a period of several hours.

The complete period of oscillation of the system, neglecting friction, may be approximated by:

$$T = 2\pi \sqrt{\frac{L A_s}{g A_t}} \tag{2}$$

where L = length of pressure tunnel, A_s = shaft area and A_t = tunnel area. As in a typical system, this is much longer than the complete period of elastic waves (4L/c) it is normal to ignore elastic effects and to consider the water as a rigid column oscillating between the upstream reservoir and the surge shaft.

In addition to being high enough to take the maximum calculated water level rise without overtopping (unless an allowance has been made for overflow in the design), the surge shaft should also have a cross-sectional area great enough to be stable. For the damping to be positive the shaft area must exceed a value known as the Thoma critical area A_{TH}, where

$$A_{TH} = \frac{L A_t}{F V_o^2 (H - F V_o^2)} \cdot \frac{V_o^2}{2g} \tag{3}$$

and V_o is the steady state velocity, H the reservoir head and FV_o^2 the steady state friction loss.

The Thoma criterion gives a first approximation to the critical area, but being based upon a number of idealisations it is common practice to add on a factor of 25-50% to ensure that fluctuations are damped out within a reasonable time.

Air Vessel

Surge shafts are limited to applications where the pipeline profile is close to the hydraulic grade line, since otherwise they would overflow. The air vessel does not suffer from this restriction.

Their most common use is to guard against adverse conditions following pump shut-down. In this case the vessel is placed downstream of the pumps and of any check valves (Fig. 1).

When an air vessel is to be installed, a check should be made to ensure that the pressure at any high spot further along the line will not fall to vapour pressure. This check can easily be done by using a computer, printing out results at intermediate points along the line and plotting a minimum head envelope (Fig.2).

The rate at which water enters and leaves an air vessel may be controlled by fitting throttles. In theory the optimum throttle loss coefficient for flow in is usually appreciably different from that for flow out. A practical way of providing for this is to have a large diameter outflow pipe fitted with a check valve and a small by-pass or a multi-door check valve with one door missing.

Preliminary estimates of air vessel sizes may conveniently be made with the aid of the approximate methods reviewed in reference (8).

Accumulators are basically the same as air vessels except that the gas (usually nitrogen) is contained within a flexible bag and there is therefore no possibility of it entering the line. In fluid power applications accumulators are often used to reduce surge pressures, and they are also often used to damp out pulsations of positive displacement pumps. Manufacturers' handbooks give approximate methods of determining the size of accumulator required to damp out a given surge pressure. The size is normally such that it is not worth carrying out a more detailed analysis or considering fitting optimum outlet throttles in the way described for larger vessels. The saving in cost from any slight reduction in size would probably not cover the increased cost of design.

Air Valves

The presence of air or gas in a liquid pipeline is a condition engineers normally strive to avoid as the collision of slugs of liquid with one another or with components in the system can lead to excessive shock loads. Air and gas cannot be eliminated entirely at all times - it would have been present when the line was initially constructed, it may be drawn in at the pump suction or through faulty joints or glands or it may be released from solution due to changes in pressure and temperature.

The primary functions of air valves may therefore be listed as

(a) the release of air/gas during pipeline filling at a rate sufficient to prevent excessive back pressure

(b) admission of air during emptying at a rate sufficient to prevent pipeline collapse

(c) to release accumulations of air/gas arising from normal pressurised operation.

Since air and gas tend to accumulate at high points and changes in pipeline slope it is relatively easy to release by the proper use of appropriate valves.

In addition to their function of ventilating pipelines modified air valves may, in some circumstances, be used to alleviate surge. For example, if the pressure is falling to vapour pressure, causing separation of the liquid and later rejoinder with a subsequent high pressure rise, it may be acceptable to place at appropriate points valves which will open when the line pressure starts to fall below atmospheric. These will let in air which will cushion the blow as the separated liquid columns come together again. The valves have to be carefully designed to allow sufficient air into the line and yet ensure that it is not expelled too rapidly. A vented non-return valve fulfils this purpose.

Relief Valves

These can be of the conventional spring-loaded type, be controlled by a hydraulically operated pilot valve or be one of the various special patented designs. The essential features are a rapid opening (i.e. much less than a pipeline period), followed usually by a slow closure. It is also essential that they should be of an adequate size and number to pass the required flow, allowing for valve isolation for maintenance purposes. It is often convenient to use two or more valves, set to open at slightly different pressures.

The choice of relief valves cannot be made in isolation. The discharge line from the valves to a dump tank will, however short, give rise to a back pressure once flow commences, and account must be taken of this. In some circumstances, such as a congested jetty head, there is not room for a large tank and it may even be desirable to utilize a back pressure through the valves to decelerate the main flow. Some specialist surge relief packages are designed with this in mind, even to the extent of having the dump tank pressurized with an inert gas, which, when the pressure in the main pipeline has been stabilized, forces the relieved volume of liquid back into the system.

Another variation on the conventional relief valve is to incorporate sensing devices to cause the valves to open in anticipation of a pressure surge.

Pressure Regulating Valves

Discharge pipelines on deep-well pump installations can be protected against high start-up pressures by the use of pressure regulating valves - see Fig. 3. The main purpose is usually to discharge to waste discoloured water from the pump riser: the element of surge protection is an added bonus. The pressure regulating valve is held in the fully open position for a predetermined time and then allowed to close gradually. As the pressure in the pump discharge increases the check valve gradually opens and no undue pressure rises occur. This arrangement offers no protection on pump trips.

By-passes

Power failure to a booster pump usually leads to high pressures on the upstream side and low pressures on the downstream side - both potentially dangerous. A by-pass line containing a check valve around the pump is usually the simplest and cheapest way of alleviating both problems together.

Check Valves

The principal use of check valves is to prevent reverse flow and reverse rotation of pumps. A major problem in high head installations and multiple pump applications is the phenomenon of check valve slam. This is usually, through not exclusively, associated with swing check valves and occurs when a significant reverse flow develops before the valve is completely closed. A very large pressure rise occurs when the flow is suddenly brought to rest.

In systems where a fast response is required a valve having the following characteristics should be selected:

i) the moving parts should be of low inertia

ii) the distance through which they move should be small

iii) spring assistance to initiate closure as the flow decreases should be provided, and be properly tuned to the pipeline system of which the valve is a part.

Feed Tanks

These may be useful in systems where air admission is undesirable. They fulfil the same purpose as by-pass arrangements around pumps and may also be located at high points in a pipeline. They offer protection against sub-atmospheric pressures and, by preventing column separation, in effect, offer protection against the high pressures associated with cavity collapse. Pumps should not be restarted after a trip until the feed tanks have been refilled.

CONCLUDING REMARKS

As mentioned previously there is no simple single solution to all pressure surge problems. Every pipe system must be treated separately and the advantages and disadvantages of the various devices and operating procedures assessed accordingly. In principle any method of surge protection may be used in any system provided it is practical, economic and gives adequate protection. Having selected and installed appropriate protective devices it is highly desirable that the commissioning procedure should include the proving of these devices and operating methods.

ACKNOWLEDGEMENTS

This paper is based in part on Chapter 3 of reference 8, with the permission of the publishers.

REFERENCES

1. Wood, D.J., and Jones, S.E., 1973 "Waterhammer charts for various types of valves""Procs. ASCE, Jo.Hyd.Div.99 HY1, 167

2. Wylie, E.B., and Streeter, V.L., 1983 "Fluid Transients", F.E.B. Press, Ann Arbor, Michigan.

3. Stephenson, D., 1976 "Pipeline Design for Water Engineers", Elsevier Scientific Publ.Co.

4. Pearsall, I.S., 1962 "A survey of surge tank design theories", National Engineering Laboratories, Scotland. Rept. No. 56.

5. B.H.R.A. 1976, 1980, Procs. 2nd and 3rd Intl.Conferences on Pressure Surge, Publ.British Hydromechanics Research Assoc. U.K.

6. Pickford, J.A., 1969, "Analysis of Surge", Macmillan, London.

7. Chaudhry, M.H., 1979 "Applied Hydraulic Transients" Van Nostrand Reinhold Co., New York.

8. Thorley, A.R.D., and Enever, K.J., 1979 "Control and Suppression of Pressure Surges in Pipelines and Tunnels" Construction Industry Research and Information Association, London. Report 84.

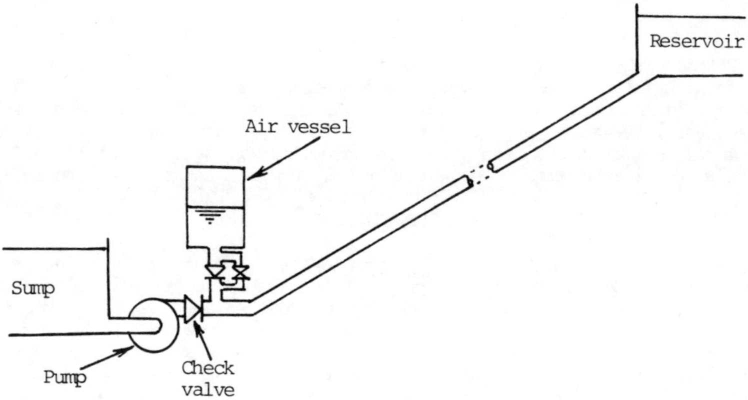

Fig.1 Air vessel downstream of a pump to control conditions after shutdown.

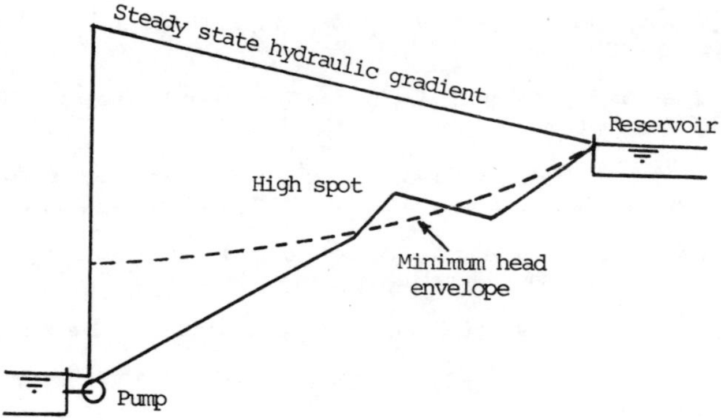

Fig.2 Typical minimum head envelope for pump shutdown showing possibility of column separation at high spot.

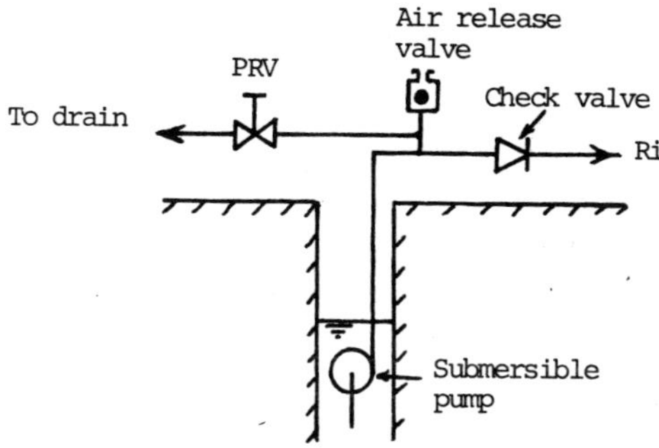

Fig.3 Schematic layout showing the use of a pressure regulating valve (PRV) for surge protection of a deep-well pump installation during pump starts.